Deutsche Forschungsgemeinschaft

List of MAK and BAT Values 2008

Commission for the Investigation of Health Hazards of Chemical Compounds in the Work Area

Report No. 44

The MAK-Collection

Recent Volumes of the MAK-Collection for Occupational Health and Safety

Part I: MAK Value Documentations, Volume 24
Greim, H. (ed.)

2007. ISBN 978-3-527-31594-9

Part II: BAT Value Documentations, Volume 4
Drexler, H. and Greim, H. (eds.)

2005. ISBN 978-3-527-27049-1

Part III: Air Monitoring Methods, Volume 10
Parlar, H. and Greim, H. (eds.)

2007. ISBN 978-3-527-31601-4

Part IV: Biomonitoring Methods, Volume 11
Angerer, J. and Greim, H. (eds.)

2007. ISBN 978-3-527-31596-3

The MAK-Collection online
www.mrw.interscience.wiley.com/makbat

Deutsche Forschungsgemeinschaft

List of MAK and BAT Values 2008

Maximum Concentrations
and
Biological Tolerance Values
at the Workplace

Commission for the
Investigation of Health Hazards
of Chemical Compounds
in the Work Area

Report No. 44

WILEY-VCH Verlag GmbH & Co. KGaA

Report No. 44 of the Commission for the Investigation of Health Hazards of Chemical Compounds in the Work Area, of July 1, 2008. This report replaces Report No. 43 of July 1, 2007 and supersedes all previous reports of the Commission.

DEUTSCHE FORSCHUNGSGEMEINSCHAFT
authorized and signed by Professor Dr. Andrea Hartwig
Chair of the Commission for the Investigation of Health Hazards of Chemical Compounds in the Work Area

Deutsche Forschungsgemeinschaft
Kennedyallee 40, D-53175 Bonn, Federal Republic of Germany
Postal address: D-53170 Bonn
Phone: ++49/228/885-2591
Telefax: ++49/228/885-2777
E-mail: postmaster@dfg.de
Internet: http://www.dfg.de

Library of Congress Card No. applied for.

Die Deutsche Bibliothek – CIP-Cataloguing-in-Publication-Data.

A catalogue record for this publication is available from Die Deutsche Bibliothek.
ISBN: 978-3-527-32305-0

Cover Design and Typography: Dieter Hüsken
Composition, Printing, Bookbinding: Konrad Triltsch, Print und digitale Medien GmbH,
D-97199 Ochsenfurt-Hohestadt

Printed in the Federal Republic of Germany

Table of Contents

Maximum Concentrations at the Workplace

List of MAK and BAT Values 2008. DFG, Deutsche Forschungsgemeinschaft

ISBN: 978-3-527-32305-0

Biological Tolerance Values

CAS Number Index

Appendix

★ Indicates a change from the 2007 MAK list
Details of the new threshold values or classifications proposed are listed in the blue pages (appendix, page I). The Commission has adopted these proposals but puts them up for discussion until 31.12.2008. New data or scientific commentary may be submitted to the Commission's scientific office (Kommissionssekretariat) until this date. This information will be examined and taken into consideration in the final ratification.

Maximum Concentrations at the Workplace

I Significance, use and derivation of MAK values

Definition

The MAK value ("maximale Arbeitsplatz-Konzentration": maximum workplace concentration) is defined as the maximum concentration of a chemical substance (as gas, vapour or particulate matter) in the workplace air which generally does not have known adverse effects on the health of the employee nor cause unreasonable annoyance (e. g. by a nauseous odour) even when the person is repeatedly exposed during long periods, usually for 8 hours daily but assuming on average a 40-hour working week. Certain ★ aspects of occupational hygiene associated with liquid substances, e. g. formation of mist with obscured visibility, dampening of clothing, or condensation on the floor, can not be taken into account in establishing the MAK value. Such effects have a wide range of variation, depending on the industrial process, the procedure, and the physical conditions at the workplace. A suitable instrument for evaluation is not yet available. Regardless of the level of the toxicologically based MAK value, it should be ensured in these cases that safety at the workplace is not placed at risk. This situation is not explicitly mentioned in the documentations because it is not known whether the substance exists as an aerosol at the MAK value. As a rule, the MAK value is given as an average concentration for a period of up to one working day or shift. MAK values are established on the basis of the effects of chemical substances; when possible, practical aspects of the industrial processes and the resulting exposure patterns are also taken into account. Scientific criteria for the prevention of adverse effects on health are decisive, not technical and economic feasibility.

For the establishment of a MAK value,

the carcinogenicity (see Section III)
the sensitizing effects (see Section IV)
the contribution to systemic toxicity after percutaneous absorption (see Section VII)
the risks during pregnancy (see Section VIII)
the germ cell mutagenicity (see Section IX)

of a substance are evaluated and the substance classified or designated accordingly. Descriptions of the procedures used by the Commission in the evaluation of these end points may be found in the appropriate sections of the *List of MAK and BAT Values*, in the "Toxikologisch-arbeitsmedizinischen Begründungen von MAK-Werten" (availa-

List of MAK and BAT Values 2008. DFG, Deutsche Forschungsgemeinschaft

ISBN: 978-3-527-32305-0

ble in English translation in the series *Occupational Toxicants*)[1] and in scientific journals.[2,3,4,5,6]

In line with the so-called "preferred value approach" also used e.g. in the European Union, MAK values are to be established preferentially as the numerical values 1, 2 or 5 ml/m³ or, for non-volatile substances, 1, 2 or 5 mg/m³, multiplied by powers of ten.

In the use of MAK values, the analytical procedures used for sampling and analysis and the sampling strategy are of great importance.

Purpose

MAK values promote the protection of health at the workplace. They provide a basis for judgement of the toxic potential or safety of the concentrations of substances in the workplace air. However, they do not provide constants from which the presence or absence of a health hazard after longer or shorter periods of exposure can be determined; nor can proven or suspected damage to health be deduced, in an isolated case, from MAK values or from the classification of a substance as carcinogenic. Such deductions can be made only on the basis of medical findings, taking into consideration all the circumstances of the particular case. Therefore, on principle, statements in the *List of MAK and BAT Values* are not to be seen as *a priori* judgements for individual cases. On principle, observation of MAK values does not eliminate the necessity for regular medical examination of the exposed individuals.

MAK values are not suitable for providing constant conversion factors for deduction of health risks associated with long-term exposure to contaminants in the non-occupational atmosphere, e.g., in the vicinity of industrial plants.

Prerequisites

In principle, the substances are dealt with according to their importance for practical occupational hygiene and the expertise of the members of the Commission. The prerequisite for the establishment of a MAK value is the availability of sufficient data for the substance from the fields of toxicology, occupational medicine or industrial hygiene. Ade-

---

1 obtainable from the publisher: WILEY-VCH, D-69451 Weinheim

2 Adler ID, Andrae U, Kreis P, Neumann HG, Thier R, Wild D (1999) Vorschläge zur Einstufung von Keimzellmutagenen. Arbeitsmed Sozialmed Umweltmed 34: 400–403.

3 Drexler H (1998) Assignment of skin notation for MAK values and its legal consequences in Germany. Int Arch Occup Environ Health 71: 503–505.

4 Hofmann A (1995) Fundamentals and possibilities of classification of occupational substances as developmental toxicants. Int Arch Occup Environ Health 67: 139–145.

5 Neumann HG, Thielmann HW, Filser JG, Gelbke HP, Greim H, Kappus H, Norpoth KH, Reuter U, Vamvakas S, Wardenbach P, Wichmann HE (1998) Changes in the classification of carcinogenic chemicals in the work area. (Section III of the German List of MAK and BAT Values). J Cancer Res Clin Oncol 124: 661–669.

6 Neumann HG, Vamvakas S, Thielmann HW, Gelbke HP, Filser JG, Reuter U, Greim H, Kappus H, Norpoth KH, Wardenbach P, Wichmann HE (1998) Changes in the classification of carcinogenic chemicals in the work area. Section III of the German List of MAK and BAT Values. Int Arch Occup Environ Health 71: 566–574.

quate documentation is not always available. The List is revised annually and suggestions for substances to be added and new information on listed substances are welcome.[7]

Derivation of MAK values

MAK values are derived by the "DFG Commission for the Investigation of Health Hazards of Chemical Compounds in the Work Area" exclusively on the basis of scientific arguments and are published in the *List of MAK and BAT Values* which is issued annually. For the derivation of MAK values, certain rules of procedure have been developed by the Commission on the basis of established toxicological and occupational medical concepts; answers to at least the more common questions are repeatedly sought in the same way. Therefore the usual procedures and the general principles for the derivation of MAK values are described below. Essentially, these principles correspond with those published by the European "Scientific Committee on Occupational Exposure Limits, SCOEL".[8]

First the most sensitive parameters described in the available data are to be identified, i.e., those effects which appear first during exposure to increasing concentrations of the substance. To be taken into account in this process are both local effects, that is, the results of effects on surfaces of the organism which are in contact with the environment (e.g. mucous membranes of the respiratory tract and the eyes, skin) and also systemic effects, that is, the results of uptake of the substance into the organism. Generally the concentration-effect relationships for these two kinds of effects are different. The derivation of the MAK value is based on the "no observed adverse effect level" for the most sensitive effect with relevance for health. A NOAEL is not equivalent with a threshold which can not be scientifically defined. The NOAEL is a concentration determined by experimental conditions at which the given effect is so low that it does not differ from the control value. It must be decided whether or not such effects may be considered to be adverse effects. At present there is no generally accepted definition for an "adverse" effect, at least in part because of the lack of clarity about the still changing definition for the state of being "healthy";[9,10] therefore this decision must be made anew in every case.

Fundamentally, known effects of a substance in man are given highest priority in the derivation of the MAK value.

In the evaluation of a substance, known effects of structural analogues may also be taken into account.

If no NOAEL may be derived from the available data, a scientifically founded MAK value cannot be established and the substance is listed in Section II b of the *List of MAK and BAT Values.*

---

7 Please contact the Geschäftsstelle der Deutschen Forschungsgemeinschaft, Kennedyallee 40, D-53175 Bonn; or the Sekretariat der Kommission: Technische Universität Berlin, Fakultät III – Lebensmittelchemie/Sekr. TIB 4/3-1, Gustav-Meyer-Allee 25, 13355 Berlin .

8 European Commission (Ed.) (1999) Methodology for the derivation of occupational exposure limits: Key documentation Cat. No. CE-NA-19253-EN-C, ISBN 92-828-8106-7, EUR 7, Office for Official Publications of the European Communities, L-2985 Luxembourg.

9 DFG (Deutsche Forschungsgemeinschaft) (Ed.) (1997) Verhaltenstoxikologie und MAK-Grenzwertfestlegungen. Wissenschaftliche Arbeitspapiere. Wiley-VCH, Weinheim.

10 Henschler D (1992) Evaluation of adverse effects in the standard-setting process. Toxicology Letters 64/65: 53–57.

a. Selection of substances and collection of data

For the substances being studied, the epidemiological data published in scientific journals, occupational medical reports, toxicological properties and any other potentially useful information is first assembled by carrying out researches in appropriate databanks. The references found in the literature search are checked for their relevance for the assessment of the substance in question and the original publications of the selected literature are examined. When necessary, unpublished internal company data in the form of complete study reports are also included. These are then identified as such in the reference list at the end of the documentation. The validity of the available information and studies is checked. Whether or not a study is relevant for the current assessment is decided on a case to case basis. Whenever possible, evaluation of the studies is based on the guidelines of the OECD or similar bodies.

The unabridged reports are made available to the Commission and are filed at the Commission's scientific central office. Information required by a third party about the company reports cited in the Commission's documentation is supplied in writing by the chairman of the Commission at his discretion. Access to company reports is not made available to third parties. Copies, even of parts of reports, are not provided.

b. Values based on effects in man

For many substances encountered at the workplace, irritation or central nervous depression is the critical effect. Valuable information – at least for these acute effects of single exposures – may be obtained from studies of volunteers exposed under controlled conditions which yield data for concentration-effect relationships and also for concentrations without effects (NOAEC). A detailed review of the methods required of such studies and of the usefulness of various parameters for the establishment of threshold concentrations has been published.[9] Such studies often demonstrate differences in sensitivity between persons who have never been exposed to the test substance and those who have been repeatedly exposed, e.g., at work.

Occupational medical and epidemiological studies provide further information from which the health risks associated with handling particular substances may be evaluated. However, not only the parameters determined in the exposed persons, but also any differences in study design, in the analytical methods and sampling strategies must be considered in evaluating such studies. Various confounders, exposure to mixtures, previous disorders or inadequate exposure records can alter or falsify any detected concentration-effect relationships.

Cross-sectional studies with only single determinations of exposure levels and only single examinations of the exposed persons do not generally permit the association of any observed symptoms with the current exposure situation. This requires information as to past exposure levels.

Therefore longitudinal studies with repeated determination of the workplace and systemic exposure levels and repeated examination of the exposed persons play a decisive role in the establishment of thresholds. Valid epidemiological studies of persons exposed for long periods to concentrations which do not produce adverse effects provide a reliable basis for the establishment of threshold levels for the workplace, especially when the study design permits statements as to both local and systemic effects.

---

[9] DFG (Deutsche Forschungsgemeinschaft) (Ed.) (1997) Verhaltenstoxikologie und MAK-Grenzwertfestlegungen. Wissenschaftliche Arbeitspapiere. Wiley-VCH, Weinheim.

The diverse sensitivities of individual employees (as determined by age, constitution, nutrition, climate, etc.) are taken into consideration in the establishment of MAK values. It is currently not possible to take sex-specific differences in toxicokinetics and toxicodynamics into account when establishing MAK and BAT values because of the lack of appropriate scientific data.

When the NOAEL has been determined from effects of the substance in man, the MAK value is generally established at the level of this NOAEL.

c. Values based on effects on animals

Because the effects in man are not known for many substances, MAK values are often derived from results obtained with experimental animals. This is carried out in the clear understanding of the problems associated with extrapolation between species and of the much smaller group sizes than is usual in epidemiological studies. On the other hand, animal studies carried out according to modern principles also offer advantages including precise characterization of exposure levels, the wide range of parameters that can be studied, and the possibility of determining dose-response relationships and NOAELs. The minimum database for the derivation of a MAK value is generally considered to be a NOAEL from a valid 90-day inhalation study with experimental animals. Of the results of studies in which substances were administered to experimental animals by the oral or dermal route, mostly only the systemic effects may be considered to be relevant for persons exposed at the workplace. Therefore, in the documentation of a MAK value such results must be accompanied by information about the local effects of the substance, especially the effects on the respiratory tract.

When the NOAEL has been determined from effects of the substance in animals, the MAK value is generally established at the level of half of this NOAEL. However, in some cases species differences in sensitivity to the substance must be taken into account and here the toxicokinetic data are particularly important.

d. Exceptional workplaces

During exposure to gaseous substances which are metabolized rapidly and for which the blood/air distribution coefficient is larger than 10, it must be taken into account that the concentrations of the substances in blood and tissues are positively correlated with the level of physical activity.

Likewise, the concentrations of inhaled gaseous substances in blood and tissues of persons working under hyperbaric pressure have been shown to correlate positively with the pressure.

This dependence of the body burden on the workplace conditions must be taken into account in the establishment of MAK and BAT values.

e. Odour, irritation and annoyance

Exposure of persons to substances at the workplace can cause smells (*nervi olfactorii*) or sensory irritation (*nervus trigeminus*). Such effects must be differentiated according to their relevance for health. This differentiation can cause difficulties because the parameters of interest can still not be determined with sufficient objectivity. Smells are mostly detected at lower concentrations than is sensory irritation. In general, if the smell and irritation are unpleasant and powerful enough, both can cause annoyance. When assessing these effects on the well-being of exposed persons, the physiological process of ha-

bituation (adaptation) must also be taken into account. In particular the sense of smell is affected markedly by habituation processes so that during constant exposure even to high concentrations the smell of a substance may no longer be noticed after a while. Excessive annoyance of workers by sensory irritation or persistent intensive or nauseous smells is taken into account when establishing thresholds.

f. Habituation

Even at constant exposure concentrations, persons can become accustomed to sensory irritation, effects on the sense of well-being or smells so that these no longer function adequately as warning signals. At present, however, not enough is known about the mechanisms and dose-response relationships involved. With many substances, on the other hand, habituation is the result of toxic effects such as inactivation of enzymes or inhibition of receptor molecules. Especially in such cases, and when the warning signals produced by sensory irritation are reduced or cancelled out by disorders of well-being or the sense of smell, it is necessary to take habituation into account when establishing thresholds.

Documentation

A detailed scientific documentation of each decision is published in the series *Toxikologisch-arbeitsmedizinische Begründung von MAK-Werten*, also available in English translation in the series *Occupational Toxicants.*[1] Annual supplements are planned. These documents present, clearly and in detail, the scientific data and the reasons for the establishment of a MAK value. Because of this system, it is sufficient to establish only general principles for the derivation of MAK values. The assessment of individual substances on the basis of all the available toxicological and occupational medical data yields a more differentiated and specific evaluation than would the observance of stringently formulated rules.

The published data for the toxicity and effects of a substance in man and animals and all other relevant information are organized according to the kind of effect and presented in the form of a review. This review of the toxicological and epidemiological data for a substance serves initially as a basis for the discussion within the Commission for the derivation of a MAK value and for detailed evaluation of the physicochemical properties, percutaneous absorption, sensitizing effects, carcinogenic effects, prenatal toxicity and germ cell mutagenicity of the substance. When new data become available, the MAK value, classification and designation of the substance are reassessed and, when necessary, altered.

Publication

Prospective changes and new entries are announced each year in the *List of MAK and BAT Values*[11] and in the periodical *Zentralblatt für Arbeitsmedizin* and in the *Bundesarbeitsblatt.* The periodical *Arbeitsmedizin, Sozialmedizin, Umweltmedizin* also publishes a detailed discussion of the list with notes of changes and new entries. Following

[1] obtainable from the publisher: WILEY-VCH, D-69451 Weinheim

[11] see yellow pages

ratification of the annual List, the organizations listed below are officially informed of the planned changes: "Länderausschuß für Arbeitsschutz und Sicherheitstechnik (LASI)" (Federal Committee for Occupational Safety and Technical Security), the "Bundesverband der Deutschen Industrie" (Federation of German Industries), the "Hauptverband der gewerblichen Berufsgenossenschaften" (Central Association of Industrial Injuries Insurance Institutes) and the "Deutsche Gewerkschaftsbund" (the German Trade Union Federation). The purpose of this measure is to give these organizations enough time to send to the Commission any available scientific documentation relevant to the planned changes and additions to the *List of MAK and BAT Values.*

Mixtures of substances

In general, the MAK value is only valid for exposure to a single, pure substance. It cannot be applied unconditionally to one component of a mixture in the workplace air or to a technical product which might contain more toxic impurities. Simultaneous or successive exposure to several substances may be much more or, in isolated cases, even less dangerous than the exposure to one of the substances on its own. A MAK value for a mixture of substances cannot be satisfactorily determined by simple calculation because the components of the mixture generally have very different kinds of effect; MAK values can presently be established for such mixtures only after specific toxicological examination or studies of the particular mixture of substances. Given the inadequacy of the currently available data, the Commission decidedly refrains from calculating MAK values for mixtures, particularly for liquid solvent mixtures. However, it is willing, on the basis of its own investigations, to provide values for defined vapour mixtures of practical relevance.

Analytical controls

The observance of the MAK, BAT and EKA values (that is, keeping the exposure levels below these values) is intended to protect the health of persons exposed to dangerous substances at work. This objective is only to be attained by regular monitoring of the concentration of the dangerous substances in the workplace air or of the concentration of the substances, their metabolites or other parameters of intermediary metabolism in the body fluids of exposed persons. For this purpose it is necessary to use analytical methods which have been tested for reliability and practicability. The Commission's analytical chemistry group has developed such methods and published them in the series *Luftanalysen* and *Analysen in biologischem Material.*[12] New issues of these publications appear

[12] *Analytische Methoden zur Prüfung gesundheitsschädlicher Arbeitsstoffe*, available from the publisher: WILEY-VCH, D-69451 Weinheim
Volume 1: *Luftanalysen* (*Analyses of Hazardous Substances in Air*)
Volume 2: *Analysen in biologischem Material* (*Analyses of Hazardous Substances in Biological Materials*)
Supplementary reports at yearly intervals are anticipated. The Commission welcomes suggestions for inclusion of new chemical compounds as well as analytical methods. Contact the group "Analytische Chemie" at the Deutsche Forschungsgemeinschaft, D-53170 Bonn. Analytical methods for carcinogenic workplace substances are published in cooperation with the analytical chemistry group from the German statutory accident insurance, 'Arbeitsgruppe Analytik des Fachausschusses Chemie der Deutschen Gesetzlichen Unfallversicherung' *Von den Berufsgenossenschaften anerkannte Analysenverfahren zur Feststellung der Konzentration krebserzeugender Arbeitsstoffe in der Luft in Arbeitsbereichen*, Carl Heymanns Verl. KG, D-50939 Köln.

regularly in both German and English. The methods are conceived as so-called standard operating procedures (SOP) which are intended to ensure comparability of the analytical results from laboratory to laboratory and with the above-mentioned thresholds. Thus they contribute to the quality control of the results. They also provide a good basis for the health protection which is the objective of the threshold values.

In the development and selection of these analytical methods, the accuracy and reliability of the results they yield is the most important factor. The methods reflect the current state of technology. They are repeatedly modified in the light of recent developments.

The methods for analyses in biological material are, whenever possible, designed so that their analytical range includes the concentration range relevant in environmental studies. This makes it also possible to differentiate the occupational from the environmental concentration range and to evaluate any differences.

II List of Substances

In the following list, maximum concentrations in the workplace air (MAK values) of gases, vapours and volatile airborne particulates are expressed in ml/m³ (millilitre (ml) of the substance per cubic metre (m³) of air, ppm), a unit which is unaffected by temperature and barometric pressure, as well as in mg/m³ (milligram (mg) of the substance per cubic metre (m³) of air), a unit which is temperature and pressure dependent and has therefore been adjusted to a temperature of 20 °C and barometric pressure of 1013 hPa;[13] the MAK values for non-volatile airborne particulates (dust, smoke, mist) are given in mg/m³ air. Non-volatile airborne particulates are substances which have such a low vapour pressure that at normal temperatures a dangerously high concentration cannot occur in the gaseous phase.

Since the health hazards associated with handling a substance can be affected by its volatility, the vapour pressure of a series of highly volatile compounds has been listed in a special column of the table. Knowledge of the vapour pressure makes it possible to estimate whether hazardous concentrations of the substance can accumulate by evaporation under the conditions prevailing at the particular workplace. The listed vapour pressure values are taken from the literature and have been rounded for practical purposes.

A,B,C,D	pregnancy risk groups or "–" (see p. 186)
H	danger of percutaneous absorption (see p. 183)
Sa	danger of sensitization of the airways (see Section IV p. 162)
Sh	danger of sensitization of the skin (see Section IV p. 160)
Sah	danger of sensitization of the airways and the skin (see Section IV p. 164)
SP	danger of photocontact sensitization (see Section IV p. 159)
°	not registered as a pesticide
I/II	peak limitation categories (excursion factors in parentheses), or "–" (see p. 182)
★	indicates a change from the 2007 MAK list, see p. 7

MAK [mg/m³] :

R	measured as the respirable fraction of the aerosol (see Section Vd p. 179)
I	measured as the inhalable fraction of the aerosol (see Section Vd p. 178)

---

[13] Under the specified atmospheric conditions (20 °C, 1013 hPa) the concentration values can be converted according to the following formula:

$$C(mg/m^3) = \frac{\text{molar mass in g}}{\text{molar volume in l}} \cdot C(ml/m^3)$$

The molar volume corresponds to 24.1 l at 20 °C and 1013 hPa (mbar).
The MAK value is generally established with the units ml/m³; the value in mg/m³ is then calculated with the formula given above. Following a suggestion from users, the calculated values are given correct to two significant figures.

List of MAK and BAT Values 2008. DFG, Deutsche Forschungsgemeinschaft

ISBN: 978-3-527-32305-0

a. Substances with MAK values
and substances listed in Sections II b and III to XV

MAK values which were established on the condition that the working week exceeds 40 hours have been retained with no change in the toxicological evaluation.

Substance [CAS number]	Formula	MAK ml/m³ (ppm)	MAK mg/m³	Peak limitation	H;S	Carcinogen category	Pregnancy risk group	Germ cell mutagen categ.	Vapour pressure in hPa at 20°C
Abietic acid [514-10-3]	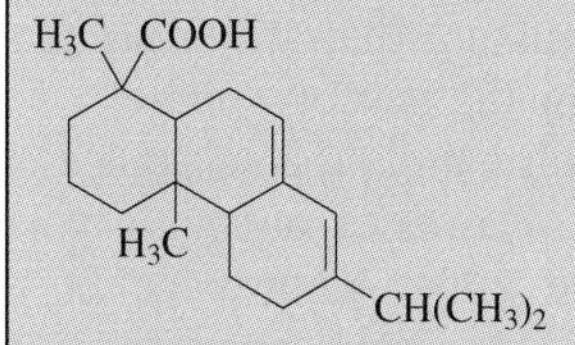	see Section IIb			Sh[14]				
Acacia melanoxylon	see Woods								
Acetaldehyde [75-07-0]	$H_3C{-}CHO$	50	91	I(1)[15]		5	C	5	
Acetamide [60-35-5]	$H_3C{-}CO{-}NH_2$	–	–	–		3B	–		
Acetic acid [64-19-7]	$H_3C{-}COOH$	10	25	I(2)			C		
Acetic acid methyl ester	see Methyl acetate								
Acetic acid 2-propoxyethyl ester	see Ethylene glycol monopropyl ether acetate								
Acetic anhydride [108-24-7]	$H_3C{-}CO{-}O{-}CO{-}CH_3$	5	21	I(1)			D		4
Acetoacetic acid ethyl ester [141-97-9]	$H_3C{-}CO{-}CH_2{-}COO{-}CH_2{-}CH_3$	see Section IIb							
Acetone [67-64-1]	$H_3C{-}CO{-}CH_3$	500 see Section XII	1200	I(2)			D		240
Acetonitrile [75-05-8]	$H_3C{-}CN$	20	34	II(2)	H		C		96.6
Acetyl acetone	see 2,4-Pentanedione								
Acetylene black	see Carbon black								
Acetylene tetrabromide	see 1,1,2,2-Tetrabromoethane								
Acetylene tetrachloride	see 1,1,2,2-Tetrachloroethane								

[14] An immunological genesis of the asthma often seen in persons working with materials containing abietic acid has not been proved.
[15] A momentary value of 100 ml/m³ (180 mg/m³) should not be exceeded.

Substance [CAS number]	Formula	MAK ml/m³ (ppm)	MAK mg/m³	Peak limitation	H;S	Carcinogen category	Pregnancy risk group	Germ cell mutagen categ.	Vapour pressure in hPa at 20°C
Acrolein [107-02-8]	$H_2C{=}CH{-}CHO$	–	–	–		3B	–		290
Acrylaldehyde	see Acrolein								
Acrylamide [79-06-1]	$H_2C{=}CH{-}CO{-}NH_2$	see Section XII		–	H Sh	2	–	2	
Acrylates and methacrylates		see Section IVe							
Acrylic acid [79-10-7]	$H_2C{=}CH{-}COOH$	10	30	I(1)			C		
Acrylic acid *n*-butyl ester [141-32-2]	$H_2C{=}CH{-}C({=}O){-}O{-}(CH_2)_3{-}CH_3$	2	11	I(2)	Sh		C		4.3
Acrylic acid *tert*-butyl ester	see *tert*-Butyl acrylate								
Acrylic acid diester with ethylene glycol	see Triethylene glycol diacrylate								
Acrylic acid 2-ethoxyethanol diester	see Diethylene glycol diacrylate								
Acrylic acid ethyl ester [140-88-5]	$H_2C{=}CH{-}COOCH_2{-}CH_3$	5	21	I(2)	Sh		C		39
Acrylic acid 2-ethylhexyl ester [103-11-7]	$H_2C{=}CH{-}C({=}O){-}O{-}CH_2{-}CH(C_2H_5){-}(CH_2)_3{-}CH_3$	5	38	I(1)	Sh		C		12
Acrylic acid 2-hydroxyethyl ester [818-61-1]	$H_2C{=}CH{-}COO{-}C_2H_4OH$	see Section IV			Sh				
Acrylic acid hydroxypropyl ester (all isomers) [25584-83-2]	$H_2C{=}CH{-}COO{-}C_3H_6OH$	see Section IIb			Sh				
Acrylic acid methyl ester [96-33-3]	$H_2C{=}CH{-}COOCH_3$	5	18	I(1)	Sh		D		89
Acrylic acid pentaerythritol triester	see Pentaerythritol triacrylate								
Acrylic acid polymer (neutralized, cross-linked)	$({-}CH_2{-}CH(COO^-){-})_n$		0.05 **R**	I(1)		4	C		
Acrylic acid resin	see Acrylic acid polymer								

Substance [CAS number]	Formula	MAK ml/m³ (ppm)	MAK mg/m³	Peak limitation	H;S	Carcinogen category	Pregnancy risk group	Germ cell mutagen categ.	Vapour pressure in hPa at 20°C
Acrylic acid tetramethylene ester	see 1,4-Butanediol diacrylate								
Acrylic acid 1,1,1-(trihydroxymethyl)propane triester	see Trimethylolpropane triacrylate								
Acrylonitrile [107-13-1]	$H_2C{=}CH{-}CN$	see Section XIII		–	H Sh	2	–		116
Actinolite (fibrous dust)	see Asbestos								
Aerosols		see Section V							
Afara	see Woods, *Terminalia superba*								
Aflatoxins [1402-68-2]		–	–	–	H	1	–	3A	
African blackwood	see Woods, *Dalbergia melanoxylon*								
African "cherry"	see Woods, *Tieghemella heckelii*								
African whitewood	see Woods, *Triplochiton scleroxylon*								
Aldrin° [309-00-2]	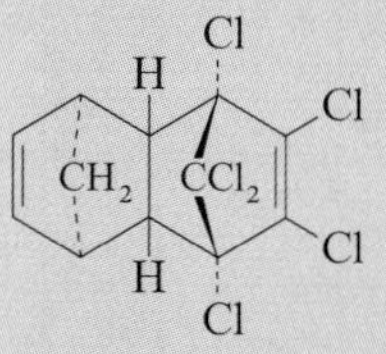		0.25 **I**	II(8)	H				
Alkali chromates	see Chromium(VI) compounds								
Alkali citrates	see Citric acid								
Alkali persulfates	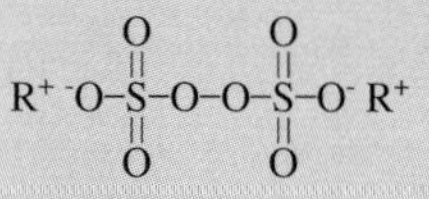 R = alkali metal ion	see Section IV			Sah				
Alkyl benzenesulfonates C10–C14, linear [69669-44-9; 85117-50-6]	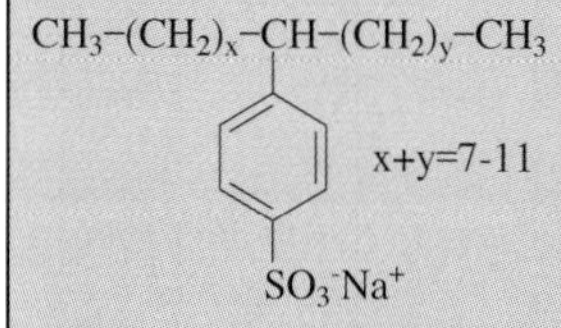	see Section IIb							
N-Alkyl-*N*,*N*-dimethyl-*N*-benzylammoniumchloride	see Benzalkonium chloride								

Substance [CAS number]	Formula	MAK ml/m³ (ppm)	MAK mg/m³	Peak limitation	H;S	Carcinogen category	Pregnancy risk group	Germ cell mutagen categ.	Vapour pressure in hPa at 20°C
Alkyl ether carboxylic acids	$RO-(CH_2-CH_2-O)_n-CH_2COOH$ $RO-(CH(CH_3)-CH_2-O)_n-CH_2COOH$ R = alkyl, n = 2-10	see Section IIb							
Allyl alcohol [107-18-6]	$H_2C=CH-CH_2OH$	–	–	–	H	3B	–		24
Allyl chloride [107-05-1]	$H_2C=CH-CH_2Cl$	–	–	–	H	3B	–		393
Allyl 2,3-epoxypropyl ether	see Allyl glycidyl ether								
Allyl glycidyl ether [106-92-3]	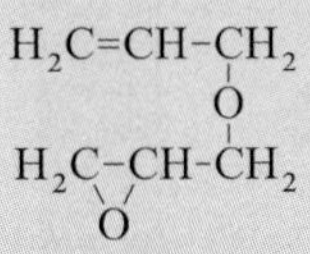	–	–	–	H Sh	2	–		
4-Allyl-2-methoxyphenol	see Eugenol								
Allyl propyl disulfide [2179-59-1]	$H_2C=CH-CH_2-S$ $H_3C-(CH_2)_2-S$	2	12	I(1)					
Aluminium- [7429-90-5], **Aluminium oxide-** [1344-28-1; 1302-74-5] and **Aluminium hydroxide-** [21645-51-2] **containing dusts** (inhalable fraction)	Al	see Section Vf, Vg and XII	4 **I**				D		
Aluminium- [7429-90-5], **Aluminium oxide-** [1344-28-1; 1302-74-5] and **Aluminium hydroxide-** [21645-51-2] **containing dusts** (respirable fraction)	Al	see Section Vf, Vg and XII	1.5 **R**				D		
Aluminium oxide [1344-28-1] (fibrous dust)	Al_2O_3	see Section III		–		2	–		
***o*-Aminoazotoluene** [97-56-3]	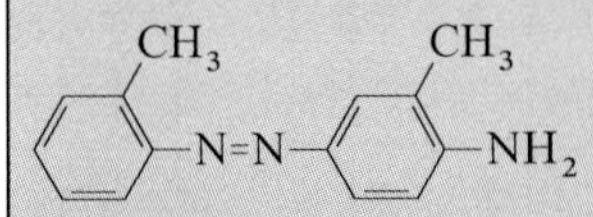	–	–	–	H Sh	2	–	3B	
4-Aminobiphenyl [92-67-1]	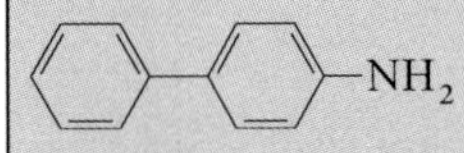	see Section XII		–	H	1	–		
1-Aminobutane	see *n*-Butylamine								

Substance [CAS number]	Formula	MAK ml/m³ (ppm)	MAK mg/m³	Peak limitation	H;S	Carcinogen category	Pregnancy risk group	Germ cell mutagen categ.	Vapour pressure in hPa at 20°C
2-Aminobutane	see *sec*-Butylamine								
1-Amino-4-chloro-benzene	see *p*-Chloroaniline								
2-Amino-5-chloro-toluene	see 4-Chloro-*o*-toluidine								
Aminocyclohexane	see Cyclohexylamine								
1-Amino-3,4-dichloro-benzene	see 3,4-Dichloroaniline								
2-Aminoethanol [141-43-5]	$H_2NCH_2{-}CH_2OH$	2	5.1	I(2)	Sh		C		0.53
2-(2-Aminoethoxy)-ethanol [929-06-6]	$HO{-}(CH_2)_2{-}O{-}(CH_2)_2{-}NH_2$	see Section IIb							2
6-Amino-2-ethoxy-naphthalene [293733-21-8]	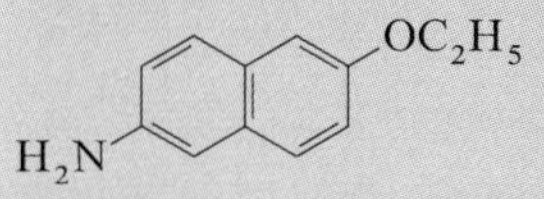	–	–	–		2	–		
3-Amino-9-ethyl-carbazole [132-32-1]	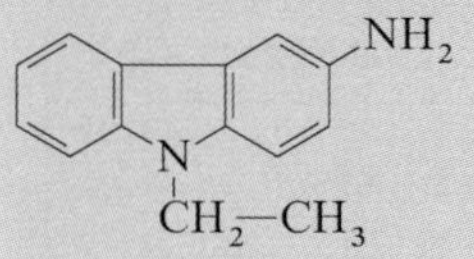	–	–	–		3B	–		
2-Amino-2-ethyl-1,3-propanediol [115-70-8]	$(HO{-}CH_2)_2C(C_2H_5)NH_2$	see Section IIb							
4-Amino-1-hydroxy-benzene	see *p*-Aminophenol								
2-Aminoisobutanol	see 2-Amino-2-methyl-1-propanol								
1-Amino-2-methoxy-5-methylbenzene	see 5-Methyl-*o*-anisidine								
3-Amino-4-methoxy-toluene	see 5-Methyl-*o*-anisidine								
4-Amino-1-methylbenzene	see *p*-Toluidine								
1-Amino-2-methylpropane	see Isobutylamine								
2-Amino-2-methylpropane	see *tert*-Butylamine								

Substance [CAS number]	Formula	MAK ml/m³ (ppm)	MAK mg/m³	Peak limitation	H;S	Carcinogen category	Pregnancy risk group	Germ cell mutagen categ.	Vapour pressure in hPa at 20°C
2-Amino-2-methyl-1-propanol [124-68-5]	$CH_3-C(CH_3)NH_2-CH_2-OH$	see Section II b							
3-Aminomethyl-3,5,5-trimethyl-cyclohexylamine (Isophorone diamine) [2855-13-2]	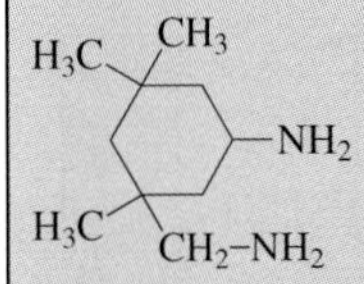	see Section II b			Sh				
Aminonitrofen	see 4-(2,4-Dichlorophenoxy)-benzenamine								
4-Amino-2-nitrophenol	see 2-Nitro-4-aminophenol								
2-Amino-4-nitrotoluene	see 5-Nitro-*o*-toluidine								
4-Aminophenol	see *p*-Aminophenol								
***p*-Aminophenol** [123-30-8]	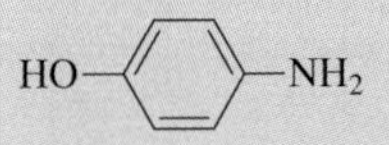	see Section IV			Sh				
2-[(4-Aminophenyl)-amino]-5-nitro-benzenesulfonic acid	see 4-Nitro-4'-aminodiphenyl-amine-2-sulfonic acid								
2-Aminopropane	see Isopropylamine								
1-Amino-2-propanol [78-96-6]	$NH_2-CH_2-CHOH-CH_3$	see Section II b							
2-Aminopyridine [504-29-0]	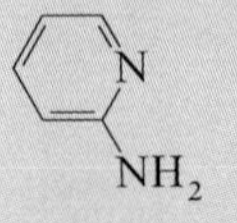	see Section II b							
4-Aminotoluene	see *p*-Toluidine								
3-Amino-*p*-toluidine	see Toluene-2,4-diamine								
5-Amino-*o*-toluidine	see Toluene-2,4-diamine								
3-Amino-1,2,4-triazole	see Amitrole								
★ **Aminotris(methylene-phosphonic acid)** [6419-19-8]	$N(CH_2PO_3H_2)_3$	see Section II b and Xc							
Amitrole [61-82-5]	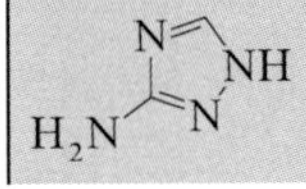		0.2 **I**	II (8)		3B	C		

Substance [CAS number]	Formula	MAK ml/m³ (ppm)	MAK mg/m³	Peak limitation	H;S	Carcinogen category	Pregnancy risk group	Germ cell mutagen categ.	Vapour pressure in hPa at 20°C
Ammonia [7664-41-7]	NH_3	20	14	I(2)			C		8570
Ammonium molybdate	see Molybdenum and its compounds								
Ammonium perfluoro-octanoate	see Perfluorooctanoic acid								
Ammonium peroxy-disulfate	see Ammonium persulfate								
Ammonium persulfate [7727-54-0]	$NH_4^+ \ {}^-O-S(=O)_2-O-O-S(=O)_2-O^- \ NH_4^+$	see Section IV			Sah				
Ammonium sulfamate [7773-06-0]	$NH_4^{\oplus} \ H_2N-SO_3^{\ominus}$	see Section IIb							
Amorphous carbon	see Carbon black								
Amosite (fibrous dust)	see Asbestos								
Amyl acetate (all isomers):	$H_3C-COOC_5H_{11}$	50	270	I(1)					<10
1,1-Dimethylpropyl acetate [625-16-1],	$CH_3COO-C(CH_3)_2CH_2CH_3$						D		
1-Methylbutyl acetate [626-38-0],	$CH_3COO-CH(CH_3)(CH_2)_2CH_3$						D		9.3
2-Methylbutyl acetate [624-41-9],	$CH_3COO-CH_2CH(CH_3)CH_2CH_3$						C		
3-Methylbutyl acetate [123-92-2],	$CH_3COO-(CH_2)_2CH(CH_3)_2$						D		5.3
1-Pentyl acetate [628-63-7],	$CH_3COO-(CH_2)_4CH_3$						C		5.3
3-Pentyl acetate [620-11-1]	$CH_3COO-CH(CH_2CH_3)_2$						D		
Amyl alcohol	see Pentanol								
α-Amylase		see Section IV			Sa				
α-Amylcinnamaldehyde [122-40-7]	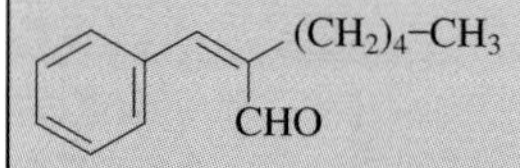	see Section IV			Sh				
Aniline [62-53-3]	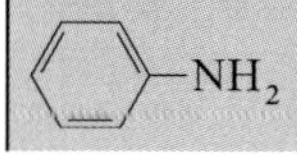	2 see Section XII	7.7	II(2)	H Sh	4	C		

Substance [CAS number]	Formula	MAK ml/m³ (ppm)	MAK mg/m³	Peak limitation	H;S	Carcinogen category	Pregnancy risk group	Germ cell mutagen categ.	Vapour pressure in hPa at 20°C
Animal hair, epithelia and other materials derived from animals		see Section IV			Sah				
***o*-Anisidine** [90-04-0]	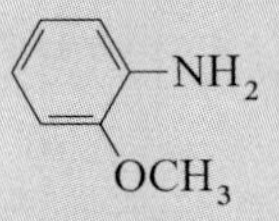	–	–	–	H	2	–		
***p*-Anisidine** [104-94-9]	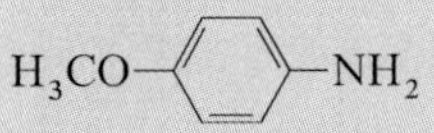	–	–	–	H	3B	–		
Anthanthrene [191-26-4]	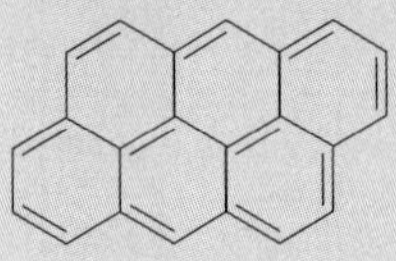	see Section III pyrolysis products of organic materials		–	H	2	–		
Anthophyllite (fibrous dust)	see Asbestos								
Anthracite dust	see Coal mine dust								
Antibiotics		see Section IVe							
Antimony [7440-36-0] and its inorganic compounds (inhalable fraction) except for stibine	Sb	see Section XII		–		2	–	3B	
ANTU	see 1-Naphthylthiourea								
***p*-Aramid** [26125-61-1] (fibrous dust)	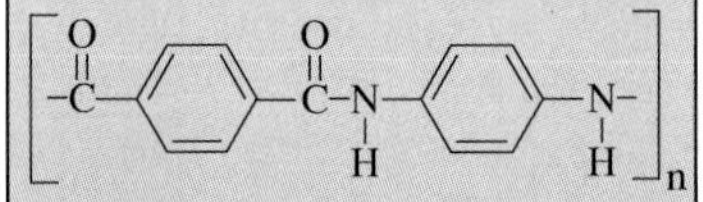	see Section III		–		3B	–		
Arborvitae	see Woods, *Thuja* spp.								
Arprocarb	see Propoxur								
Arsenic and inorganic arsenic compounds Metallic arsenic [7440-38-2], Arsenic trioxide [1327-53-3], Arsenous acid [13464-58-9] and its salts, e.g.	 As As_2O_3 H_3AsO_3	see Section XII		–		1	–	3A	

Substance [CAS number]	Formula	MAK ml/m³ (ppm)	MAK mg/m³	Peak limitation	H;S	Carcinogen category	Pregnancy risk group	Germ cell mutagen categ.	Vapour pressure in hPa at 20°C
Sodium arsenite [7784-46-5], Arsenic pentoxide [1303-28-2], Arsenic acid [7778-39-4] and its salts, e. g. Lead arsenate [3687-31-8], Calcium arsenate [7778-44-1]	$NaAsO_2$ As_2O_5 H_3AsO_4 $Pb_3(AsO_4)_2$ $Ca_3(AsO_4)_2$								
Arsenic(III) oxide	see Arsenic								
Arsenic(V) oxide	see Arsenic								
Arsine [7784-42-1]	AsH_3	see Section IIb							
Artificial almond oil	see Benzaldehyde								
Asbestos [1332-21-4] (fibrous dust)	Actinolite, Amosite, Anthophyllite, Chrysotile, Crocidolite and Tremolite	see Section III		–		1	–		
Atrazine [1912-24-9]	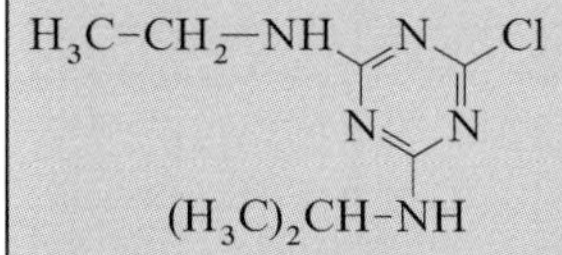		2 **I**	II(8)					
Attapulgite [12174-11-7] (fibrous dust)	$Mg_5Si_8O_{20}(OH)_2(H_2O)_4 \cdot 4H_2O$	see Section III		–		2	–		
Auramine [492-80-8] and Auramine hydrochloride [2465-27-2]	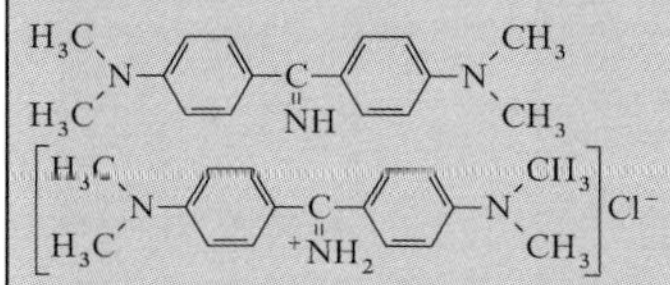	–	–	–	H	2	–		
Australian blackwood	see Woods, *Acacia melanoxylon*								
Australian silky oak	see Woods, *Grevillea robusta*								
Ayan	see Woods, *Distemonanthus benthamianus*								

Substance [CAS number]	Formula	MAK ml/m³ (ppm)	MAK mg/m³	Peak limitation	H;S	Carcinogen category	Pregnancy risk group	Germ cell mutagen categ.	Vapour pressure in hPa at 20°C
Azinphos-methyl [86-50-0]	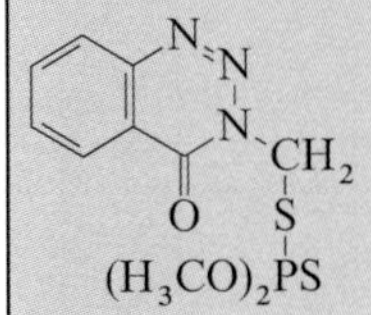		0.2 **I**	II(8)	H				
Aziridine	see Ethylenimine								
Azo colourants		see Section III		–			–		
Azoimide	see Hydrazoic acid								
Barium compounds (soluble) (as Ba [7440-39-3])			0.5 **I**	II(2)					
★ **Barium sulfate** [7727-43-7] (inhalable fraction)	$BaSO_4$	see Section Vf and Vg	4 **I**				C		
★ **Barium sulfate** [7727-43-7] (respirable fraction)	$BaSO_4$	see Section Vf and Vg	1.5 **R**				C		
Beech wood dust		–	–	–		1	–		
Behenic acid [112-85-6]	$CH_3(CH_2)_{20}COOH$	see Section IIb							
Benomyl [17804-35-2]	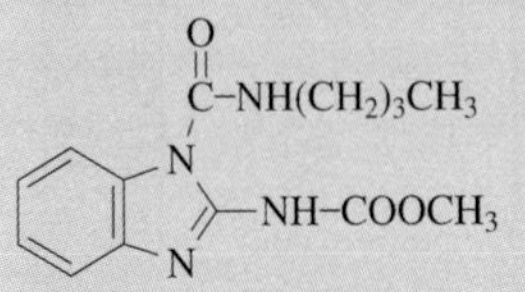				Sh			3A	
Benzal chloride	see Benzyl dichloride								
Benzaldehyde [100-52-7]	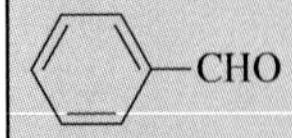	see Section IIb							
★ **Benzalkonium chloride** [8001-54-5]	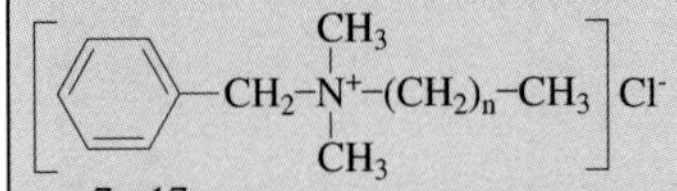 n = 7 - 17	see Section IIb							
Benzene [71-43-2]	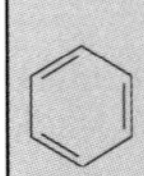	see Section XIII		–	H	1	–	3A	101
1,2-Benzenedicarboxylic acid	see Phthalic acid								

Substance [CAS number]	Formula	MAK ml/m³ (ppm)	MAK mg/m³	Peak limitation	H;S	Carcinogen category	Pregnancy risk group	Germ cell mutagen categ.	Vapour pressure in hPa at 20°C
1,2-Benzenedicarboxylic acid di-2-propenyl ester	see Diallyl phthalate								
1,3-Benzenediol	see Resorcinol								
Benzidine [92-87-5] and its salts	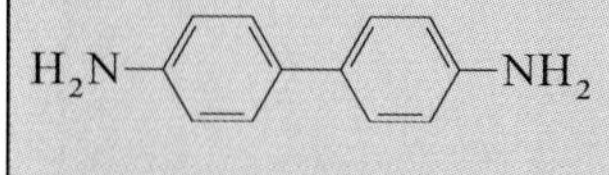	see Section XII		–	H	1	–		
Benzilidene chloride	see Benzyl dichloride								
1*H*-Benzimidazole-2-carbamic acid, methyl ester	see Carbendazim								
1,2-Benzisothiazol-3(2*H*)-one [2634-33-5]	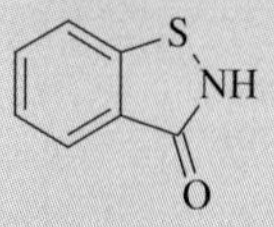	see Section IIb			Sh				
Benzo[*a*]anthracene [56-55-3]	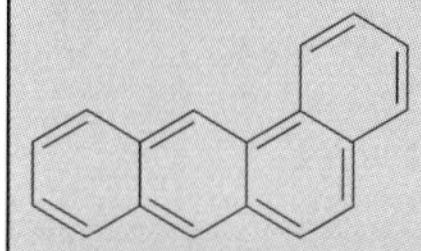	see Section III pyrolysis products of organic materials		–	H	2	–	3A	
Benzo[*b*]fluoranthene [205-99-2]	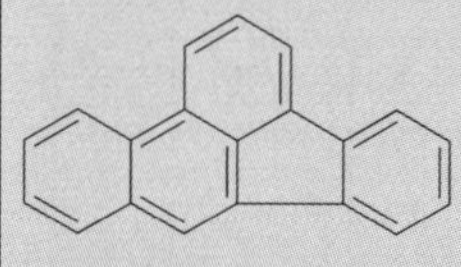	see Section III pyrolysis products of organic materials		–	H	2	–	3B	
Benzo[*j*]fluoranthene [205-82-3]	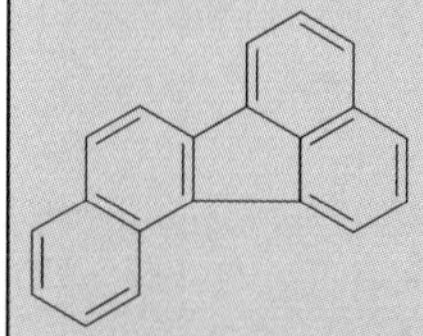	see Section III pyrolysis products of organic materials		–	H	2	–	3B	
Benzo[*k*]fluoranthene [207-08-9]	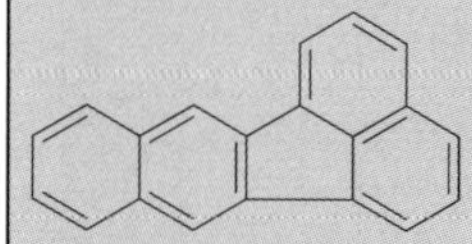	see Section III pyrolysis products of organic materials		–	H	2	–	3B	
Benzoic acid [16] [65-85-0]	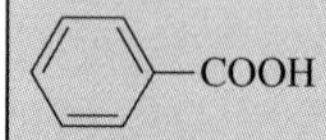	see Section IIb							
Benzoic aldehyde	see Benzaldehyde								

[16] causes pseudoallergic reactions, see *Toxikologisch-arbeitsmedizinische Begründung von MAK-Werten* (21st issue 1995)

Substance [CAS number]	Formula	MAK ml/m³ (ppm)	MAK mg/m³	Peak limitation	H;S	Carcinogen category	Pregnancy risk group	Germ cell mutagen categ.	Vapour pressure in hPa at 20°C
Benzo[*b*]naphtho[2,1-*d*]-thiophene [239-35-0]	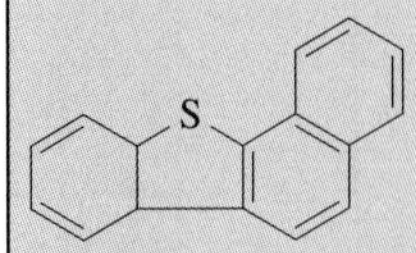	see Section III pyrolysis products of organic materials		–	H	2	–	3B	
Benzo[*a*]pyrene [50-32-8]	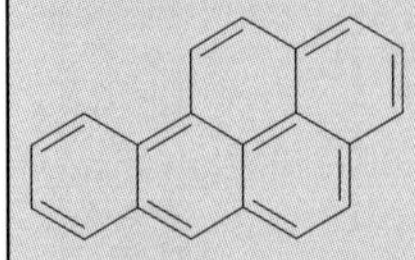	see Section III pyrolysis products of organic materials		–	H	2	–	2	
p-Benzoquinone	see Quinone								
1*H*-Benzotriazole [95-14-7]	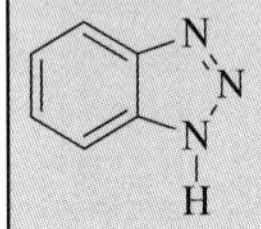	see Section II b							
Benzotrichloride	see Benzyl trichloride								
Benzoyl chloride [98-88-4] see also α-Chlorinated toluenes	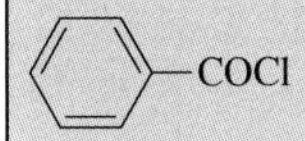					3B			
Benzoyl peroxide	see Dibenzoyl peroxide								
Benzyl alcohol [100-51-6]	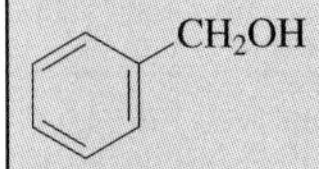	see Section II b							
Benzyl alcohol mono-(poly)hemiformal [17] [14548-60-8]	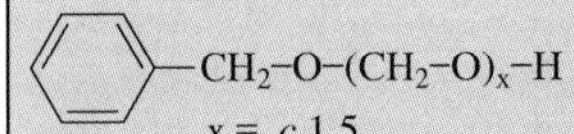 x = *c* 1.5	see Section II b			Sh				
Benzyl chloride [100-44-7] see also α-Chlorinated toluenes	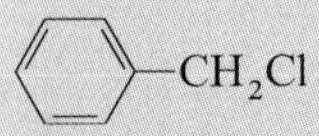	–	–	–	H	2	–		
Benzyl dichloride [98-87-3] see also α-Chlorinated toluenes	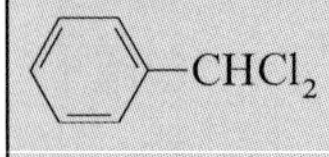	–	–	–	H	2	–		
Benzyl trichloride [98-07-7] see also α-Chlorinated toluenes	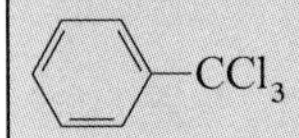	–	–	–	H	2	–		
Beryllium [7440-41-7] and its inorganic compounds	Be	see Section XII		–	Sah	1	–		

[17] releases formaldehyde

Substance [CAS number]	Formula	MAK ml/m³ (ppm)	MAK mg/m³	Peak limitation	H;S	Carcinogen category	Pregnancy risk group	Germ cell mutagen categ.	Vapour pressure in hPa at 20°C
Bété	see Woods, *Mansonia altissima*								
Bethabara	see Woods, *Tabebuia serratifolia*								
BHT	see 3,5-Di-*tert*-butyl-*p*-cresol								
N,N'-Bianiline	see Hydrazobenzene								
Biformyl	see Glyoxal								
2,2'-Bioxirane	see Diepoxybutane								
Biphenyl [92-52-4]	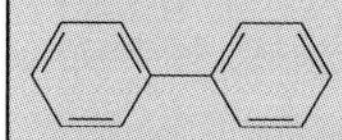	–	–	–	H	3B	–		
3,3',4,4'-Biphenyl-tetramine	see 3,3'-Diaminobenzidine								
Bis(2-aminoethyl)amine	see Diethylenetriamine								
N,N'-Bis(2-aminoethyl)-1,2-ethanediamine	see Triethylenetetramine								
1,3-Bis(aminomethyl)-benzene	see *m*-Xylylenediamine								
Bis[*O,O*-bis(2-ethylhexyl) phosphorodithioato-*S,S'*]-zinc	see *Zinc,* O,O'-di-2-ethylhexyl dithiophosphate								
Bis(2-chloroethyl)ether	see 2,2'-Dichlorodiethyl ether								
Bis(2-chloroethyl)sulfide	see Bis(β-chloroethyl)sulfide								
Bis(β-chloroethyl)sulfide (mustard gas) [505-60-2]	$ClCH_2{-}CH_2{-}S{-}CH_2{-}CH_2Cl$	–	–	–	H	1	–		
Bischloromethyl ether [542-88-1]	$ClCH_2{-}O{-}CH_2Cl$	–	–	–		1	–		
4,4'-Bis(dimethyl-amino)benzophenone	see Michler's ketone								
1,3-Bis(2,3-epoxy-propoxy)benzene	see Diglycidyl resorcinol ether								
1,4-Bis(2,3-epoxy-propoxy)butane	see 1,4-Butanediol diglycidyl ether								

Substance [CAS number]	Formula	MAK ml/m³ (ppm)	MAK mg/m³	Peak limitation	H;S	Carcinogen category	Pregnancy risk group	Germ cell mutagen categ.	Vapour pressure in hPa at 20°C
2,2-Bis(4-(2,3-epoxypropyloxy)phenyl)propane	see Bisphenol A diglycidyl ether								
2,2-Bis(*p*-glycidyloxyphenyl)propane	see Bisphenol A diglycidyl ether								
1,2-Bis(2-hydroxyethoxy)ethane	see Triethylene glycol								
Bis(2-hydroxyethyl) ether	see Diethylene glycol								
Bis(hydroxymethyl)acetylene	see Butynediol								
1,3-Bis(hydroxymethyl)-5,5-dimethyl-2,4-imidazolidinedione	see 1,3-Dimethylol-5,5-dimethyl hydantoin								
1,3-Bis(hydroxymethyl)urea [17] [140-95-4]	$(HOCH_2{-}NH)_2CO$	see Section II b							
2,2-Bis(4-hydroxyphenyl)propane	see Bisphenol A								
1,2-Bis(2-(methacryloyloxy)ethoxy)ethane	see Triethylene glycol dimethacrylate								
Bis(2-methoxyethyl)ether	see Diethylene glycol dimethyl ether								
Bis(2-methoxypropyl)ether	see Dipropylene glycol monomethyl ether								
Bismorpholino methane	see 4,4'-Methylenedimorpholine								
Bisphenol A [80-05-7]	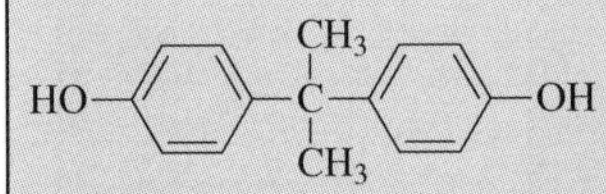	see Section XII	5 **I**	I(1)	SP		C		
Bisphenol A diglycidyl ether [1675-54-3]	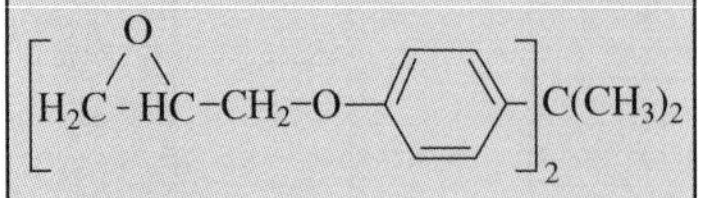	–	–	–	H Sh	3A	–		
Bisphenol A diglycidyl methacrylate [1565-94-2]	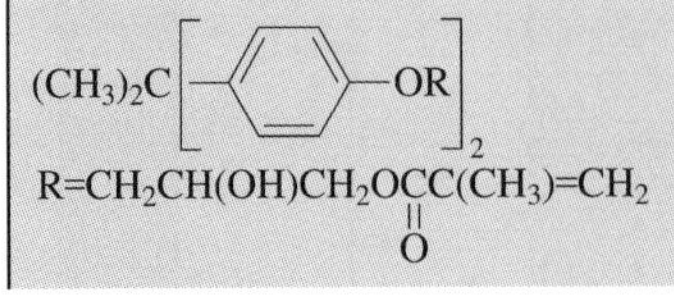	see Section IV			Sh				

[17] releases formaldehyde

Substance [CAS number]	Formula	MAK ml/m^3 (ppm)	MAK mg/m^3	Peak limitation	H;S	Carcinogen category	Pregnancy risk group	Germ cell mutagen categ.	Vapour pressure in hPa at 20°C
Bithionol [97-18-7]	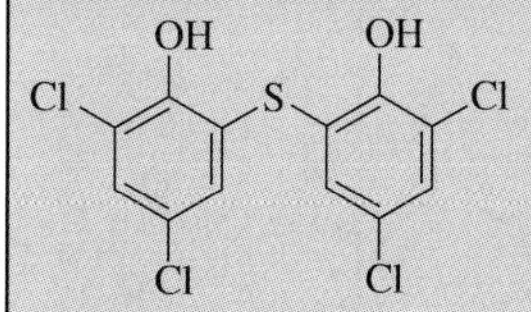	see Section IIb			SP				
Bitumen [8052-42-4] (vapour and aerosol)		–	–	–	H	2	–		
Black coal dust	see Coal mine dust								
Bombay blackwood	see Woods, *Dalbergia latifolia*								
Boric acid [10043-35-3]	$B(OH)_3$	see Section IIb							
Boron oxide [1303-86-2]	B_2O_3	see Section IIb							
Boron trifluoride [7637-07-2]	BF_3	see Section IIb							
Bowdichia nitida	see Woods								
Bromelain [9001-00-7]		see Section IV			Sa				
Bromine [7726-95-6]	Br_2	see Section IIb							
2-Bromo-2-(bromomethyl)glutaronitrile	see 1,2-Dibromo-2,4-dicyanobutane								
2-Bromo-2-(bromomethyl)pentanedinitrile	see 1,2-Dibromo-2,4-dicyanobutane								
Bromochloromethane [74-97-5]	CH_2BrCl	–	–	–	H	3B	–		147
2-Bromo-2-chloro-1,1,1-trifluoroethane	see Halothane								
Bromodichloromethane [75-27-4]	$CHBrCl_2$	–	–	–	H	2	–	3B	
Bromoethane [74-96-4]	$H_3C{-}CH_2Br$	–	–	–	H	2	–		507
Bromoform	see Tribromomethane								

Substance [CAS number]	Formula	MAK ml/m³ (ppm)	MAK mg/m³	Peak limitation	H;S	Carcinogen category	Pregnancy risk group	Germ cell mutagen categ.	Vapour pressure in hPa at 20°C
Bromomethane	see Methyl bromide								
2-Bromo-2-nitro-1,3-propanediol [18] [52-51-7]	$HOCH_2{-}CBr(NO_2){-}CH_2OH$	see Section IIb			H Sh				
Bromotrifluoromethane [75-63-8]	$BrCF_3$	1000	6200	II(8)			C		
Brown coal tars (soft coal tars)	see Pyrolysis products of organic materials								
Brucite (fibrous dust)	see Nemalite								
Brya ebenus	see Woods								
1,3-Butadiene [106-99-0]	$H_2C{=}CH{-}CH{=}CH_2$	see Section XIII		–		1	–	2	2477
1,3-Butadiene diepoxide	see Diepoxybutane								
Butane (both isomers): *n*-Butane [106-97-8], Isobutane [75-28-5]	$H_3C{-}(CH_2)_2{-}CH_3$ $(H_3C)_3CH$	1000	2400	II(4)			D		
1,4-Butane diglycidyl ether	see 1,4-Butanediol diglycidyl ether								
1,4-Butanediol diacrylate [1070-70-8]	$H_2C{=}CH{-}CO{-}(CH_2)_4{-}OC{-}HC{=}CH_2$ (both CO groups with =O)	see Section IV			Sh				
1,4-Butanediol diglycidyl ether [2425-79-8]	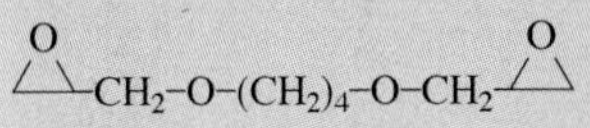	see Section IV			Sh				
1,4-Butanediol dimethacrylate [2082-81-7]	$CH_2{-}CH_2{-}O{-}OC{-}C(CH_3){=}CH_2$ $CH_2{-}CH_2{-}O{-}OC{-}C(CH_3){=}CH_2$	see Section IV			Sh				
Butane sulfone	see 1,4-Butane sultone								
1,4-Butane sultone [1633-83-6]	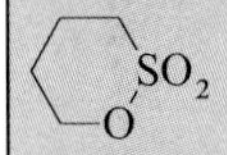	–	–	–		3B	–		
2,4-Butane sultone [1121-03-5]	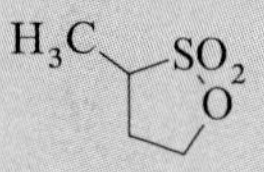	–	–	–		2	–		

[18] Use in metal-working fluids is not permitted: see TRGS 611.

Substance [CAS number]	Formula	MAK ml/m³ (ppm)	MAK mg/m³	Peak limitation	H;S	Carcinogen category	Pregnancy risk group	Germ cell mutagen categ.	Vapour pressure in hPa at 20°C
δ-Butane sultone	see 1,4-Butane sultone								
Butanethiol [109-79-5]	$H_3C{-}(CH_2)_2{-}CH_2SH$	0.5	1.9	II(2)			C		40
Butanol (all isomers)	see Butyl alcohol								
2-Butanone [78-93-3]	$H_3C{-}CH_2{-}CO{-}CH_3$	200 see Section XII	600	I(1)	H		C		105
Butanone oxime [96-29-7]	$H_3C{-}C({=}N{-}OH){-}CH_2{-}CH_3$	–	–	–	H Sh	2	–		
2-Butanone peroxide	see Methyl ethyl ketone peroxide								
2-Butenal (*trans-*)	see Crotonaldehyde								
1,2-Butene oxide	see 1,2-Butylene oxide								
Butoxydiglycol	see Diethylene glycol monobutyl ether								
1-*n*-Butoxy-2,3-epoxy-propane	see *n*-Butyl glycidyl ether								
1-*tert*-Butoxy-2,3-epoxy-propane	see *tert*-Butyl glycidyl ether								
2-Butoxyethanol	see Ethylene glycol monobutyl ether								
2-(2-Butoxyethoxy)-ethanol	see Diethylene glycol monobutyl ether								
2-Butoxyethyl acetate	see Ethylene glycol monobutyl ether acetate								
***n*-Butyl acetate** [123-86-4]	$H_3C{-}COOCH_2{-}(CH_2)_2{-}CH_3$	100	480	I(2)			C		13.3
***sec*-Butyl acetate** [105-46-4]	$H_3C{-}COOCH(CH_3){-}CH_2{-}CH_3$	see Section IIb							
***tert*-Butyl acetate** [540-88-5]	$H_3C{-}COOC(CH_3)_3$	20	96	II(4)			C		
n-Butyl acrylate	see Acrylic acid *n*-butyl ester								
***tert*-Butyl acrylate** [1663-39-4]	$(CH_3)_3C{-}O{-}C({=}O){-}CH{=}CH_2$	see Section IV			Sh				
***n*-Butyl alcohol** [71-36-3]	$H_3C{-}(CH_2)_2{-}CH_2OH$	100 see Section XII	310	I(1)			C		6.3

Substance [CAS number]	Formula	MAK ml/m³ (ppm)	MAK mg/m³	Peak limi-tation	H;S	Car-cino-gen cate-gory	Preg-nancy risk group	Germ cell muta-gen categ.	Vapour pres-sure in hPa at 20°C
***sec*-Butyl alcohol** [78-92-2]	$H_3C-CH_2-CHOH-CH_3$	see Section IIb							
***tert*-Butyl alcohol** [75-65-0]	$(H_3C)_3COH$	20	62	II (4)			C		40.8
2-Butylamine	see *sec*-Butylamine								
***n*-Butylamine** [109-73-9]	$H_3C-(CH_2)_2-CH_2NH_2$	2	6.1	I (2)[19]			C		
***sec*-Butylamine** [13952-84-6]	$H_3C-CH_2-CH(NH_2)-CH_3$	2	6.1	I (2)[19]			C		
***tert*-Butylamine** [75-64-9]	$(H_3C)_3CNH_2$	see Section IIb							
4-*tert*-Butylbenzoic acid [98-73-7]	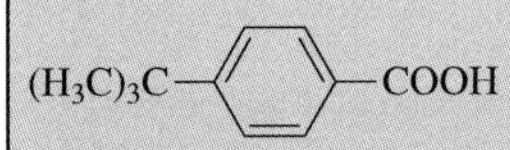	see Section Xc	2 **I**	II (2)	H		D		
Butylcarbamic acid 3-iodo-2-propynyl ester	see 3-Iodo-2-propynyl butyl-carbamate								
1-(Butylcarbamoyl)-2-benzimidazolecarbamic acid methyl ester	see Benomyl								
***p-tert*-Butylcatechol** [98-29-3; 27213-78-1]	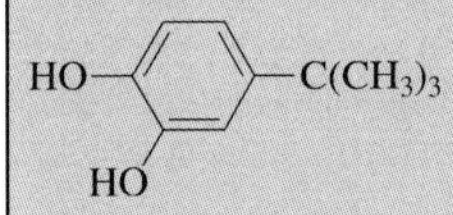	see Section IV			Sh				
n-Butyl chloroformate	see Chloroformic acid butyl ester								
2-*tert*-Butyl-*p*-cresol [2409-55-4]	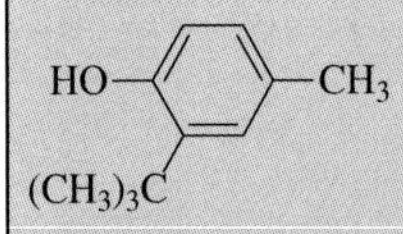	see Section IIb							
Butyldiglycol	see Diethylene glycol monobutyl ether								
1,4-Butylene glycol diacrylate	see 1,4-Butanediol diacrylate								
1,2-Butylene oxide [106-88-7]	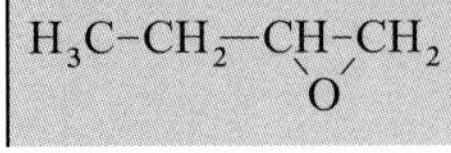	–	–	–	H	2	–		188

[9] A momentary value of 10 ml/m³ (30 mg/m³) should not be exceeded.

Substance [CAS number]	Formula	MAK ml/m³ (ppm)	MAK mg/m³	Peak limitation	H;S	Carcinogen category	Pregnancy risk group	Germ cell mutagen categ.	Vapour pressure in hPa at 20°C
***n*-Butyl glycidyl ether** (BGE) [2426-08-6]	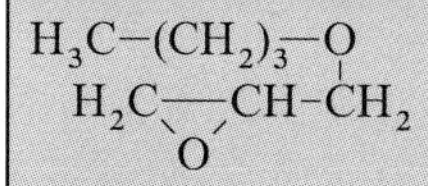	–	–	–	H Sh	3B	–	2	
***tert*-Butyl glycidyl ether** [7665-72-7]	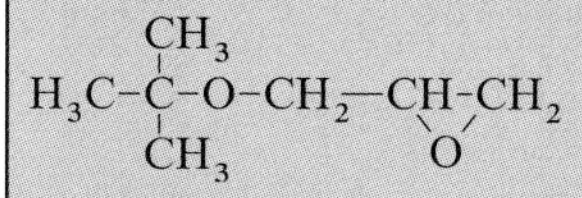	–	–	–	H Sh	3B	–		
Butyl glycolate	see Hydroxyacetic acid butyl ester								
***tert*-Butyl hydroperoxide** [75-91-2]	$(H_3C)_3C{-}OOH$	see Section Xa							
***tert*-Butyl-4-hydroxy-anisole** (BHA) [25013-16-5]	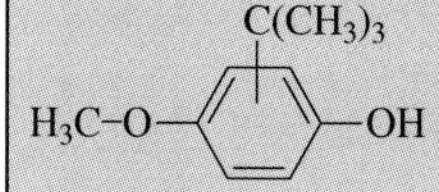	see Section IIb							
Butyl mercaptan	see Butanethiol								
***n*-Butyl methacrylate** [97-88-1]	$CH_3{-}(CH_2)_3{-}O{-}OC{-}C(CH_3){=}CH_2$	see Section IV			Sh				
***tert*-Butyl methyl ether** [1634-04-4]	$(CH_3)_3C{-}O{-}CH_3$	50 see Section XII	180	I(1.5)		3B	C		~300
***tert*-Butyl peracetate** [107-71-1]	$H_3C{-}CO{-}OO{-}C(CH_3)_3$	see Section Xa							
***p-tert*-Butyl phenol** [98-54-4]	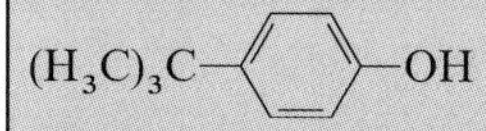	0.080 see Section XII	0.5	II(2)	H Sh		D		
p-tert-Butylphenol	see also Formaldehyde condensation products with *p-tert*-butylphenol								
***n*-Butyltin compounds** (as Sn [7440-31-5])		0.004	0.02	I(1)	H[20]	4	C		
***p-tert*-Butyl toluene** [98-51-1]	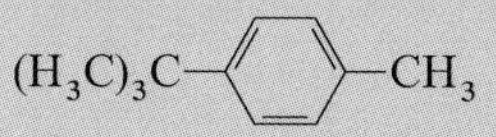	see Section IIb							
Butynediol [110-65-6]	$HO{-}CH_2{-}C{\equiv}C{-}CH_2{-}OH$		0.2 **I**	I(1)	H Sh		C		$1.7 \cdot 10^{-3}$
Cadmium [7440-43-9] and its inorganic compounds (inhalable fraction)	Cd	see Section XII		–	H	1	–	3A	

[20] For n-butyltin compounds whose organic ligands were already designated with "Sa" or "Sh", these designations also apply.

Substance [CAS number]	Formula	MAK ml/m³ (ppm)	MAK mg/m³	Peak limitation	H;S	Carcinogen category	Pregnancy risk group	Germ cell mutagen categ.	Vapour pressure in hPa at 20°C
Calcium arsenate	see Arsenic								
Calcium carbimide	see Calcium cyanamide								
Calcium chromate	see Chromium(VI) compounds								
Calcium cyanamide [156-62-7]	$CaCN_2$		1 **I**	II(2)	H		C		
Calcium molybdate	see Molybdenum and its compounds								
Calcium oxide [1305-78-8]	CaO	see Section II b							
Calcium sodium metaphosphate [23209-59-8] (fibrous dust)	$x CaO \cdot x Na_2O \cdot P_2O_5$	see Section III		–		3B	–		
★ **Calcium sulfate** Anhydrite [7778-18-9] Hemihydrate [10034-76-1] Dihydrate [10101-41-4] Gypsum [13397-24-5] (inhalable fraction)	$CaSO_4$	see Section V f, Vg and page 156	4 **I**				C		
★ **Calcium sulfate** Anhydrite [7778-18-9] Hemihydrate [10034-76-1] Dihydrate [10101-41-4] Gypsum [13397-24-5] (respirable fraction)	$CaSO_4$	see Section V f, Vg and page 156	1.5 **R**				C		
Calocedrus decurrens	see Woods								
CAM	see Chloroacetamide-*N*-methylol								
Camphor [76-22-2]	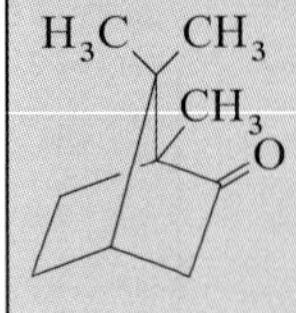	2	13	II(2)					
ε-Caprolactam [105-60-2] (vapour and dust)	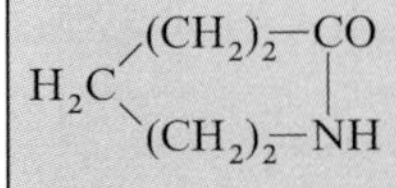		5 **I**	I(2)			C		
Carbamic acid ethyl ester [51-79-6]	$H_2N{-}CO{-}O{-}CH_2{-}CH_3$	–	–	–	H	2	–	3A	

Substance [CAS number]	Formula	MAK ml/m³ (ppm)	MAK mg/m³	Peak limitation	H;S	Carcinogen category	Pregnancy risk group	Germ cell mutagen categ.	Vapour pressure in hPa at 20°C
Carbaryl [63-25-2]	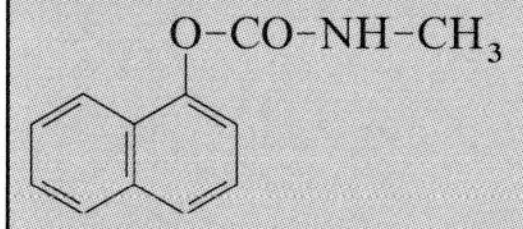		5 **I**	II(4)	H				
Carbendazim [10605-21-7]	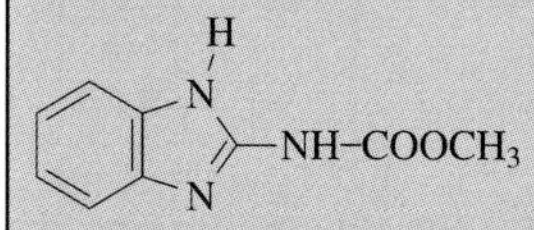							3A	
Carbodicyclohexylimide	see Dicyclohexylcarbodiimide								
Carbon black (inhalable fraction) [1333-86-4]		–	–	–		3B	–		
Carbon dioxide [124-38-9]	CO_2	5000	9100	II(2)					
Carbon disulfide [75-15-0]	CS_2	5	16	II(2)	H		B		400
		see Section XII							
Carbon monoxide [630-08-0]	CO	30	35	II(1)			B		
		see Section XII							
Carbon silicide	see Silicon carbide								
Carbon tetrachloride [56-23-5]	CCl_4	0.5	3.2	II(2)	H	4	C		120
		see Section XII							
Carbonyl chloride	see Phosgene								
Carborundum	see Silicon carbide								
***N*-Carboxyanthranilic anhydride** [118-48-9]	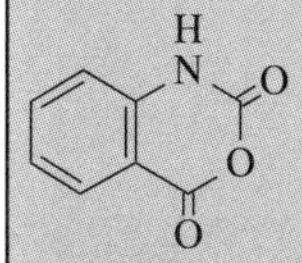	see Section IV			Sh				
Cedar	see Woods, *Thuja* spp., *Calocedrus* spp.								
Cellulases		see Section IV			Sa				
Cement	see Portland cement								
Ceramic fibres (fibrous dust)		see Section III		–		2	–		
Cereal flour dusts Rye		see Section IV			Sa				

Substance [CAS number]	Formula	MAK ml/m³ (ppm)	MAK mg/m³	Peak limitation	H;S	Carcinogen category	Pregnancy risk group	Germ cell mutagen categ.	Vapour pressure in hPa at 20°C
Wheat									
Cherry mahogany	see Woods, *Tieghemella heckelii*								
Chloramine	see *N*-Methyl-bis(2-chloroethyl)-amine								
Chlordane° [57-74-9]	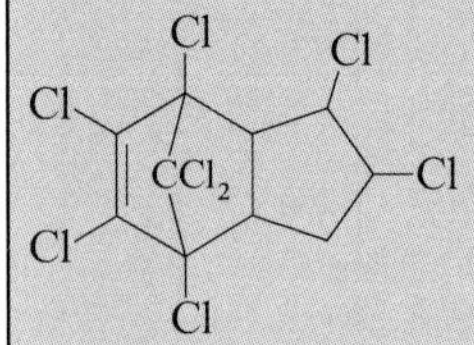		0.5 **I**	II(8)	H	3B			
Chlordecone° [143-50-0]	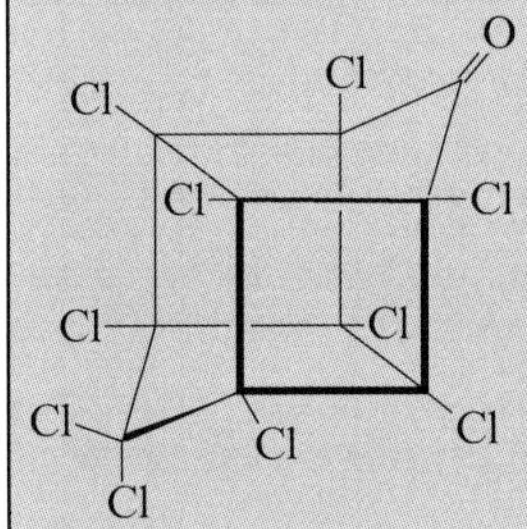	–	–	–		3B	–		
Chlorinated biphenyls (42% chlorine) [53469-21-9]	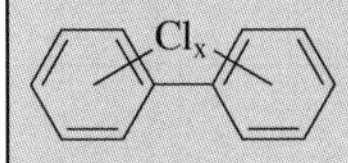 x = 1 - 10, mainly 3	0.1	1.1	II(8)	H	3B	B		
Chlorinated biphenyls (54% chlorine) [11097-69-1]	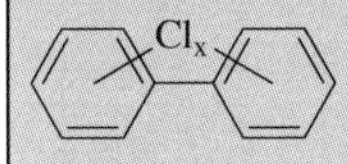 x = 1 - 10, mainly 5	0.05	0.70	II(8)	H	3B	B		
Chlorinated biphenyl oxides several CAS Nos, e.g. [55720-99-5]	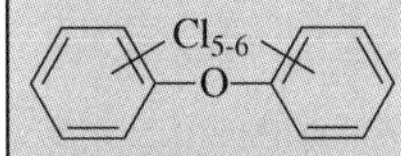	see Section II b			H				
Chlorinated camphene [8001-35-2]	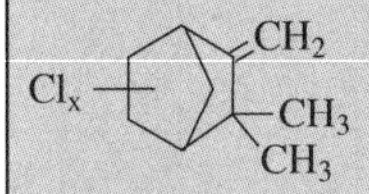 x = 4 - 12 on average 8	–	–	–	H	2	–		
Chlorinated naphthalenes	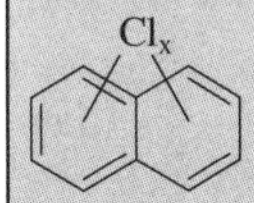 x = 1 - 8	see Section II b			H				
Chlorinated paraffins several CAS Nos, e.g. [63449-39-8]	from $C_{10}H_{22-n}Cl_n$ to $C_{30}H_{62-n}Cl_n$, unbranched chains, n = 1–28 (20% – 70% chlorine)	–	–	–		3B	–		

Substance [CAS number]	Formula	MAK ml/m³ (ppm)	MAK mg/m³	Peak limitation	H;S	Carcinogen category	Pregnancy risk group	Germ cell mutagen categ.	Vapour pressure in hPa at 20°C
α-Chlorinated toluenes: mixture of Benzoyl chloride [98-88-4], Benzyl chloride [100-44-7], Benzyl dichloride [98-87-3], Benzyl trichloride [98-07-7]		–	–	–	H	1	–		
Chlorine [7782-50-5]	Cl_2	0.5	1.5	I(1)			C		
Chlorine dioxide [10049-04-4]	ClO_2	0.1	0.28	I(1)			D		
Chlorine trifluoride [7790-91-2]	ClF_3	see Section IIb							
Chlorite	see Talc								
Chloroacetaldehyde [107-20-0]	$ClCH_2{-}CHO$	–	–	–	H	3B	–		133
Chloroacetamide-*N*-methylol (CAM) [17] [2832-19-1]	$H_2CCl{-}CO{-}NH{-}CH_2OH$	see Section Xc		–	Sh	3B	–		
Chloroacetic acid [79-11-8]	$ClCH_2{-}COOH$	see Section IIb							
Chloroacetic acid methyl ester [96-34-4]	$Cl{-}CH_2{-}CO{-}OCH_3$	1	4.5	I(1)	H Sh		C		~7
Chloroacetyl chloride [79-04-9]	$ClCH_2{-}COCl$	see Section IIb			H				
2-Chloroacrylonitrile [920-37-6]	$H_2C{=}CClCN$	–	–	–		3B	–		
γ-Chloroallyl chloride	see 1,3-Dichloropropene								
4-Chloroaniline	see *p*-Chloroaniline								
***o*-Chloroaniline** [95-51-2]	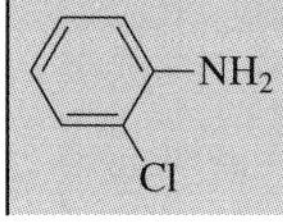	see Section IIb			H				

[17] releases formaldehyde

Substance [CAS number]	Formula	MAK ml/m³ (ppm)	MAK mg/m³	Peak limitation	H;S	Carcinogen category	Pregnancy risk group	Germ cell mutagen categ.	Vapour pressure in hPa at 20°C
***m*-Chloroaniline** [108-42-9]	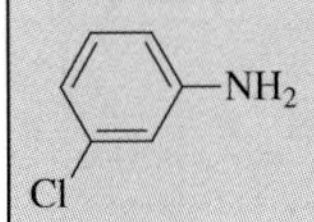	see Section IIb			H Sh				
★ ***p*-Chloroaniline** [106-47-8]	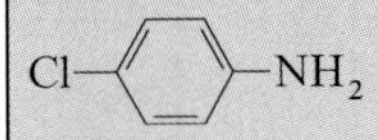	–	–	–	H Sh	2	–		
Chlorobenzene [108-90-7]	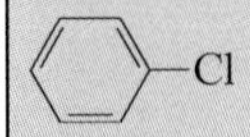	10 see Section XII	47	II(2)			C		12
Chlorobenzoic acid (all isomers): *o*-Chlorobenzoic acid [118-91-2] *m*-Chlorobenzoic acid [535-80-8] *p*-Chlorobenzoic acid [74-11-3]	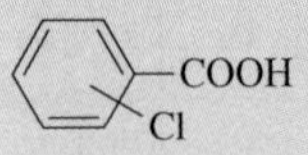	see Section IIb							
***p*-Chlorobenzotrichloride** [5216-25-1]	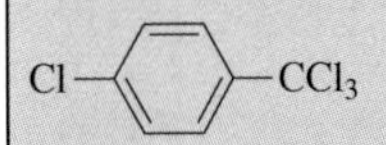	–	–	–	H	2	–		
Chlorobromomethane	see Bromochloromethane								
2-Chloro-1,3-butadiene	see Chloroprene								
***p*-Chloro-*m*-cresol** [59-50-7]	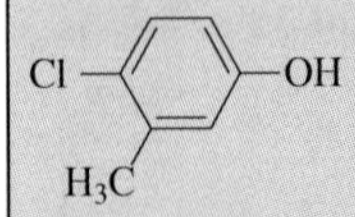	see Section IIb			Sh				
1-Chloro-1,1-difluoroethane (FC-142b) [75-68-3]	$ClF_2C{-}CH_3$	1000	4200	II(8)			D		
Chlorodifluoromethane[21] (FC-22) [75-45-6]	$CHClF_2$	500	1800	II(8)			C		
2-Chloro-1-(difluoromethoxy)-1,1,2-trifluoroethane	see Enflurane								

[21] applies only to the pure substance; for samples contaminated with chlorofluoromethane [593-70-4] see *Toxikologisch-arbeitsmedizinische Begründung von MAK-Werten*, 12th issue, 1986 and in English translation in *Occupational Toxicants*, Vol. 3, available from the publisher: WILEY-VCH, D-69451 Weinheim

Substance [CAS number]	Formula	MAK ml/m³ (ppm)	MAK mg/m³	Peak limi-tation	H;S	Car-cino-gen cate-gory	Preg-nancy risk group	Germ cell muta-gen categ.	Vapour pres-sure in hPa at 20°C
(*R*)-*N*-[(5-Chloro-3,4-dihydro-8-hydroxy-3-methyl-1-oxo-1*H*-2-benzopyran-7-yl)car-bonyl]-L-phenylalanine	see Ochratoxin A								
2-Chloro-10-(3-dimethyl-aminopropyl)pheno-thiazine	see Chlorpromazine								
Chlorodimethyl ether	see Monochlorodimethyl ether								
1-Chloro-2,4-dinitro-benzene [97-00-7]	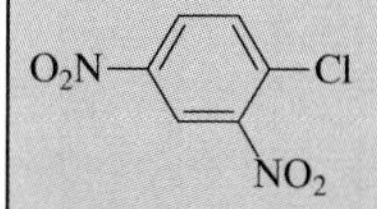	see Section IV			Sh				
1-Chloro-2,3-epoxy-propane	see Epichlorohydrin								
Chloroethane [75-00-3]	H_3C-CH_2Cl	–	–	–	H	3B	–		
Chloroethanoic acid	see Chloroacetic acid								
2-Chloroethanol [107-07-3]	$ClCH_2-CH_2OH$	1	3.3	II(1)	H		C		7
Chlorofluoromethane (FC-31) [593-70-4]	CH_2ClF	–	–	–		2	–		
Chloroform [67-66-3]	$CHCl_3$	0.5	2.5	II(2)	H	4	C		210
Chloroformic acid butyl ester [543-27-1];[592-34-7]	$Cl-\overset{\overset{O}{\|}}{C}-O-CH_2-CH(CH_3)_2$ $Cl-\overset{\overset{O}{\|}}{C}-O-(CH_2)_3-CH_3$	0.2	1.1	I(2)			C		7
Chloroformic acid ethyl ester [541-41-3]	$Cl-COO-CH_2-CH_3$	–	–	–		3B	–		54
Chloroformic acid methyl ester [79-22-1]	$Cl-\overset{\overset{O}{\|}}{C}-O-CH_3$	0.2	0.78	I(2)			C		137
***N*-Chloroformyl-morpholine** [15159-40-7]	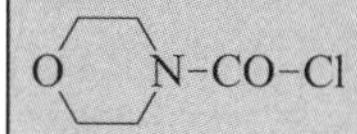	–	–	–		2	–		

Substance [CAS number]	Formula	MAK ml/m³ (ppm)	MAK mg/m³	Peak limitation	H;S	Carcinogen category	Pregnancy risk group	Germ cell mutagen categ.	Vapour pressure in hPa at 20°C
2-Chloro-*N*-hydroxymethylacetamide	see Chloroacetamide-*N*-methylol								
N-(((3*R*)-5-Chloro-8-hydroxy-3-methyl-1-oxo-7-isochromanyl)carbonyl)-3-phenyl-L-alanine	see Ochratoxin A								
1-Chloro-4-isocyanatobenzene	see 4-Chlorophenyl isocyanate								
Chloromethane	see Methyl chloride								
4-Chloromethylbiphenyl [1667-11-4]	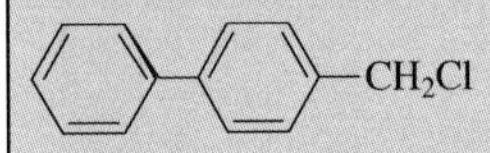	see Section II b							
5-Chloro-2-methyl-2,3-dihydroisothiazol-3-one [26172-55-4] **and** **2-Methyl-2,3-dihydroisothiazol-3-one** [2682-20-4] mixture in ratio 3:1	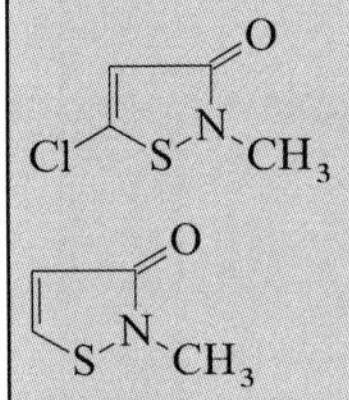	see Section Xc	0.2 **I**	I(2)	Sh		C		
bis-Chloromethyl ether	see Bischloromethyl ether								
3-Chloro-2-methylpropene [563-47-3]	$ClH_2C-C(CH_3)=CH_2$	–	–	–		3B	–		140
1-Chloro-2-nitrobenzene	see *o*-Chloronitrobenzene								
1-Chloro-4-nitrobenzene	see *p*-Chloronitrobenzene								
***o*-Chloronitrobenzene** [88-73-3]	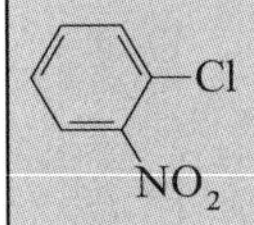	–	–	–	H	3B	–		6
***m*-Chloronitrobenzene** [121-73-3]	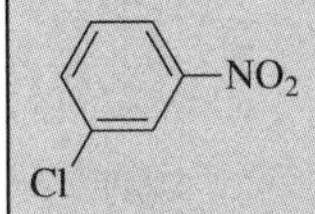	see Section II b			H				
***p*-Chloronitrobenzene** [100-00-5]	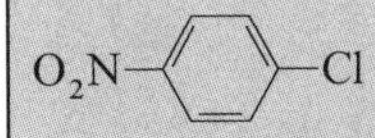	–	–	–	H	3B	–		
1-Chloro-1-nitropropane [600-25-9]	$H_3C-CH_2-CHClNO_2$	see Section II b							

Substance [CAS number]	Formula	MAK ml/m³ (ppm)	MAK mg/m³	Peak limitation	H;S	Carcinogen category	Pregnancy risk group	Germ cell mutagen categ.	Vapour pressure in hPa at 20°C
4-Chlorophenyl isocyanate [104-12-1]	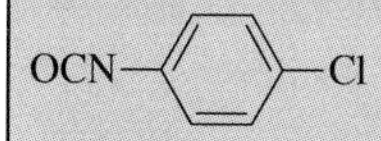	–	–	–		3B	–		
Chlorophora excelsa	see Woods								
Chloropicrin [76-06-2]	Cl_3CNO_2	0.1	0.68	I(1)					25
Chloroprene [126-99-8]	$H_2C{=}CCl{-}CH{=}CH_2$	–	–	–	H	2	–		267
3-Chloro-1,2-propanediol (α-Chlorohydrin) [96-24-2]	$HOCH_2{-}CHOH{-}CH_2Cl$	see Section IIb							
3-Chloro-1-propene	see Allyl chloride								
2-Chloro-2-propene nitrile	see 2-Chloroacrylonitrile								
Chlorothalonil [1897-45-6]	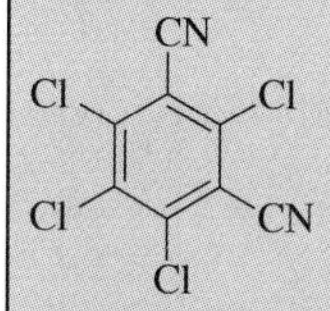	–	–	–	Sh	3B	–		
4-Chloro-*o*-toluidine [95-69-2]	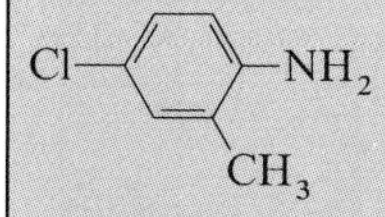	–	–	–	H	1	–	3A	
5-Chloro-*o*-toluidine [95-79-4]	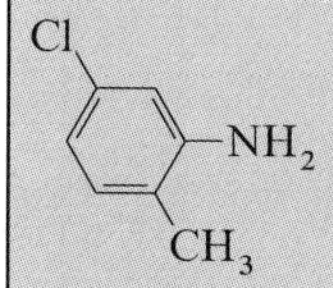	–	–	–		3B	–		
1-Chloro-4-(trichloromethyl)benzene	see *p*-Chlorobenzotrichloride								
2-Chloro-1,1,2-trifluoroethyl difluoromethyl ether	see Enflurane								
Chlorotrifluoromethane (FC-13) [75-72-9]	$CClF_3$	1000	4300	II(8)			D		

Substance [CAS number]	Formula	MAK ml/m³ (ppm)	MAK mg/m³	Peak limitation	H;S	Carcinogen category	Pregnancy risk group	Germ cell mutagen categ.	Vapour pressure in hPa at 20°C
Chlorpromazine (2-Chloro-10-(3-dimethylaminopropyl)-phenothiazine) [50-53-3]	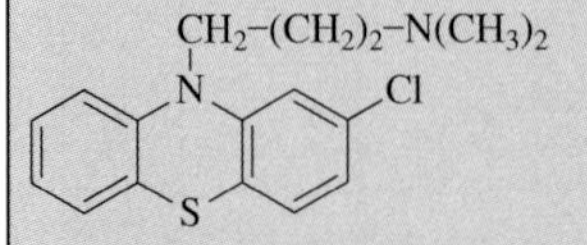	see Section IV			SP				
Chrome yellow	see Lead chromate								
Chromic acid	see Chromium(VI) compounds								
Chromium	see Chromium(VI) compounds								
Chromium carbonyl [13007-92-6]	$Cr(CO)_6$	–	–	–		3B	–		
Chromium-III-chromate (“Chromic-chromate”)	see Chromium(VI) compounds								
★ **Chromium(III) compounds**		see Section II b			Sh[22]				
Chromium(VI) compounds (inhalable fraction), with the exception of those practically insoluble in water such as lead chromate, barium chromate (but zinc chromate Section III Category 1)		see Section XII		–	Sh	2	–		
Chromium(VI) oxide	see Chromium(VI) compounds								
Chromium oxychloride	see Chromium(VI) compounds								
Chromium trioxide	see Chromium(VI) compounds								
Chromyl chloride	see Chromium(VI) compounds								
Chrysene [218-01-9]	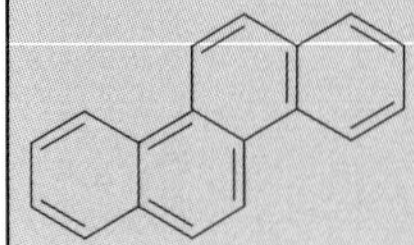	see Section III pyrolysis products of organic materials		–	H	2	–		
Chrysotile (fibrous dust)	see Asbestos								
Cinnamaldehyde [104-55-2]	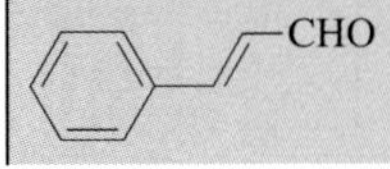	see Section IV			Sh				

22 does not apply for chromium(III) oxide and similar poorly soluble chromium(III) compounds

Substance [CAS number]	Formula	MAK ml/m³ (ppm)	MAK mg/m³	Peak limitation	H;S	Carcinogen category	Pregnancy risk group	Germ cell mutagen categ.	Vapour pressure in hPa at 20°C
Cinnamic alcohol	see Cinnamyl alcohol								
Cinnamic aldehyde	see Cinnamaldehyde								
Cinnamyl alcohol [104-54-1]	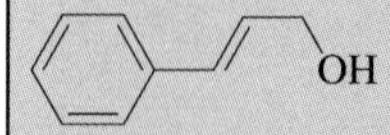	see Section IV			Sh				
C.I. Pigment Red 104	see Lead chromate as well as Lead and its inorganic compounds								
C.I. Pigment Yellow 34	see Lead chromate								
Citrates	see Citric acid								
Citric acid [77-92-9] and its alkali metal salts	CH_2–COOH HO–C–COOH CH_2–COOH	see Section II b							
Coal mine dust (respirable fraction)		–	–	–		3B	–		
Coal tars, coal tar pitches, coal tar oils	see Pyrolysis products of organic materials								
★ **Cobalt and cobalt compounds** (inhalable fraction):		see Section XIII		–	H Sah	2	–	3A	
Metallic cobalt [7440-48-4],	Co								
Cobalt(II) carbonate [513-79-1],	$CoCO_3$								
Cobalt(II) oxide [1307-96-6],	CoO								
Cobalt(II,III) oxide [1308-06-1],	Co_3O_4								
Cobalt(II) sulfate [10026-24-1] and similar salts,	$Co_2SO_4 \cdot 7H_2O$								
Cobalt(II) sulfide [1317-42-6]	CoS								
Cobalt alloys					[23]				
Cobalt	see also Hard metal containing tungsten carbide and cobalt								
Cocobolo	see Woods, *Dalbergia retusa*								
Cocus wood	see Woods, *Brya ebenus*								

[23] For cobalt alloys containing bio-available cobalt see Cobalt and cobalt compounds.

Substance [CAS number]	Formula	MAK ml/m³ (ppm)	MAK mg/m³	Peak limitation	H;S	Carcinogen category	Pregnancy risk group	Germ cell mutagen categ.	Vapour pressure in hPa at 20°C
Coke oven emissions	see Pyrolysis products of organic materials								
Colophony	see Rosin								
Copper [7440-50-8] and its inorganic compounds	Cu		0.1 **I**	II(2)			C		
Coromandel	see Woods, *Diospyros celebica*								
Cotton dust [24]		see Section V	1.5 **I**	I(1)			C		
p-Cresidine	see 5-Methyl-*o*-anisidine								
Cresol (all isomers) [1319-77-3] *o*-Cresol [95-48-7], *m*-Cresol [108-39-4], *p*-Cresol [106-44-5]	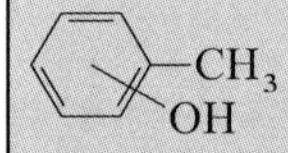	see Section XII		–	H	3A	–		
Cristobalite	see Silica, crystalline								
Crocidolite (fibrous dust)	see Asbestos								
Crotonaldehyde [123-73-9; 4170-30-3]	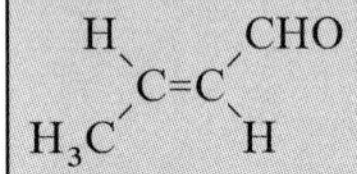	–	–	–	H	3B	–	3B	25
Cumene [98-82-8]	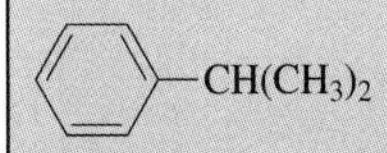	50 see Section XII	250	II(4)	H		C		4
Cumene hydroperoxide	see α,α-Dimethylbenzyl hydroperoxide								
Cyanamide [420-04-2]	$H_2N{-}CN$		1 **I**	II(2)	H Sh		C		0.005
Cyanides (as CN)			2 **I**	II(1)	H		C		
2-Cyanoacrylic acid methyl ester	see Methyl 2-cyanoacrylate								

[24] applies only to raw cotton

Substance [CAS number]	Formula	MAK ml/m³ (ppm)	MAK mg/m³	Peak limitation	H;S	Carcinogen category	Pregnancy risk group	Germ cell mutagen categ.	Vapour pressure in hPa at 20°C
Cyano(4-fluoro-3-phenoxyphenyl)methyl-3-(2,2-dichloroethenyl)-2,2-dimethylcyclopropane carboxylate	see Cyfluthrin								
Cyanogen [460-19-5]	NC–CN	5	11	II(2)	H		D		
Cyanogen chloride [506-77-4]	CNCl	see Section IIb							
Cyanoguanidine	see Dicyanodiamide								
Cyclohexane [110-82-7]	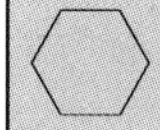	200 see Section XII	700	II(4)			D		104
Cyclohexanol [108-93-0]	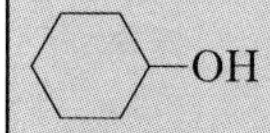	50	210	I(1)	H		D		
Cyclohexanone [108-94-1]	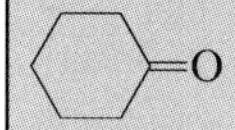	see Section XIII		–	H	3B	–		5
Cyclohexanone peroxide	see 1-Hydroxy-1'-hydroperoxy-dicyclohexyl peroxide								
Cyclohexene [110-83-8]	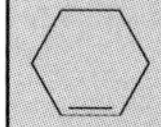	see Section IIb							
Cyclohexylamine [108-91-8]	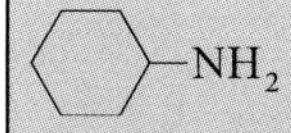	2	8.2	I(2)			C		
Cyclopentadiene [542-92-7]	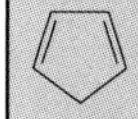	see Section IIb							451
Cyclopenta[*cd*]pyrene [27208-37-3]	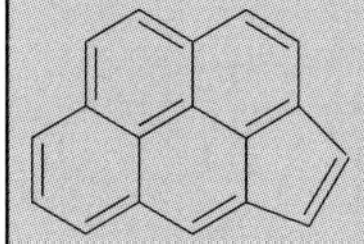	see Section III pyrolysis products of organic materials		–	H	2	–	3B	
Cyfluthrin [68359-37-5]	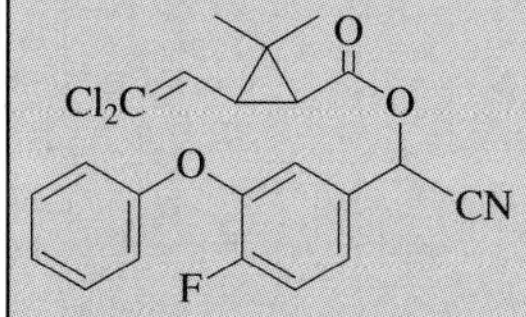		0.01 **I**	I(1)			C		
β-Cyfluthrin	see Cyfluthrin								
2,4-D	see 2,4-Dichlorophenoxyacetic acid								

Substance [CAS number]	Formula	MAK ml/m³ (ppm)	MAK mg/m³	Peak limitation	H;S	Carcinogen category	Pregnancy risk group	Germ cell mutagen categ.	Vapour pressure in hPa at 20°C
Dalapon	see 2,2-Dichloropropionic acid								
Dalbergia spp.	see Woods								
Dawsonite [12011-76-6] (fibrous dust)	$NaAl(CO_3)(OH)_2$	see Section III		–		2	–		
DDT (Dichlorodiphenyl-trichloroethane) [50-29-3]	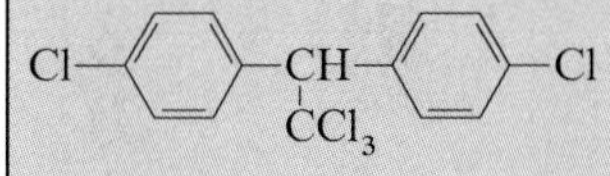		1 **I**	II(8)	H				
DDVP	see Dichlorvos								
Decaborane [17702-41-9]	$B_{10}H_{14}$	0.05	0.25	II(2)	H				
Decachlorotetracyclo-decanone	see Chlordecone								
Decyl 9-octadecenoate	see Decyl oleate								
Decyl oleate [3687-46-5]	$CH_2{-}(CH_2)_6{-}COO{-}(CH_2)_9{-}CH_3$ / $HC{=}CH{-}(CH_2)_7{-}CH_3$	see Section IIb							
Demeton° [25] [8065-48-3]	$SP(OCH_2{-}CH_3)_2$ / $O{-}(CH_2)_2{-}S{-}CH_2{-}CH_3$ + $OP(OCH_2{-}CH_3)_2$ / $S{-}(CH_2)_2{-}S{-}CH_2{-}CH_3$	see Section IIb			H				
Demeton-methyl [8022-00-2]	$SP(OCH_3)_2$ / $O{-}(CH_2)_2{-}S{-}CH_2{-}CH_3$ + $OP(OCH_3)_2$ / $S{-}(CH_2)_2{-}S{-}CH_2{-}CH_3$	0.5	4.8	II(2)	H				
Diacetone alcohol [123-42-2]	$H_3C{-}COH(CH_3){-}CH_2{-}CO{-}CH_3$	20	96	I(2)	H		D		
Diacetyl peroxide [110-22-5]	$H_3C{-}CO{-}OO{-}CO{-}CH_3$	see Section Xa							
Diallyl phthalate [131-17-9]	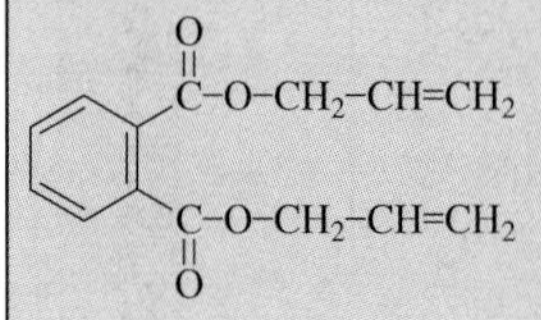	see Section IIb							

[25] see Section XII, List of BAT Values, Acetylcholinesterase inhibitors

Substance [CAS number]	Formula	MAK ml/m³ (ppm)	MAK mg/m³	Peak limitation	H;S	Carcinogen category	Pregnancy risk group	Germ cell mutagen categ.	Vapour pressure in hPa at 20°C
2,4-Diaminoanisole [615-05-4]	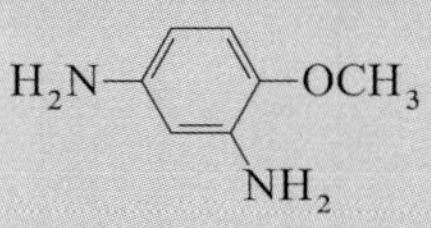	–	–	–	H	2	–		
1,2-Diaminobenzene	see *o*-Phenylenediamine								
1,3-Diaminobenzene	see *m*-Phenylenediamine								
1,4-Diaminobenzene	see *p*-Phenylenediamine								
3,3'-Diaminobenzidine [91-95-2] and its tetrahydrochloride [7411-49-6]	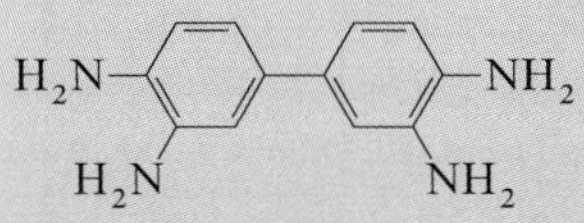	–	–	–		3B	–		
4,4'-Diamino-3,3'-dichlorodiphenylmethane	see 4,4'-Methylene-bis(2-chloroaniline)								
2,2'-Diaminodiethylamine	see Diethylenetriamine								
4,4'-Diaminodiphenyl	see Benzidine								
4,4'-Diaminodiphenylmethane [101-77-9]	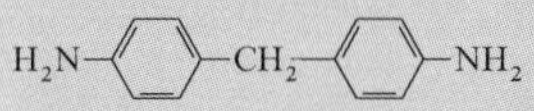	see Section XII		–	H Sh	2	–		
4,4'-Diaminodiphenyl sulfide	see 4,4'-Thiodianiline								
1,2-Diaminoethane	see Ethylenediamine								
3,8-Diamino-5-ethyl-6-phenylphenanthridinium bromide	see Ethidium bromide								
1,5-Diaminonaphthalene [2243-62-1]	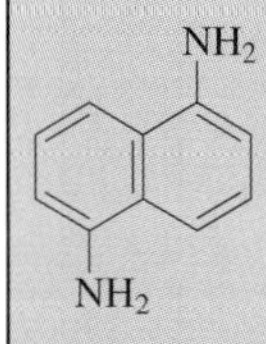	–	–	–	H Sh	2	–		
o-Dianisidine	see 3,3'-Dimethoxybenzidine								
Diatomaceous earth	see Silica, amorphous								

Substance [CAS number]	Formula	MAK ml/m³ (ppm)	MAK mg/m³	Peak limitation	H;S	Carcinogen category	Pregnancy risk group	Germ cell mutagen categ.	Vapour pressure in hPa at 20°C
Diazinon [333-41-5]	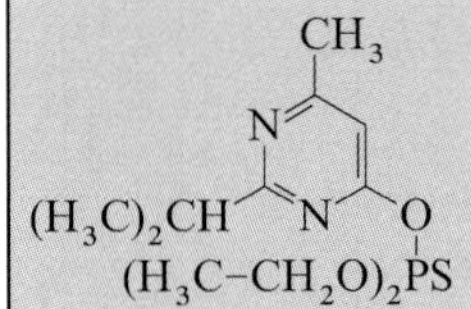		0.1 **I**	II(2)	H		C		
Diazomethane [334-88-3]	$H_2C{=}\overset{\oplus}{N}{=}\overset{\ominus}{N} \longleftrightarrow H_2\overset{\ominus}{C}{-}\overset{\oplus}{N}{\equiv}N$	–	–	–		2	–		
Dibenz[*a,h*]anthracene [53-70-3]	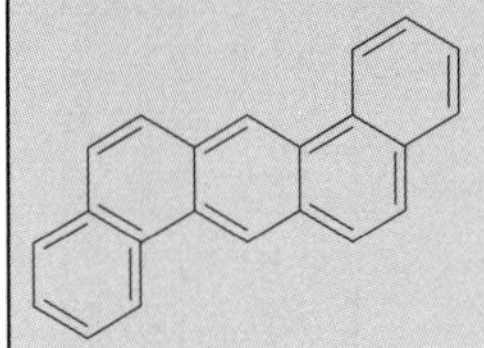	see Section III pyrolysis products of organic materials		–	H	2	–	3A	
Dibenzo[*a,e*]pyrene [192-65-4]	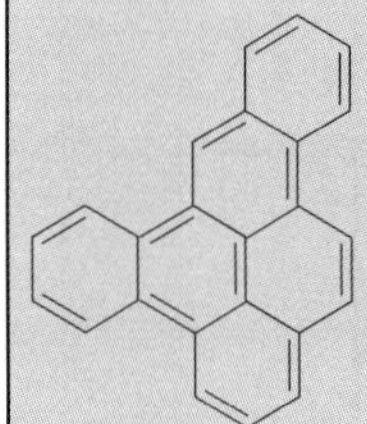	see Section III pyrolysis products of organic materials		–	H	2	–	3B	
Dibenzo[*a,h*]pyrene [189-64-0]	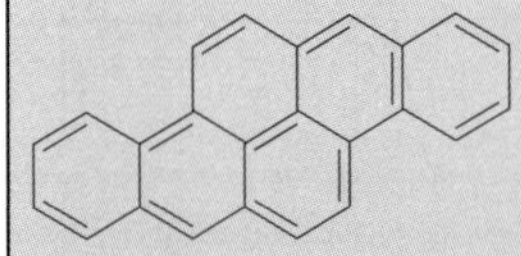	see Section III pyrolysis products of organic materials		–	H	2	–	3B	
Dibenzo[*a,i*]pyrene [189-55-9]	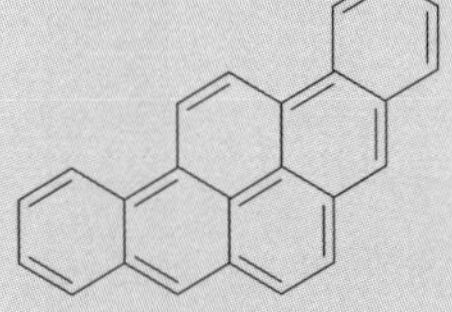	see Section III pyrolysis products of organic materials		–	H	2	–	3B	
Dibenzo[*a,l*]pyrene [191-30-0]	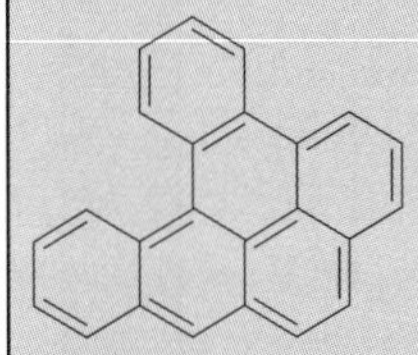	see Section III pyrolysis products of organic materials		–	H	2	–	3B	
Dibenzo-1,4-thiazine	see Phenothiazine								
Dibenzoyl peroxide [94-36-0]	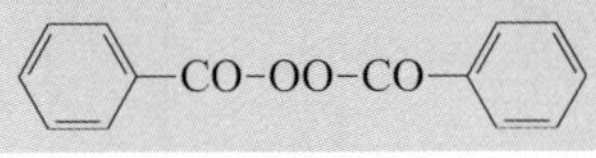	see Section Xa	5 **I**	I(1)					

Substance [CAS number]	Formula	MAK ml/m³ (ppm)	MAK mg/m³	Peak limitation	H;S	Carcinogen category	Pregnancy risk group	Germ cell mutagen categ.	Vapour pressure in hPa at 20°C
Dibenzyl disulfide [150-60-7]	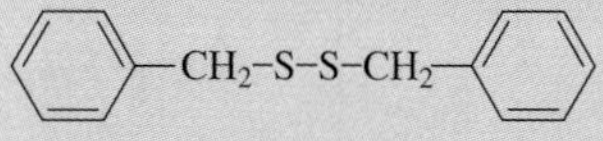	see Section IIb							
Diborane [19287-45-7]	H_3B-BH_3	see Section IIb							
1,2-Dibromo-3-chloropropane° [96-12-8]	$H_2CCl-CHBr-CH_2Br$	–	–	–	H	2	–	2	
1,2-Dibromo-2,4-dicyanobutane [35691-65-7]	$BrCH_2-CBr(CN)-CH_2-CH_2-CN$	see Section IIb			Sh				
Dibromodifluoromethane [75-61-6]	CBr_2F_2	see Section IIb							
1,2-Dibromoethane [106-93-4]	BrH_2C-CH_2Br	–	–	–	H	2	–		15
Dibromohydroxymercurifluorescein disodium salt	see Merbromin								
2,6-Di-*tert*-butyl-*p*-cresol (3,5-Di-*tert*-butyl-4-hydroxytoluene) (BHT) [128-37-0]	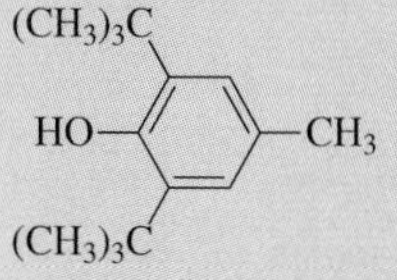		20 **I**	II(2)		4	C		
3,5-Di-*tert*-butyl-4-hydroxytoluene	see 3,5-Di-*tert*-butyl-*p*-cresol								
N,N-Di-*n*-butylnitrosoamine	see *N*-Nitrosodi-*n*-butylamine								
Di-*tert*-butyl peroxide [110-05-4]	$(H_3C)_3C-OO-C(CH_3)_3$	see Section Xa							
2,6-Di-*tert*-butylphenol [128-39-2]	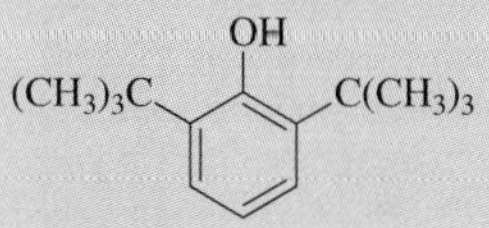	see Section IIb							
★ **Di-*n*-butyl phosphate** [107-66-4] and its technical mixtures	$HO-P(=O)(O-(CH_2)_3-CH_3)_2$	see Section Xc		–		3A	–		7.4·10[illegible]
Dicarboxylic acid anhydrides		see Section IVe							

Substance [CAS number]	Formula	MAK ml/m³ (ppm)	MAK mg/m³	Peak limitation	H;S	Carcinogen category	Pregnancy risk group	Germ cell mutagen categ.	Vapour pressure in hPa at 20°C
Dicarboxylic acid (C4–C6) dimethylester, mixture [95481-62-2]	16.5% Dimethyl adipate, 16.9% Dimethyl succinate, 66.6% Dimethyl glutarate (purity > 99.5%)	0.75	5	I(1)			C		
Dichloroacetylene [7572-29-4]	ClC≡CCl	–	–	–		2	–		
3,4-Dichloroaniline [95-76-1]	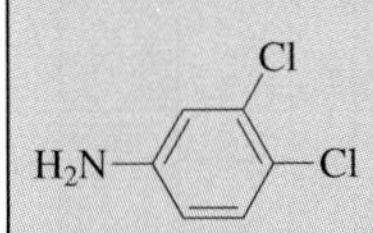	see Section IIb			H Sh				
3,4-Dichlorobenzenamine	see 3,4-Dichloroaniline								
1,2-Dichlorobenzene [95-50-1]	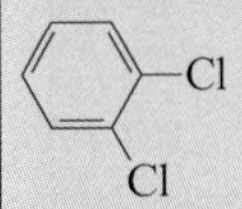	10 see Section XII	61	II(2)	H		C		1.33
1,3-Dichlorobenzene [541-73-1]	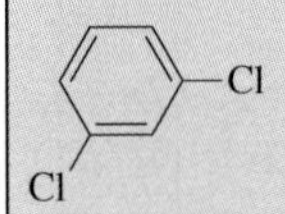	2	12	II(2)			C		
1,4-Dichlorobenzene [106-46-7]	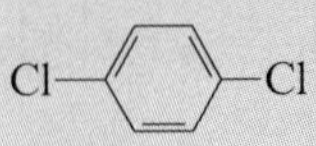	see Section XIII		–	H	2	–	3B	1.7
3,3'-Dichlorobenzidine [91-94-1]	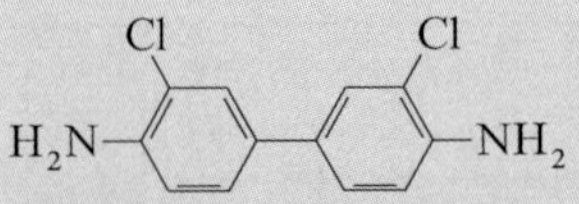	–	–	–	H	2	–		
1,4-Dichloro-2-butene [764-41-0]	$ClCH_2-CH=CH-CH_2Cl$	–	–	–	H	2	–	3A	
2,2'-Dichlorodiethyl ether [111-44-4]	$ClCH_2-CH_2-O-CH_2-CH_2Cl$	10	59	I(1)	H				
Dichlorodifluoromethane (FC-12) [75-71-8]	CCl_2F_2	1000	5000	II(2)			C		
Dichlorodimethyl ether	see Bischloromethyl ether								
Dichlorodioxochromium	see Chromium(VI) compounds								
1,1-Dichloroethane [75-34-3]	$H_3C-CHCl_2$	100	410	II(2)			C		240
1,2-Dichloroethane [107-06-2]	ClH_2C-CH_2Cl	–	–	–	H	2	–		87

Substance [CAS number]	Formula	MAK ml/m³ (ppm)	MAK mg/m³	Peak limitation	H;S	Carcinogen category	Pregnancy risk group	Germ cell mutagen categ.	Vapour pressure in hPa at 20°C
1,2-Dichloroethene	see 1,2-Dichloroethylene								
1,1-Dichloroethylene	see Vinylidene chloride								
1,2-Dichloroethylene *sym* [540-59-0] (*cis* [156-59-2] and *trans* [156-60-5])	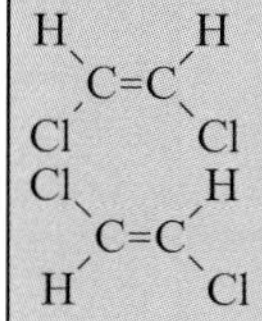	200	800	II(2)					220
1,2-Dichloroethyl methyl ether	see 1,2-Dichloromethoxyethane								
Di-(2-chloroethyl)sulfide	see Bis(β-chloroethyl)sulfide								
2,2'-Dichloroethyl sulfide	see Bis(β-chloroethyl)sulfide								
Dichlorofluoromethane (FC-21) [75-43-4]	$CHCl_2F$	10	43	II(2)					
Dichlorohydrin	see 1,3-Dichloro-2-propanol								
Dichloromethane [75-09-2]	CH_2Cl_2	see Section XIII		–		3A	–		475
1,2-Dichloromethoxy-ethane [41683-62-9]	$H_2CCl{-}CHCl{-}OCH_3$	–	–	–	H	3B	–		
2,2'-Dichloro-*N*-methyl-diethylamine	see *N*-Methyl-bis(2-chloroethyl)-amine								
2,2'-Dichloro-4,4'-methylene dianiline	see 4,4'-Methylene-bis(2-chloro-aniline)								
Dichloronaphthalenes	see Chlorinated naphthalenes								
3,4-Dichloronitrobenzene [99-54-7]	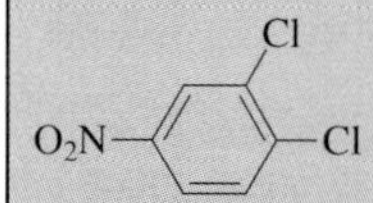	–	–		H	3B			
1,1-Dichloro-1-nitro-ethane [594-72-9]	$H_3C{-}CCl_2NO_2$	see Section IIb							

Substance [CAS number]	Formula	MAK ml/m³ (ppm)	MAK mg/m³	Peak limitation	H;S	Carcinogen category	Pregnancy risk group	Germ cell mutagen categ.	Vapour pressure in hPa at 20°C
2,4-Dichlorophenoxy-acetic acid [94-75-7] (including salts and esters)	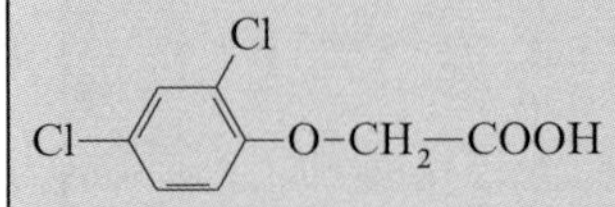		1 **I**	II(8)	H		C		
4-(2,4-Dichlorophenoxy)-benzenamine [14861-17-7]	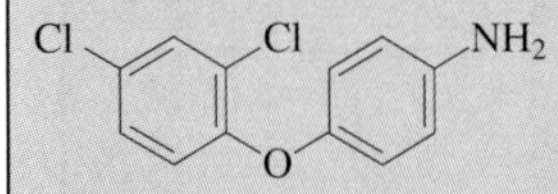	–	–	–	H	3B	–		
1,2-Dichloropropane [78-87-5]	$H_3C{-}CHCl{-}CH_2Cl$	–	–	–		3B	–		51
1,3-Dichloro-2-propanol [96-23-1]	$ClH_2C{-}CHOH{-}CH_2Cl$	–	–	–	H	2	–		
1,3-Dichloropropene [542-75-6] (*cis* and *trans*)	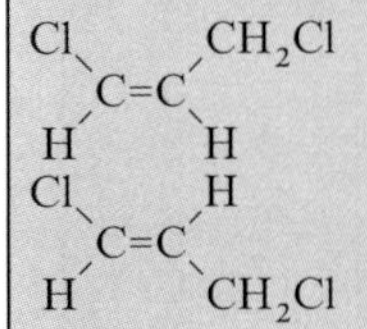	–	–	–	H Sh	2	–		40
2,2-Dichloropropionic acid [75-99-0] and its sodium salt [127-20-8]	$H_3C{-}CCl_2{-}COOH$ $H_3C{-}CCl_2{-}COO^{\ominus}Na^{\oplus}$	see Section II b							
1,2-Dichloro-1,1,2,2-tetrafluoroethane (FC-114) [76-14-2]	$ClF_2C{-}CClF_2$	1000	7100	II(8)			D		
α,α-Dichlorotoluene	see Benzyl dichloride								
2,2-Dichloro-1,1,1-trifluoroethane (FC-123) [306-83-2]	$F_3C{-}CHCl_2$	–	–	–		3B	–		13.2
Dichlorvos (DDVP) [62-73-7]	$Cl_2C{=}CH{-}O{-}PO(OCH_3)_2$	0.11	1	II(2)	H		C		
Dicyanodiamide [461-58-5]	$N{\equiv}C{-}NH{-}C({=}NH){-}NH_2$	see Section II b							$2.3 \cdot 10^{-3}$
1,3-Dicyanotetrachloro-benzene	see Chlorothalonil								

Substance [CAS number]	Formula	MAK ml/m³ (ppm)	MAK mg/m³	Peak limitation	H;S	Carcinogen category	Pregnancy risk group	Germ cell mutagen categ.	Vapour pressure in hPa at 20°C
Dicyclohexylamine[26] [101-83-7]	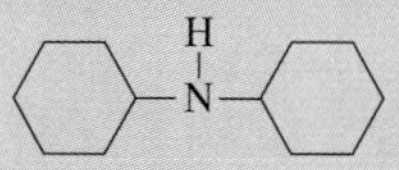	see Section IIb			H				
Dicyclohexylamine nitrite [3129-91-7]	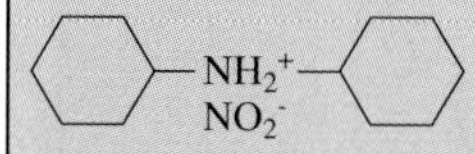	see Section IIb							
Dicyclohexylcarbodiimide [538-75-0]	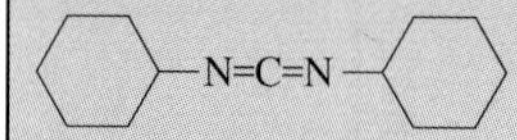	see Section IV			Sh				
Dicyclohexyl peroxide [1758-61-8]	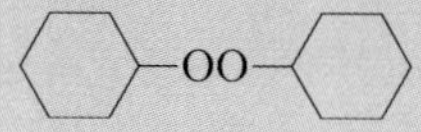	see Section Xa							
Dicyclopentadiene [77-73-6]	 *endo* *exo*	0.5	2.7	I(1)			D		
Dieldrin° [60-57-1]	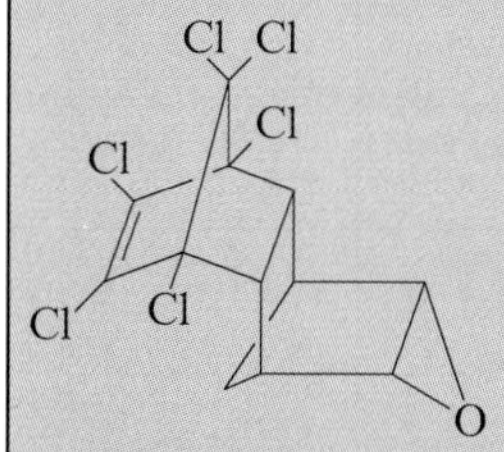		0.25 **I**	II(8)	H				
Diepoxybutane [1464-53-5]	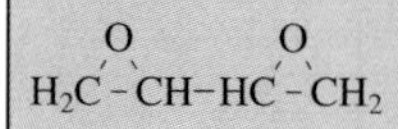							2	
Diesel engine emissions[27]		see Section III pyrolysis products of organic materials		–		2	–		

[26] Reaction with nitrosating agents can result in the formation of carcinogenic *N*-Nitrosodicyclohexylamine, see Section III "Amines which form carcinogenic nitrosamines on nitrosation", p. 147.

[27] Because of the new diesel engine technology the emissions have changed significantly in quality and quantity. Since it must be assumed that these new diesel engines were introduced at the end of the 1990s, all the available epidemiological studies which were evaluated in 2007 are based on exposures to emissions from older diesel engines. The emissions from the new diesel engines can not be evaluated until appropriate studies become available.

Substance [CAS number]	Formula	MAK ml/m³ (ppm)	MAK mg/m³	Peak limitation	H;S	Carcinogen category	Pregnancy risk group	Germ cell mutagen categ.	Vapour pressure in hPa at 20°C
Diethanolamine[28] [111-42-2]	$HO-(CH_2)_2-NH-(CH_2)_2-OH$		1 **I**	I(1)	H Sh	3B	C		$4 \cdot 10^{-4}$
N,N-Diethanolnitrosoamine	see *N*-Nitrosodiethanolamine								
Diethylamine[29] [109-89-7]	$(H_3C-CH_2)_2NH$	5	15	I(2)[30]			D		260
2-Diethylaminoethanol [100-37-8]	$(H_3C-CH_2)_2N-CH_2-CH_2OH$	5	24	I(1)	H		C		1.9
Diethylcarbamoyl chloride [88-10-8]	$(H_3C-CH_2)_2N-CO-Cl$	–	–	–		3B	–		
Diethyldithiocarbamate sodium	see Sodium diethyldithiocarbamate								
Diethylene dioxide	see 1,4-Dioxane								
Diethylene glycol [111-46-6]	$HO-(CH_2)_2-O-(CH_2)_2-OH$	10	44	II(4)			C		0.027
Diethylene glycol diacrylate [4074-88-8]	$(CH_2C=CH-COO-(CH_2)_2)_2O$	see Section IV			Sh				
Diethylene glycol dimethacrylate [2358-84-1]	$O-(CH_2)_2-O-OC-C(CH_3)=CH_2$ / $(CH_2)_2-O-OC-C(CH_3)=CH_2$	see Section IV			Sh				
Diethylene glycol dimethyl ether [111-96-6]	$H_3C-O-[(CH_2)_2-O]_2-CH_3$	5	28	II(8)	H		B		2
Diethylene glycol dinitrate [693-21-0]	$O((CH_2)_2-ONO_2)_2$	see Section IIb			H				
Diethylene glycol ethyl ether [111-90-0]	$CH_3-(CH_2-O-CH_2)_2-CH_2OH$		50 **I**	I(2)			C		

28 Reaction with nitrosating agents can result in the formation of carcinogenic *N*-nitrosodiethanolamine, see Section III "Amines which form carcinogenic nitrosamines on nitrosation", p. 147.

29 Reaction with nitrosating agents can result in the formation of carcinogenic *N*-nitrosodiethylamine, see Section III "Amines which form carcinogenic nitrosamines on nitrosation", p. 147.

30 A momentary value of 10 ml/m³ (30 mg/m³) should not be exceeded.

Substance [CAS number]	Formula	MAK ml/m³ (ppm)	MAK mg/m³	Peak limitation	H;S	Carcinogen category	Pregnancy risk group	Germ cell mutagen categ.	Vapour pressure in hPa at 20°C
Diethylene glycol monobutyl ether [112-34-5]	$H_3C{-}(CH_2)_3{-}O{-}(CH_2)_2{-}O{-}(CH_2)_2{-}OH$	10 [31]	67	I(1.5)			C		
Diethylene glycol monobutyl ether acetate [124-17-4]	$CH_3{-}C(=O){-}O{-}((CH_2)_2{-}O)_2{-}(CH_2)_3{-}CH_3$	10 [31]	85	I(1.5)			C		
Diethylenetriamine [111-40-0]	$(H_2N{-}CH_2{-}CH_2)_2NH$	see Section IV			Sh				
Diethylenetriaminepenta-(methylenephosphonic acid) [15827-60-8] and its sodium salts [22042-96-2]	$CH_2{-}PO_3H_2$ $N((CH_2)_2{-}N(CH_2{-}PO_3H_2)_2)_2$	see Section IIb							
Diethyl ether	see Ethyl ether								
Di(2-ethylhexyl) phthalate (DEHP) [117-81-7]	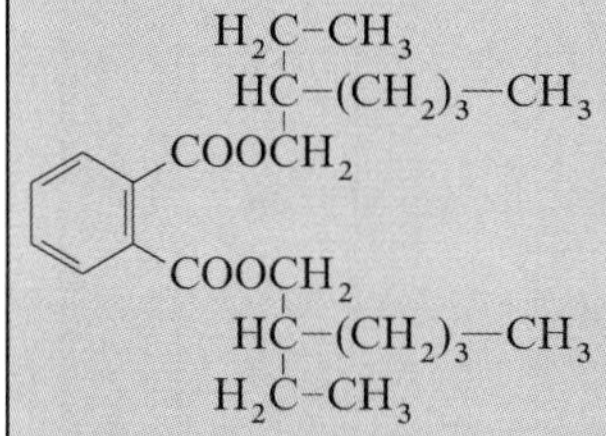		10	II(8)		4	C		
N,N-Diethylnitrosoamine	see *N*-Nitrosodiethylamine								
Diethyl sulfate [64-67-5]	$(H_3C{-}CH_2{-}O)_2SO_2$	–	–	–		2	–	2	
Difluorodibromomethane	see Dibromodifluoromethane								
1,1-Difluoroethylene [75-38-7]	$H_2C{=}CF_2$	–	–	–		3B	–		
Diformyl	see Glyoxal								
Diglycidyl ether (DGE) [2238-07-5]	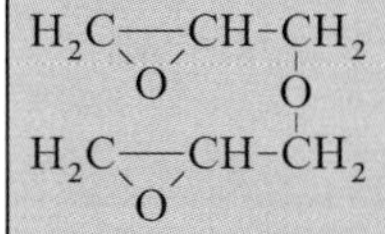	–	–	–	H	3B	–		
Diglycidyl hexanediol [16096-31-4]	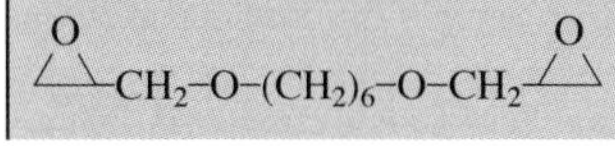	see Section IV			Sh				

[31] MAK value applies for the sum of the concentrations of diethylene glycol monobutyl ether and its acetate in the air.

Substance [CAS number]	Formula	MAK ml/m³ (ppm)	MAK mg/m³	Peak limitation	H;S	Carcinogen category	Pregnancy risk group	Germ cell mutagen categ.	Vapour pressure in hPa at 20°C
1,3-Diglycidyloxybenzene	see Diglycidyl resorcinol ether								
Diglycidyl resorcinol ether [101-90-6]	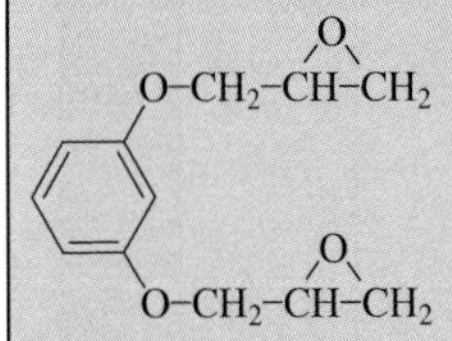	–	–	–	H Sh	2	–		
Diglycolamine	see 2-(2-Aminoethoxy)ethanol								
1,2-Dihydro-5-nitroacenaphthylene	see 5-Nitroacenaphthene								
1,4-Dihydroxybenzene	see Hydroquinone								
4,4'-Dihydroxydiphenylpropane	see Bisphenol A								
1,2-Dihydroxyethane	see Ethylene glycol								
2,2'-Dihydroxyethyl ether	see Diethylene glycol								
1,2-Dihydroxypropane	see Propylene glycol								
4-(Diiodomethylsulfonyl)-toluene [20018-09-1]	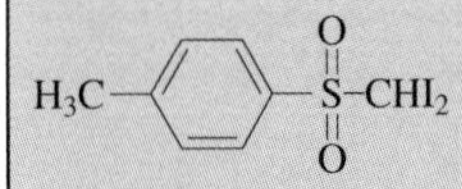	see Section IIb							
Diisobutyl ketone [108-83-8]	$(H_3C)_2CH-CH_2$ CO $(H_3C)_2CH-CH_2$	see Section IIb							
Diisocyanates		see Section IVe							
N,N-Diisopropylnitrosoamine	see *N*-Nitrosodiisopropylamine								
Diketene [674-82-8]	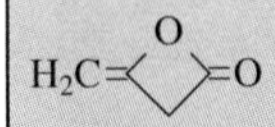	see Section IIb							
Dilauroyl peroxide [105-74-8]	$H_3C-(CH_2)_{10}-CO$ O O $H_3C-(CH_2)_{10}-CO$	see Section Xa							

Substance [CAS number]	Formula	MAK ml/m³ (ppm)	MAK mg/m³	Peak limitation	H;S	Carcinogen category	Pregnancy risk group	Germ cell mutagen categ.	Vapour pressure in hPa at 20°C
3,3'-Dimethoxybenzidine [119-90-4]	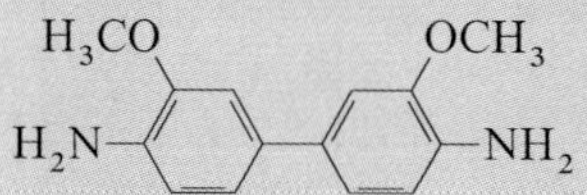	–	–	–		2	–		
2,5-Dimethoxy-4-chloro-aniline [6358-64-1]	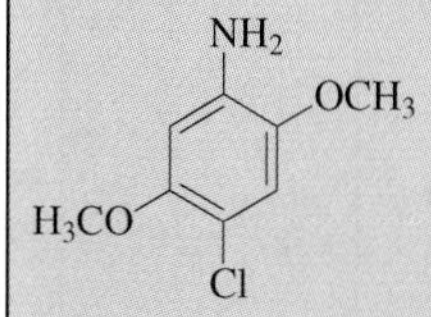	–	–	–	H	3B	–		
Dimethoxymethane [109-87-5]	$H_3CO-CH_2-OCH_3$	1000	3200	II(2)			C		440
***N,N*-Dimethyl acetamide** [127-19-5]	$H_3C-CO-N(CH_3)_2$	10 see Section XII	36	II(2)	H		C		1.3
Dimethyl adipate [627-93-0] see also dicarboxylic acid (C4-C6) dimethylester	$CH_3-OOC-(CH_2)_4-COO-CH_3$	see Section IIb							
Dimethylamine [32] [124-40-3]	$HN(CH_3)_2$	2	3.7	I(2)			D		
1,1-Dimethylaminoethane	see *tert*-Butylamine								
Dimethylaminopropio-nitrile [1738-25-6]	$(H_3C)_2N-CH_2-CH_2-CN$	see Section IIb							
Dimethylaminosulfo-chloride	see Dimethylsulfamoyl chloride								
***N,N*-Dimethylaniline** [121-69-7]	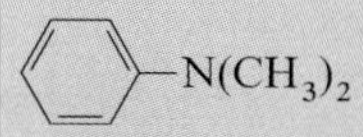	5	25	II(2)	H	3B	D		
3,3'-Dimethylbenzidine [119-93-7]	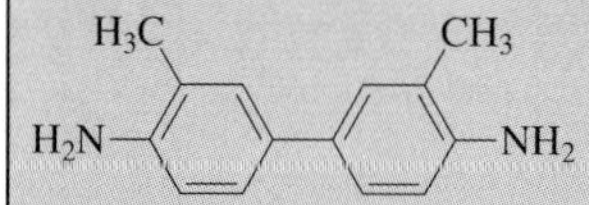	–	–	–		2	–		
α,α-Dimethylbenzyl hydroperoxide [80-15-9]	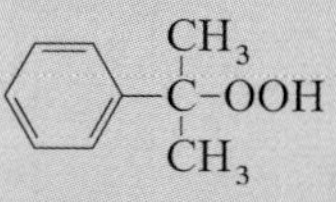	see Section Xa							
2,2-Dimethylbutane	see Hexane (all isomers except *n*-Hexane)								

[32] Reaction with nitrosating agents can result in the formation of carcinogenic *N*-nitrosodimethylamine, see Section III "Amines whic form carcinogenic nitrosamines on nitrosation", p. 147.

Substance [CAS number]	Formula	MAK ml/m³ (ppm)	MAK mg/m³	Peak limitation	H;S	Carcinogen category	Pregnancy risk group	Germ cell mutagen categ.	Vapour pressure in hPa at 20°C
2,3-Dimethylbutane	see Hexane (all isomers except *n*-Hexane)								
Dimethyl butanedioate	see Dimethyl succinate								
1,3-Dimethylbutyl acetate	see *sec*-Hexyl acetate								
Dimethylcarbamoyl chloride [79-44-7]	$Cl{-}CO{-}N(CH_3)_2$	–	–	–	H	2	–		
3,3'-Dimethyl-4,4'-diaminodiphenylmethane	see 4,4'-Methylene-bis(2-methylaniline)								
Dimethyl ether [115-10-6]	$H_3C{-}O{-}CH_3$	1000	1900	II(8)			D		5200
***N,N*-Dimethyl ethylamine**[33] [598-56-1]	$H_3C{-}CH_2{-}N(CH_3)_2$	2	6.1	I(2)			D		527–580
4-(1,1-Dimethylethyl)-1,2-benzenediol	see *p-tert*-Butylcatechol								
Dimethylformamide [68-12-2]	$HCO{-}N(CH_3)_2$	5 see Section XII	15	II(4)	H		B		
Dimethyl glutarate [1119-40-0] see also dicarboxylic acid (C4-C6) dimethylester	$CH_3{-}OOC{-}(CH_2)_3{-}COO{-}CH_3$	see Section IIb							
2,6-Dimethyl-4-heptanone	see Diisobutyl ketone								
Dimethyl hexanedioate	see Dimethyl adipate								
1,1-Dimethylhydrazine[34] [57-14-7]	$H_2N{-}N(CH_3)_2$	–	–	–	H Sh	2	–		
1,2-Dimethylhydrazine[34] [540-73-8]	$H_3C{-}NH{-}NH{-}CH_3$	–	–	–	H Sh	2	–		

33 Reaction with nitrosating agents can result in the formation of carcinogenic *N*-nitrosodimethylamine and *N*-nitrosomethylethylamine, see Section III "Amines which form carcinogenic nitrosamines on nitrosation", p. 147.

34 no longer produced in Germany

Substance [CAS number]	Formula	MAK ml/m³ (ppm)	MAK mg/m³	Peak limitation	H;S	Carcinogen category	Pregnancy risk group	Germ cell mutagen categ.	Vapour pressure in hPa at 20°C
Dimethyl hydrogen phosphite [868-85-9]	$(H_3CO)_2P(H)=O$	–	–	–		3B	–		
3,7-Dimethyl-7-hydroxy-octanal	see Hydroxycitronellal								
***N,N*-Dimethylisopropyl-amine** [996-35-0]	$(CH_3)_2CH-N(CH_3)_2$	1	3.6	I(2)			D		170
N,N-Dimethylnitroso-amine	see *N*-Nitrosodimethylamine								
Dimethylol dihydroxy-ethyleneurea [1854-26-8]	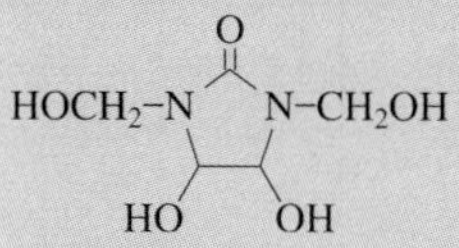	see Section IV			Sh				
1,3-Dimethylol-5,5-dimethyl hydantoin [6440-58-0]	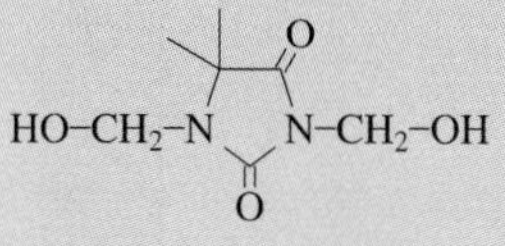	see Section II b			Sh				
Dimethyl pentanedioate	see Dimethyl glutarate								
Dimethyl phosphonate	see Dimethyl hydrogen phosphite								
N,N-Dimethyl-2-propan-amine	see *N,N*-Dimethylisopropylamine								
1,1-Dimethylpropyl acetate	see Amylacetate								
Dimethyl succinate [106-65-0] see also dicarboxylic acid (C4-C6) dimethylester	$CH_3-OOC-(CH_2)_2-COO-CH_3$	see Section II b							
Dimethylsulfamoyl chloride [13360-57-1]	$(H_3C)_2N-SO_2-Cl$	–	–	–	H	2	–		
Dimethyl sulfate [77-78-1]	$(H_3CO)_2SO_2$	see Section XIII		–	H	2	–		
Dimethyl sulfide [75-18-3]	$H_3C-S-CH_3$	see Section II b							
★ **Dimethyl sulfoxide** [67-68-5]	$H_3C-SO-CH_3$	50	160	I(2)	H		D		

Substance [CAS number]	Formula	MAK ml/m³ (ppm)	MAK mg/m³	Peak limitation	H;S	Carcinogen category	Pregnancy risk group	Germ cell mutagen categ.	Vapour pressure in hPa at 20°C
Dinitrobenzene (all isomers) [25154-54-5]	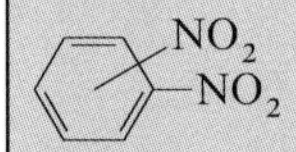	–	–	–	H	3B	–		
4,6-Dinitro-*o*-cresol [534-52-1]	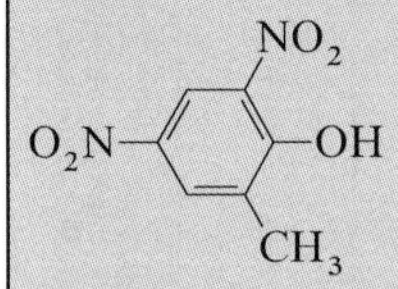	see Section IIb			H				
Dinitrogen monoxide	see Nitrous oxide								
Dinitronaphthalene (all isomers) [27478-34-8]	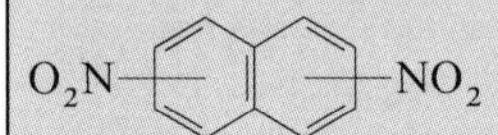	–	–	–		3B	–		
Dinitrotoluene (mixtures of isomers) [25321-14-6]	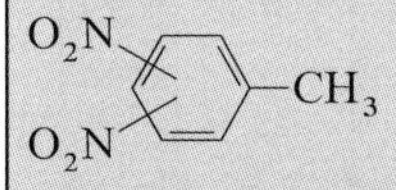	–	–	–	H	2	–		
4,4'-Dioctyldiphenylamine [101-67-7]	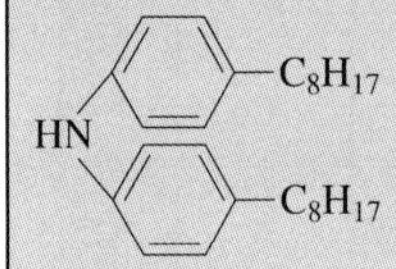	see Section IIb							
Di-*sec*-octyl phthalate	see Di(2-ethylhexyl)phthalate								
Di-*n*-octyltin compounds	see *n*-Octyltin compounds								
Diospyros spp.	see Woods								
Dioxacyclopentane	see 1,3-Dioxolane								
1,4-Dioxane [123-91-1]	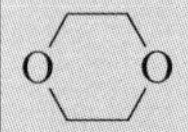	20 see Section XII	73	I(2)	H	4	C		41
1,3-Dioxolane (Dioxacyclopentane) [646-06-0]	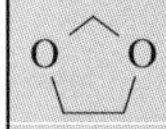	100	310	II(2)	H		C		105
3,6-Dioxyoctane-1,8-diyl dimethacrylate	see Triethylene glycol dimethacrylate								
Diphenyl	see Biphenyl								
Diphenyl cresyl phosphate [26444-49-5]	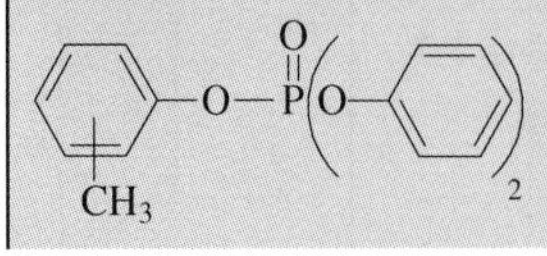	see Section IIb							<0.01

Substance [CAS number]	Formula	MAK ml/m³ (ppm)	MAK mg/m³	Peak limitation	H;S	Carcinogen category	Pregnancy risk group	Germ cell mutagen categ.	Vapour pressure in hPa at 20°C
Diphenyl ether (vapour) [101-84-8]	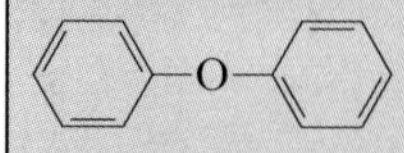	1	7.1	I(1)			C		
1,2-Diphenylhydrazine	see Hydrazobenzene								
Diphenylmethane-4,4'-diisocyanate	see 4,4'-Methylene diphenyl isocyanate (MDI)								
N,N-Diphenylnitrosamine	see *N*-Nitrosodiphenylamine								
Diphosphorus pentoxide	see Phosphorus pentoxide								
Dipropylene glycol [25265-71-8]	$CH_3-CH(OH)-CH_2-O-CH_2-CH(OH)-CH_3$	see Section Xc	200 **I**	II(2)			C		
Dipropylene glycol monomethyl ether (mixture of isomers) [34590-94-8]	$H_3CO-C_3H_6-O-C_3H_6-OH$	50	310	I(1)			D		
N,N-Di-*n*-propylnitrosoamine	see *N*-Nitrosodi-*n*-propylamine								
Disodium 2',7'-dibromo-4'-(hydroxymercury) fluorescein	see Merbromin								
Dispers blue 106/124 [68516-81-4; 15141-18-1]	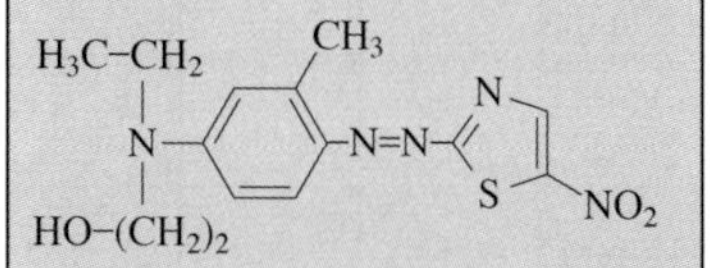	see Section IV			Sh				
★ **Disperse Orange 3** [730-40-5]	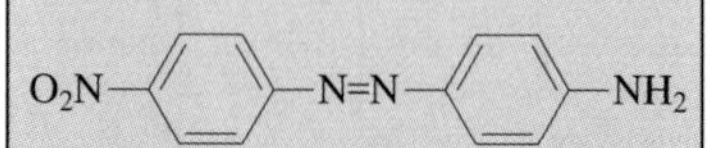	see Section IV			Sh				
★ **Disperse Red 1** [2872-52-8]	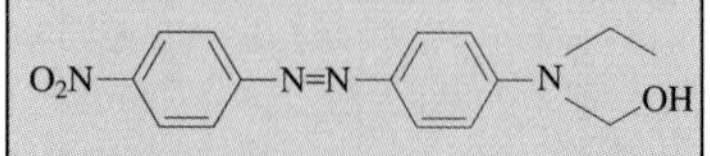	see Section IV			Sh				
★ **Disperse Red 17** [3179-89-3]	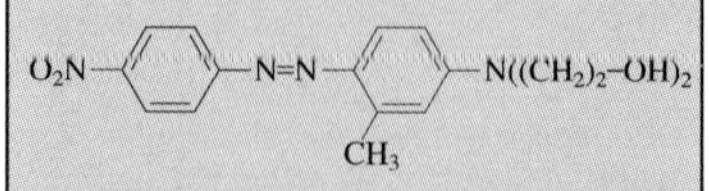	see Section IV			Sh				
★ **Disperse Yellow 3** [2832-40-8]	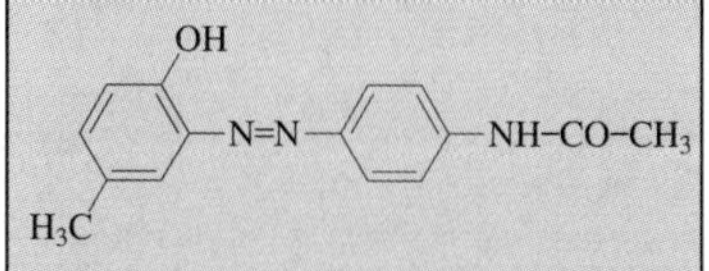	see Section IV			Sh				
Distemonanthus benthamianus	see Woods								

Substance [CAS number]	Formula	MAK ml/m³ (ppm)	MAK mg/m³	Peak limitation	H;S	Carcinogen category	Pregnancy risk group	Germ cell mutagen categ.	Vapour pressure in hPa at 20°C
Disulfiram [29] [97-77-8]	$S-CS-N(CH_2-CH_3)_2$ $S-CS-N(CH_2-CH_3)_2$		2 **I**	II(8)	Sh		D		
Disulfur chloride	see Sulfur monochloride								
Disulfur decafluoride	see Sulfur pentafluoride								
2,2'-Dithiobis(*N*-methylbenzamide) [2527-58-4]	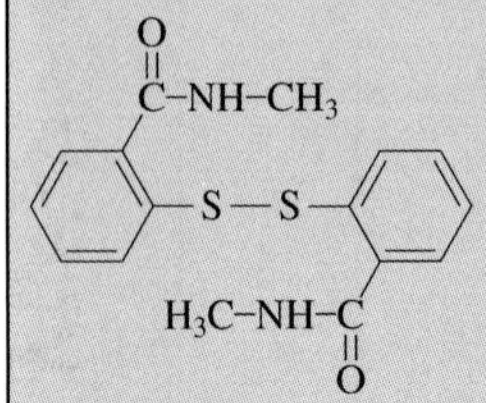	see Section IIb			Sh				
Dithiocarb	see Sodium diethyldithiocarbamate								
Ditiocarb sodium	see Sodium diethyldithiocarbamate								
Divinylbenzene (all isomers) [1321-74-0]	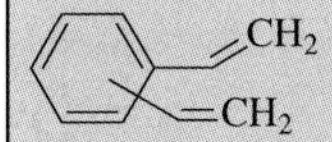	see Section IIb							
Docosanoic acid	see Behenic acid								
Dodecanedioic acid [693-23-2]	$HOOC(CH_2)_{10}COOH$	see Section IIb							
Dodecanoic acid	see Lauric acid								
1-Dodecanol [112-53-8]	$CH_3-(CH_2)_8-CH_2OH$	see Section IIb [35]							
Dodecyl alcohol	see 1-Dodecanol								
DOP	see Di(2-ethylhexyl)phthalate								
Douka	see Woods, *Tieghemella africana*								
Dust, general threshold limit value (inhalable fraction)		see Section Vf and Vg	4 **I**						
Dust, general threshold limit value (respirable fraction)		see Section Vf and Vg	1.5 **R**						

[29] Reaction with nitrosating agents can result in the formation of carcinogenic *N*-nitrosodiethylamine, see Section III "Amines which form carcinogenic nitrosamines on nitrosation", p. 147.
[35] Provided the technical exposure limit of 10 mg/m³ I for metal-working fluids is observed, adverse effects on health are not to be expected.

Substance [CAS number]	Formula	MAK ml/m³ (ppm)	MAK mg/m³	Peak limitation	H;S	Carcinogen category	Pregnancy risk group	Germ cell mutagen categ.	Vapour pressure in hPa at 20°C
Dusts		see Section V							
Dusts containing enzymes		see Section IVe							
East Indian rosewood	see Woods, *Dalbergia latifolia*								
Ebony	see Woods, *Diospyros* spp.								
EDTA	see Ethylenediaminetetraacetic acid								
Endrin [72-20-8]	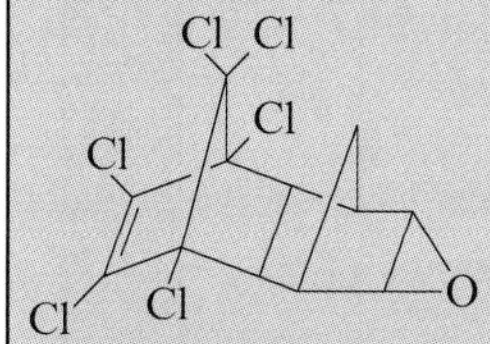		0.1 **I**	II(8)	H		C		
Enflurane [13838-16-9]	$HF_2C{-}O{-}CF_2{-}CHFCl$	20	150	II(8)			C		232
Entandrophragma spp.	see Woods								
Epichlorohydrin [106-89-8]	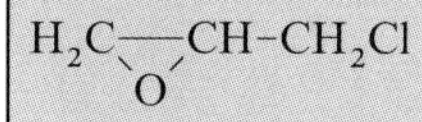	–	–	–	H Sh	2	–	3B	
EPN°, *O*-Ethyl-*O*-(4-nitrophenyl)phenyl-thiophosphonate [2104-64-5]	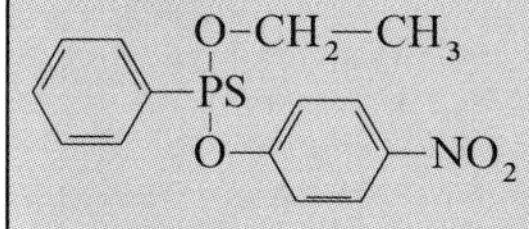		0.5 **I**	II(2)	H				
1,2-Epoxy-3-allyloxy-propane	see Allyl glycidyl ether								
1,2-Epoxybutane	see 1,2-Butylene oxide								
1,2-Epoxy-4-(epoxy-ethyl)cyclohexane	see 4-Vinyl-1-cyclohexene dioxide								
1,2-Epoxy-3-isopropoxy-propane	see Isopropyl glycidyl ether								
1,2-Epoxypropane	see Propylene oxide								
2,3-Epoxy-1-propanol	see Glycidol								
(2,3-Epoxypropyl)tri-methylammonium chloride	see Glycidyl trimethylammonium chloride								
Erionite [12510-42-8] (fibrous dust)	$(Ca,Na,K)_2[Al_3Si_9O_{24}] \cdot 9\,H_2O$	see Section III		–		1	–		

Substance [CAS number]	Formula	MAK ml/m³ (ppm)	MAK mg/m³	Peak limitation	H;S	Carcinogen category	Pregnancy risk group	Germ cell mutagen categ.	Vapour pressure in hPa at 20°C
Ethanedial	see Glyoxal								
1,2-Ethanediol	see Ethylene glycol								
N,N'-1,2-Ethane diylbis-[*N*-(carboxymethyl)-glycine]	see Ethylenediaminetetraacetic acid								
Ethanethiol [75-08-1]	H_3C-CH_2SH	0.5	1.3	II(2)			D		590
Ethanol [64-17-5]	H_3C-CH_2OH	500	960	II(2)		5	C	5	59
Ethanolamine	see 2-Aminoethanol								
Ethene	see Ethylene								
N-Ethenylcarbazole	see Vinylcarbazole								
4-Ethenylcyclohexene	see 4-Vinylcyclohexene								
Ethidium bromide [1239-45-8]	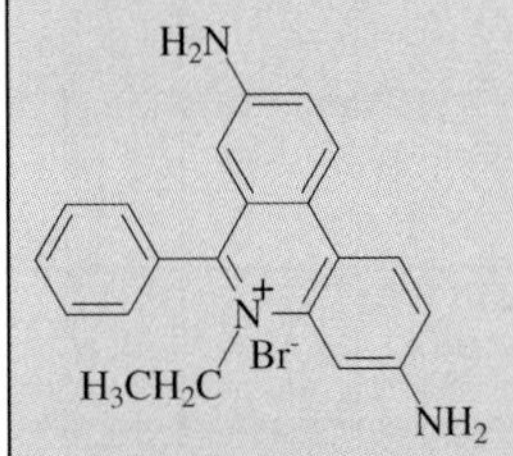	–	–	–		3B	–	3B	
2-Ethoxy-6-amino-naphthalene	see 6-Amino-2-ethoxynaphthalene								
2-Ethoxyethanol	see Ethylene glycol monoethyl ether								
2-(2-Ethoxyethoxy)ethanol	see Diethylene glycol ethyl ether								
2-Ethoxyethyl acetate	see Ethylene glycol monoethyl ether acetate								
1-Ethoxy-2-propanol [1569-02-4]	$CH_3-CH_2-O-CH_2-CH(OH)-CH_3$	50 [36] see Section XII	220	II(2)	H		C		10
1-Ethoxy-2-propyl acetate [54839-24-6]	$CH_3-C(=O)-O-CH(CH_3)-CH_2-O-CH_2-CH_3$	50 [36] see Section XII	300	II(2)			C		2
Ethyl acetate [141-78-6]	$H_3C-COOCH_2-CH_3$	400	1500	I(2)			C		97

36 MAK value applies for the sum of the concentrations of 1-ethoxy-2-propanol and 1-ethoxy-2-propyl acetate in the air.

Substance [CAS number]	Formula	MAK ml/m³ (ppm)	MAK mg/m³	Peak limitation	H;S	Carcinogen category	Pregnancy risk group	Germ cell mutagen categ.	Vapou pressure ir hPa at 20°C
Ethyl acrylate	see Acrylic acid ethyl ester								
Ethyl alcohol	see Ethanol								
Ethylamine [75-04-7]	$H_3C{-}CH_2NH_2$	5	9.4	I(2)[37]			D		1130
Ethylbenzene [100-41-4]	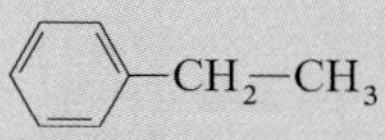	see Section XIII		–	H	3A	–		9
Ethyl bromide	see Bromoethane								
Ethyl carbamate	see Carbamic acid ethyl ester								
Ethyl chloride	see Chloroethane								
Ethyl 2-cyanoacrylate [7085-85-0]	$H_2C{=}CCN{-}CO{-}OCH_2{-}CH_3$	see Section IIb							
5-Ethyl-3,7-dioxa-1-aza-bicyclo[3.3.0]octane (EDAO)[17] [7747-35-5]	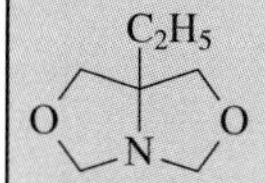	see Section IIb			Sh				
Ethylene [74-85-1]	$H_2C{=}CH_2$	see Section XIII		–		3B	–		
Ethylenebis(oxyethylene) methacrylate	see Triethylene glycol dimethacrylate								
Ethylene chlorohydrin	see 2-Chloroethanol								
Ethylenediamine [107-15-3]	$H_2NCH_2{-}CH_2NH_2$	see Section IIb			Sah				
★ **Ethylenediaminetetra-acetic acid** (EDTA)[38] [60-00-4]	$(HO_2C{-}CH_2)_2N{-}CH_2{-}CH_2{-}N(CH_2{-}CO_2H)_2$	see Section IIb							
Ethylene dibromide	see 1,2-Dibromoethane								
Ethylene dichloride	see 1,2-Dichloroethane								
Ethylene glycol [107-21-1]	CH_2OH / CH_2OH	10	26	I(2)	H		C		
Ethylene glycol-bis-(2-hydroxyethyl)ether	see Triethylene glycol								

[37] A momentary value of 10 ml/m³ (19 mg/m³) should not be exceeded.
[17] releases formaldehyde
[38] Avoid exposure to mixtures with iron compounds (formation of FeEDTA).

Substance [CAS number]	Formula	MAK ml/m³ (ppm)	MAK mg/m³	Peak limitation	H;S	Carcinogen category	Pregnancy risk group	Germ cell mutagen categ.	Vapour pressure in hPa at 20°C
Ethylene glycol dimethacrylate [97-90-5]	$H_2C=C(CH_3)-COO-(CH_2)_2-OOC-C(CH_3)=CH_2$	see Section IV			Sh				
Ethylene glycol dinitrate [39] [628-96-6]	$O_2N-O-(CH_2)_2-O-NO_2$	0.05 see Section XII	0.32	II(1)	H				
Ethylene glycol isopropyl ether	see 2-Isopropoxyethanol								
Ethylene glycol methacrylate	see 2-Hydroxyethyl methacrylate								
Ethylene glycol monoacrylate	see Acrylic acid 2-hydroxyethyl ester								
Ethylene glycol monobutyl ether [111-76-2]	$H_3C-(CH_2)_3-O$ $HOCH_2-CH_2$	10 [40] see Section XII	49	I(2)	H	4	C		
Ethylene glycol monobutyl ether acetate [112-07-2]	$H_3C-(CH_2)_3-O-CH_2$ $H_3C-COOCH_2$	10 [40] see Section XII	66	I(2)	H	4	C		
Ethylene glycol monoethyl ether [110-80-5]	$H_3C-CH_2O-CH_2-CH_2OH$	2 [41] see Section XII	7.5	II(8)	H		B		~5
Ethylene glycol monoethyl ether acetate [111-15-9]	$H_3C-CH_2O-CH_2$ $H_3C-COOCH_2$	2 [41] see Section XII	11	II(8)	H		B		
★ **Ethylene glycol monomethyl ether** [109-86-4]	$H_3CO-CH_2-CH_2OH$	1 see Section XII	3.2	II(8)	H		B		~11
★ **Ethylene glycol monomethyl ether acetate** [110-49-6]	$H_3CO-CH_2-CH_2OOC-CH_3$	1 see Section XII	4.9	II(8)	H		B		9
Ethylene glycol monophenyl ether	see 2-Phenoxyethanol								
Ethylene glycol mono-*n*-propyl ether [2807-30-9]	$CH_3-(CH_2)_2-O-(CH_2)_2-OH$	20	86	I(2)	H		C		1.3

[39] only applies for work areas where skin contact with the substance does not occur
[40] MAK value applies for the sum of the concentrations of ethylene glycol monobutyl ether and its acetate in the air.
[41] MAK value applies for the sum of the concentrations of ethylene glycol monoethyl ether and its acetate in the air.

Substance [CAS number]	Formula	MAK ml/m³ (ppm)	MAK mg/m³	Peak limitation	H;S	Carcinogen category	Pregnancy risk group	Germ cell mutagen categ.	Vapour pressure in hPa at 20°C
Ethylene glycol monopropyl ether acetate [20706-25-6]	$CH_3-(CH_2)_2-O-(CH_2)_2-O-C(=O)-CH_3$	20	120	I(2)	H		C		
Ethylene oxide [75-21-8]		see Section XIII		–	H	2	–	2	
Ethylene thiourea [96-45-7]	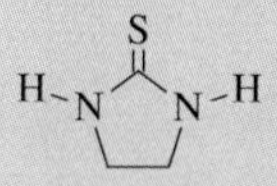	–	–	–		3B	–		
Ethylenimine [151-56-4]		–	–	–	H	2	–	2	214
Ethyl ether [60-29-7]	$H_3C-CH_2-O-CH_2-CH_3$	400	1200	I(1)			D		587
Ethyl-3-ethoxypropionate [763-69-9]	$CH_3-CH_2-O-(CH_2)_2-C(=O)O-CH_2-CH_3$	100	610	I(1)	H		C		
Ethyl formate	see Formic acid ethyl ester								
Ethyl glycol	see Ethylene glycol monoethyl ether								
2-Ethyl-1,3-hexanediol [94-96-2]	$CHOH-(CH_2)_2-CH_3$ $CH(C_2H_5)-CH_2-OH$	see Section IIb							
2-Ethylhexanoic acid [149-57-5]	$CH_3-(CH_2)_3-CH(C_2H_5)-COOH$	see Section IIb							
2-Ethylhexanol [104-76-7]	$CH_3-(CH_2)_3-CH(C_2H_5)-CH_2OH$	20 see Section Xc	110	I(1)			C		0.3
2-Ethylhexyl acrylate	see Acrylic acid 2-ethylhexyl ester								
2-Ethylhexyl alcohol	see 2-Ethylhexanol								
2-Ethyl-2-(hydroxymethyl)-1,3-propanediol triacrylate	see Trimethylolpropane triacrylate								
Ethylidene chloride	see 1,1-Dichloroethane								
Ethyl mercaptan	see Ethanethiol								
Ethyl(2-mercaptobenzoato-*S*)mercury sodium salt	see Thimerosal								
Ethyl mercury	see Mercury, organic compounds								
Ethyl methacrylate	see Methacrylic acid ethyl ester								

Substance [CAS number]	Formula	MAK ml/m³ (ppm)	MAK mg/m³	Peak limitation	H;S	Carcinogen category	Pregnancy risk group	Germ cell mutagen categ.	Vapour pressure in hPa at 20°C
Ethyl methyl ketoxime	see Butanone oxime								
Ethyl 2-methyl-2-propenoate	see Methacrylic acid ethyl ester								
N-Ethylmorpholine [100-74-3]	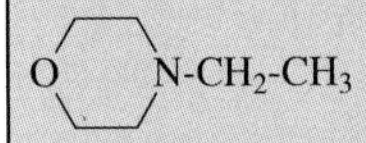	see Section IIb							
N-Ethyl-*N*-nitrosoaniline	see *N*-Nitrosoethylphenylamine								
Ethyl silicate	see Silicic acid tetraethyl ester								
Eugenol [97-53-0]	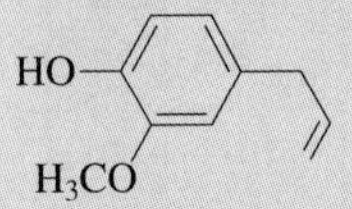	see Section IV			Sh				
F 134a	see 1,1,1,2-Tetrafluoroethane								
Farnesol [4602-84-0]	$HOCH_2(CH{=}C(CH_3){-}CH_2CH_2)_2CH{=}C(CH_3)_2$	see Section IV			Sh				
Fenthion [55-38-9]	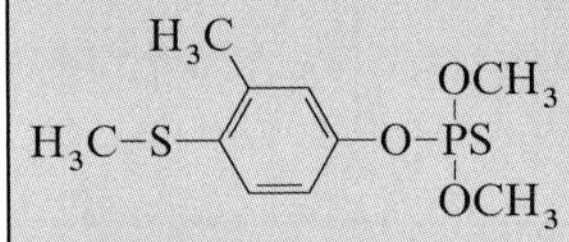		0.2 **I**	II(2)	H				
Ferbam [14484-64-1]	$Fe[S{-}CS{-}N(CH_3)_2]_3$	see Section IIb							
Ferrovanadium [12604-58-9]		see Section IIb							
Fibrous dust, inorganic		see Section III							
Fluorides (as Fluoride)		see Section XII	1 **I**	II(4)	H		C		
Fluorine [7782-41-4]	F_2	see Section IIb							
Fluorocarbon 134a	see 1,1,1,2-Tetrafluoroethane								
Fluorotrichloromethane	see Trichlorofluoromethane								
Formaldehyde [50-00-0]	HCHO	0.3	0.37 [42]	I(2)[43]	Sh	4	C	5	

42 During exposure to mixtures it should be ensured that irritant effects do not occur.
43 A momentary value of 1 ml/m³ (1.2 mg/m³) should not be exceeded.

Substance [CAS number]	Formula	MAK ml/m³ (ppm)	MAK mg/m³	Peak limitation	H;S	Carcinogen category	Pregnancy risk group	Germ cell mutagen categ.	Vapour pressure in hPa at 20°C
Formaldehyde condensation products with p-tert-butylphenol (low-molecular)		see Section IV			Sh				
Formaldehyde condensation products with phenol (low-molecular)		see Section IV			Sh				
Formamide [75-12-7]	NH_2–CHO	see Section IIb			H				
Formic acid [64-18-6]	HCOOH	5	9.5	I(2)			C		42
Formic acid ethyl ester [109-94-4]	$HCOOCH_2$–CH_3	100	310	I(1)	H		C		256
Formic acid methyl ester [107-31-3]	HCO–OCH_3	50 see Section XII	120	II(4)	H		C		640
Fragrance components		see Section IVe							
Fraké	see Woods, *Terminalia superba*								
Framiré	see Woods, *Terminalia ivorensis*								
Fumes		see Section V							
2-Furaldehyde	see Furfural								
Furan [110-00-9]	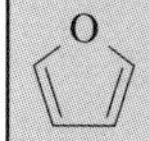	–	–		H	2	–		
Furfural [98-01-1]	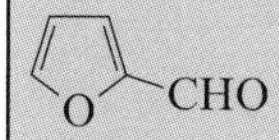	–	–	–	H	3B	–		
Furfuryl alcohol [98-00-0]	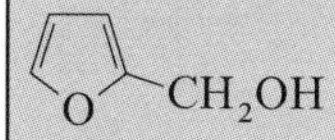	–	–	–	H	3B	–		
Gasolines		see Section Xb							
Gedu nohor	see Woods, *Entandrophragma angolense*								
Geraniol [106-24-1]	CH_3–C(CH_3)=CH–$(CH_2)_2$–C(CH_3)=CH–CH_2OH	see Section IV			Sh				
Germanium tetrahydride [7782-65-2]	GeH_4	see Section IIb							

Substance [CAS number]	Formula	MAK ml/m³ (ppm)	MAK mg/m³	Peak limitation	H;S	Carcinogen category	Pregnancy risk group	Germ cell mutagen categ.	Vapour pressure in hPa at 20°C
Glass fibres (fibrous dust)		see Section III		–		2	–		
Glutaraldehyde [111-30-8]	$OCH-(CH_2)_3-CHO$	0.05	0.21	I(2)[44]	Sah	4	C		
Glycerin [56-81-5]	$HOCH_2-CH(OH)-CH_2OH$		50 **I** see Section Xc	I(2)			C		
Glycerol trinitrate	see Nitroglycerin								
Glyceryl monothio-glycolate [30618-84-9]	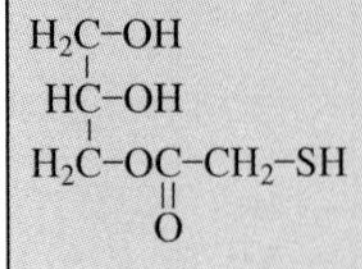	see Section IV			Sh				
Glycidol (Glycide) [556-52-5]	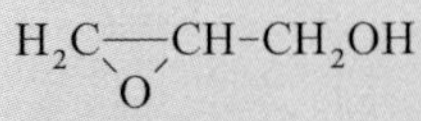	–	–	–	H	2	–		
Glycidyl compounds (epoxides)		see Section IVe							
Glycidyl trimethyl-ammonium chloride [3033-77-0]	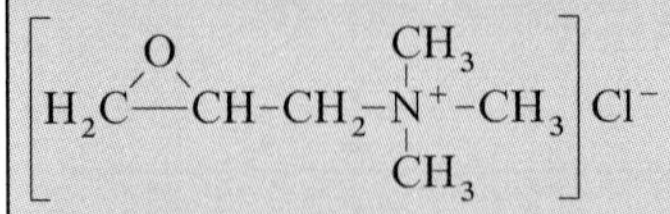	–	–	–	H Sh	2	–		
Glycol	see Ethylene glycol								
Glycol dinitrate	see Ethylene glycol dinitrate								
Glycolic acid *n*-butylester	see Hydroxyacetic acid butyl ester								
Glyoxal [107-22-2]	OHC–CHO	–	–	–	H Sh	3B	–		
Gold [7440-57-5] and its inorganic compounds	Au	see Section IIb			Sh[45]				
Gonystylus bancanus	see Woods								
Graphite [7782-42-5] (inhalable fraction)	C		4 **I** see Section Vf and Vg				C		

[44] A momentary value of 0.2 ml/m³ (0.83 mg/m³) should not be exceeded.
[45] only soluble gold compounds

Substance [CAS number]	Formula	MAK ml/m³ (ppm)	MAK mg/m³	Peak limitation	H;S	Carcinogen category	Pregnancy risk group	Germ cell mutagen categ.	Vapour pressure in hPa at 20°C
Graphite [7782-42-5] (respirable fraction)	C	see Section Vf and Vg	1.5 **R**				C		
Grevillea robusta	see Woods								
Hafnium [7440-58-6]	Hf	see Section II b							
Halloysite [12298-43-0] (fibrous dust)	$Al_2(Si_2O_7) \cdot xH_2O$	see Section III		–		3B	–		
Halothane [151-67-7]	$BrClHC{-}CF_3$	5 see Section XII	41	II(8)			B		242
Hard coal dust	see Coal mine dust								
Hard metal containing tungsten carbide and cobalt (inhalable fraction)		–	–	–	HSah	1	–	3A	
HDDA	see 1,6-Hexanediol diacrylate								
Hemicellulases	see Xylanases								
Hemimellitene (1,2,3-Trimethyl-benzene)	see Trimethylbenzene								
Hempa	see Hexamethylphosphoric acid triamide								
★ **Heptachlor** [76-44-8]	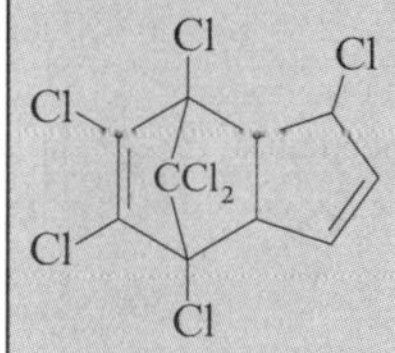		0.05 **I**	II(8)	H	4	D		
***n*-Heptane** [142-82-5]	$H_3C{-}C_5H_{10}{-}CH_3$	500 see Section XII	2100	I(1)			D		48
3-Heptanone [106-35-4]	$CH_3{-}CH_2{-}CO{-}(CH_2)_3{-}CH_3$	10	47	I(2)			D		1.5

Substance [CAS number]	Formula	MAK ml/m³ (ppm)	MAK mg/m³	Peak limitation	H;S	Carcinogen category	Pregnancy risk group	Germ cell mutagen categ.	Vapour pressure in hPa at 20°C
Hexachlorobenzene [118-74-1]	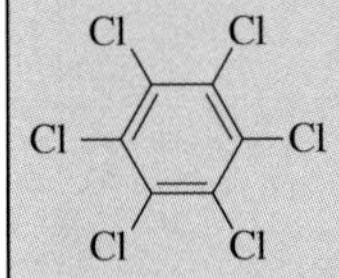	see Section XII			H	4	D		
Hexachloro-1,3–butadiene [87-68-3]	$Cl_2C{=}CCl{-}CCl{=}CCl_2$	–	–	–	H	3B	–		
1,2,3,4,5,6-Hexachlorocyclohexane° (techn. mixture of α-HCH [319-84-6] and β-HCH [319-85-7])	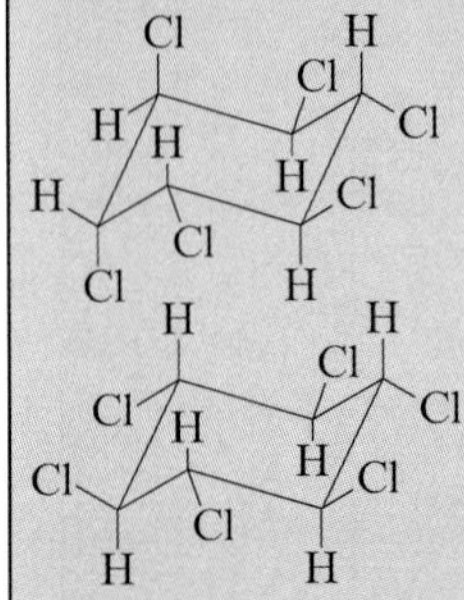		0.5[46] **I**	II (8)	H				
γ-Hexachlorocyclohexane	see Lindane								
Hexachlorocyclopentadiene [77-47-4]	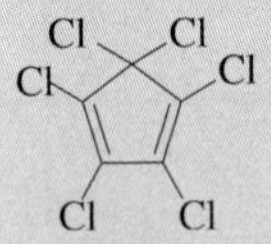	see Section II b			H				
Hexachloroethane [67-72-1]	$Cl_3C{-}CCl_3$	1	9.8	II (2)					
Hexachloronaphthalenes	see Chlorinated naphthalenes								
Hexadecanoic acid	see Palmitic acid								
1-Hexadecanol [36653-82-4]	$HO{-}(CH_2)_{15}{-}CH_3$	see Section II b[35]							
Hexahydrophthalic anhydride [85-42-7]	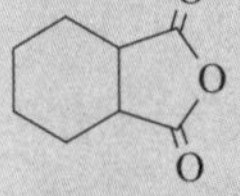	see Section IV			Sa				
Hexahydro-1,3,5-triethyl-s-triazine	see 1,3,5-Triethylhexahydro-1,3,5-triazine								

[46] 0.5 = (Conc. α-HCH divided by 5) + Conc. β-HCH

[35] Provided the technical exposure limit of 10 mg/m³ I for metal-working fluids is observed, adverse effects on health are not to be expected.

Substance [CAS number]	Formula	MAK ml/m³ (ppm)	MAK mg/m³	Peak limitation	H;S	Carcinogen category	Pregnancy risk group	Germ cell mutagen categ.	Vapour pressure in hPa at 20°C
1,6-Hexamethylene diacrylate	see 1,6-Hexanediol diacrylate								
1,6-Hexamethylene diisocyanate [822-06-0]	$OCN-(CH_2)_6-NCO$	0.005	0.035	I (1)[47]	Sah		D		0.007
Hexamethylene-tetramine [17] [100-97-0]	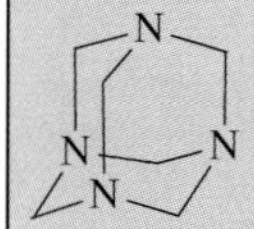	see Section IIb			Sh				
Hexamethylphosphoric acid triamide [680-31-9]	$OP[N(CH_3)_2]_3$	–	–	–	H	2	–		
Hexane (*n*-Hexane) [110-54-3]	$H_3C-(CH_2)_4-CH_3$	50 see Section XII	180	II (8)			C		160
★ **Hexane** (all isomers except *n*-Hexane): 2-Methylpentane [107-83-5], 3-Methylpentane [96-14-0], 2,2-Dimethylbutane [75-83-2] 2,3-Dimethylbutane [79-29-8] Methylcyclopentane [96-37-7]	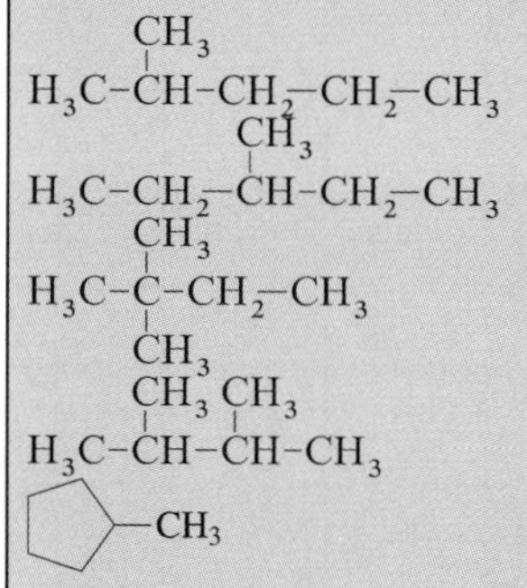	500	1800	II (2)			D		
1,6-Hexanediol diacrylate [13048-33-4]	$H_2C=CH-COO-(CH_2)_6-OOC-CH=CH_2$	see Section IV			Sh				
2,2'-[1,6-Hexanediylbis-(oxymethylene)]bisoxirane	see Diglycidyl hexanediol								
1-Hexanol [111-27-3]	$H_3C-(CH_2)_4-CH_2OH$	see Section IIb							
2-Hexanone [591-78-6]	$H_3C-(CH_2)_3-CO-CH_3$	5 see Section XII	21	II (8)	H				
Hexone [108-10-1]	$(H_3C)_2CH-CH_2-CO-CH_3$	20 see Section XII	83	I (2)	H		C		21

[47] A momentary value of 0.01 ml/m³ (0.070 mg/m³) should not be exceeded.
[17] releases formaldehyde

Substance [CAS number]	Formula	MAK ml/m³ (ppm)	MAK mg/m³	Peak limitation	H;S	Carcinogen category	Pregnancy risk group	Germ cell mutagen categ.	Vapour pressure in hPa at 20°C
***sec*-Hexyl acetate** [108-84-9]	$H_3C-COOCH(CH_3)-CH_2-CH(CH_3)_2$	see Section IIb							
2-Hexyl-1-decanol [2425-77-6]	$HO-CH_2-CH(C_6H_{13})-(CH_2)_7-CH_3$	see Section IIb							
Hexylene glycol [107-41-5]	$H_3C-CH(OH)-CH_2-C(OH)(CH_3)_2$	10 see Section Xc	49	I(2)			D		0.06
HFC 134a	see 1,1,1,2-Tetrafluoroethane								
Hydraulic fluids		see Section Xd							
Hydrazine [302-01-2]	H_2N-NH_2	see Section XIII		–	H Sh	2	–		13
Hydrazine hydrate [7803-57-8] and hydrazine salts	$H_2N-NH_2 \cdot H_2O$	see Section IV			Sh				
Hydrazobenzene [122-66-7]	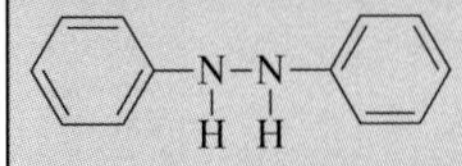	–	–	–		2	–		
Hydrazoic acid [7782-79-8]	HN_3	0.1	0.18	I(2)					
Hydrochloric acid	see Hydrogen chloride								
Hydrocyanic acid	see Hydrogen cyanide								
Hydrogen bromide [10035-10-6]	HBr	2	6.7	I(1)			D		
Hydrogen chloride [7647-01-0]	HCl	2	3.0	I(2)			C		
Hydrogen cyanide [74-90-8]	HCN	1.9	2.1	II(2)	H		C		800
Hydrogen fluoride [7664-39-3]	HF	1 see Section XII	0.83	I(2)			C		1033
Hydrogen peroxide [7722-84-1]	H_2O_2	0.5	0.71	I(1)		4	C		
Hydrogen selenide [7783-07-5]	H_2Se	0.015	0.050	I(2)		3B	C		
Hydrogen sulfide [7783-06-4]	H_2S	5	7.1	I(2)			C		

Substance [CAS number]	Formula	MAK ml/m³ (ppm)	MAK mg/m³	Peak limitation	H;S	Carcinogen category	Pregnancy risk group	Germ cell mutagen categ.	Vapour pressure in hPa at 20°C
α-Hydro-ω-hydroxy-poly[oxy(methyl-1,2-ethandiyl)]	see Polypropylene glycol								
Hydroquinone [123-31-9]	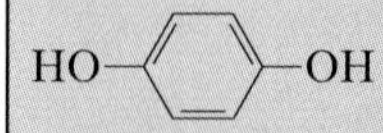	–	–	–	H Sh	2	–	3A	
Hydroxyacetic acid butyl ester [7397-62-8]	$HO-CH_2-CO-O-CH_2-CH_2-CH_2-CH_3$	see Section IIb							
p-Hydroxyaniline	see *p*-Aminophenol								
Hydroxycitronellal [107-75-5]	$HC(=O)-CH_2-CH(CH_3)-(CH_2)_3-C(OH)(CH_3)_2$	see Section IV			Sh				
2-(2-Hydroxyethoxy)-ethylamine	see 2-(2-Aminoethoxy)ethanol								
2-Hydroxyethyl acrylate	see Acrylic acid 2-hydroxyethyl ester								
1-Hydroxyethyl-2-heptadecenyl-imidazoline [21652-27-7]	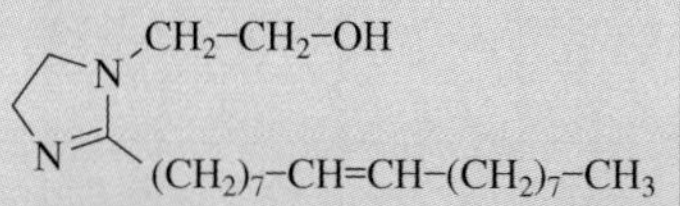	see Section IIb							
2-Hydroxyethyl methacrylate [868-77-9]	$H_2C=C(CH_3)-COO-CH_2-CH_2OH$	see Section IIb			Sh				
N-(2-Hydroxyethyl)-3-methyl-2-quinoxaline-carboxamide 1,4-dioxide	see Olaquindox								
β-Hydroxyethyl phenyl ether	see 2-Phenoxyethanol								
1-Hydroxy-1'-hydroperoxydicyclohexyl peroxide [78-18-2]	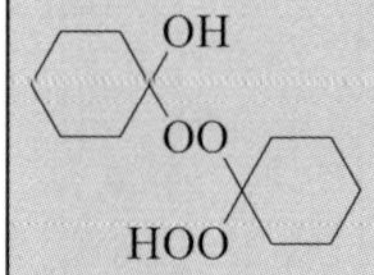	see Section Xa							
Hydroxylamine [7803-49-8] and its salts	NH_2-OH	see Section IV			Sh				
1-Hydroxy-2-methoxy-4-(1-propenyl)benzene	see Isoeugenol								

Substance [CAS number]	Formula	MAK ml/m³ (ppm)	MAK mg/m³	Peak limitation	H;S	Carcinogen category	Pregnancy risk group	Germ cell mutagen categ.	Vapour pressure in hPa at 20°C
2-Hydroxymethyl-2-nitro-1,3-propanediol [126-11-4] [18]	$C(CH_2{-}OH)_3(NO_2)$	see Section II b							
4-Hydroxy-4-methyl-pentan-2-one	see Diacetone alcohol								
4-(4-Hydroxy-4-methyl pentyl)-3-cyclohexene-1-carboxaldehyde (Lyral) [31906-04-4]	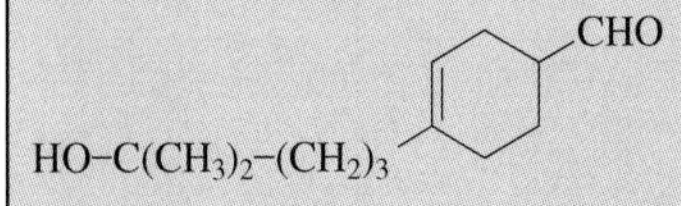	see Section IV			Sh				
N-(4-((2-Hydroxy-5-methyl-phenyl)azo)phenyl)-acetamide	see Disperse Yellow 3								
3-Hydroxy-2-naphthalenecarboxylic acid [92-70-6]	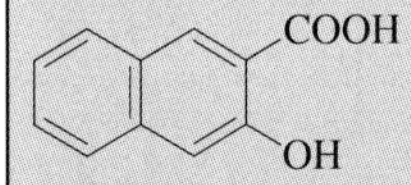	see Section II b							
3-Hydroxy-2-naphthoic acid	see 3-Hydroxy-2-naphthalene-carboxylic acid								
4-Hydroxy-3-nitroaniline	see 2-Nitro-4-aminophenol								
3-Hydroxyphenol	see Resorcinol								
1-Hydroxy-2-phenoxy-ethane	see 2-Phenoxyethanol								
2-Hydroxy-1,2,3–propanetricarboxylic acid	see Citric acid								
Hydroxypropyl acrylate	see Acrylic acid hydroxypropyl ester								
2-Hydroxypropylamine	see 1-Amino-2-propanol								
2-Hydroxypropyl meth-acrylate	see Methacrylic acid 2-hydroxy-propyl ester								
2-Hydroxypropyl 2-methyl-2-propenoate	see Methacrylic acid 2-hydroxy-propyl ester								
1-Hydroxy-2(1*H*)-pyridinethione sodium salt	see Sodium pyrithione								
Hydroxytoluene	see Benzyl alcohol								

Use in metal-working fluids is not permitted: see TRGS 611.

Substance [CAS number]	Formula	MAK ml/m³ (ppm)	MAK mg/m³	Peak limitation	H;S	Carcinogen category	Pregnancy risk group	Germ cell mutagen categ.	Vapour pressure hPa at 20°C
1-Hydroxy-2,4,5-trichlorobenzene	see 2,4,5-Trichlorophenol								
Idigbo	see Woods, *Terminalia ivorensis*								
Imidazole [288-32-4]	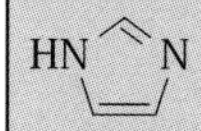	see Section II b							3.3·10
2-Imidazolidinethione	see Ethylene thiourea								
Incense cedar	see Woods, *Calocedrus decurrens*								
Indeno[1,2,3-*cd*]pyrene [193-39-5]	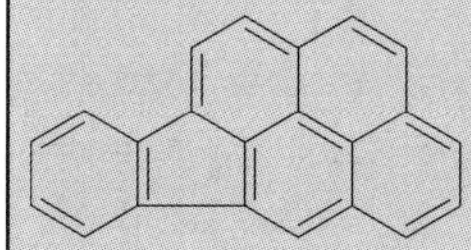	see Section III pyrolysis products of organic materials		–	H	2	–		
Indium phosphide [22398-80-7]	InP	–	–	–		2	–		
Iodine [7553-56-2]	I_2	see Section II b							
Iodomethane	see Methyl iodide								
3-Iodo-2-propynyl butylcarbamate [55406-53-6]	$I{-}C{\equiv}C{-}CH_2{-}O{-}\overset{O}{\overset{\Vert}{C}}{-}NH{-}C_4H_9$	see Section II b			Sh				
Ipe	see Woods, *Tabebuia* spp.								
Ipe peroba	see Woods, *Paratecoma peroba*								
Iroko	see Woods, *Chlorophora excelsa*								
Iron oxides [1345-25-1] [1309-37-1]	FeO Fe_2O_3	see Section Vf and Vg	1.5 **R**						
Iron pentacarbonyl [13463-40-6]	$Fe(CO)_5$	0.1	0.81	II(2)			D		
Isatoic anhydride	see *N*-Carboxyanthranilic anhydride								
Isoamyl alcohol	see Pentanol (3-Methyl-1-butanol)								
Isobutenyl chloride	see 3-Chloro-2-methylpropene								
Isobutyl acetate [110-19-0]	$H_3C{-}COOCH_2{-}CH(CH_3)_2$	100	480	I(2)			C		18

Substance [CAS number]	Formula	MAK ml/m³ (ppm)	MAK mg/m³	Peak limitation	H;S	Carcinogen category	Pregnancy risk group	Germ cell mutagen categ.	Vapour pressure in hPa at 20°C
Isobutyl alcohol [78-83-1]	$(H_3C)_2CH{-}CH_2OH$	100	310	I(1)			C		11.7
Isobutylamine [78-81-9]	$(H_3C)_2CH{-}CH_2NH_2$	2	6.1	I(2)[19]			C		
Isobutyl chloroformate	see Chloroformic acid butyl ester								
Isobutyl phosphate	see Triisobutyl phosphate								
Isocyanatobenzene	see Phenyl isocyanate								
Isocyanic acid *p*-chlorophenyl ester	see 4-Chlorophenyl isocyanate								
Isodecyl oleate [59231-34-4]	$CH_2{-}(CH_2)_5{-}COO{-}(CH_2)_7{-}CH(CH_3)_2$ $CH_2{-}CH{=}CH{-}(CH_2)_7{-}CH_3$	see Section IIb							
Isoeugenol [97-54-1] *cis*-Isoeugenol [5912-86-7] *trans*-Isoeugenol [5932-68-3]	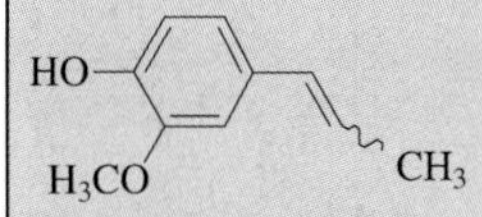	see Section IV			Sh				
Isoflurane [26675-46-7]	$F_3C{-}CHCl{-}O{-}CHF_2$	see Section IIb							
★ **Isononanoic acid** [3302-10-1] [26896-18-4]	$H_3C{-}C(CH_3)_2{-}CH_2{-}CH(CH_3){-}CH_2{-}CO_2H$	see Section IIb and Xc							
Isophorone [78-59-1]	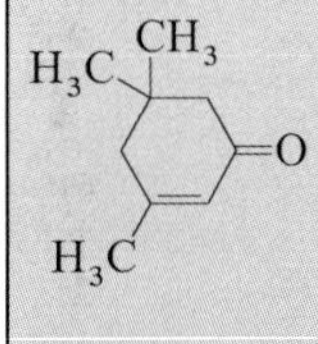	2	11	I(2)		3B	C		
Isophorone diamine	see 3-Aminomethyl-3,5,5-trimethylcyclohexylamine								
Isophorone diisocyanate [4098-71-9]	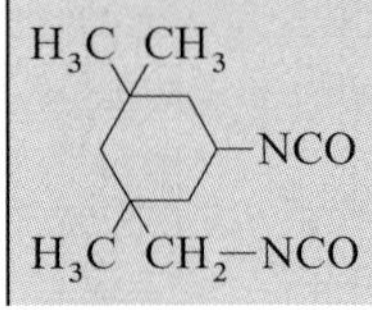	0.005	0.046	I(1)[48]	Sah		D		

[19] A momentary value of 10 ml/m³ (30 mg/m³) should not be exceeded.
[48] A momentary value of 0.01 ml/m³ (0.092 mg/m³) should not be exceeded.

Substance [CAS number]	Formula	MAK ml/m³ (ppm)	MAK mg/m³	Peak limitation	H;S	Carcinogen category	Pregnancy risk group	Germ cell mutagen categ.	Vapour pressure in hPa at 20°C
★ **Isoprene** (2-Methyl-1,3-butadiene) [78-79-5]	$H_2C=C(CH_3)-CH=CH_2$	3	8.5	II(8)		5	C	5	733
Isopropanolamine	see 1-Amino-2-propanol								
Isopropenyl acetate [108-22-5]	$H_3C-COO-CH_2-CH=CH_2$	10	46	I(2)			D		
Isopropenylbenzene	see α-Methyl styrene								
2-Isopropoxyethanol [109-59-1]	$(CH_3)_2CH-O-CH_2-CH_2OH$	5	22	II(8)	H		C		
Isopropyl acetate	see Propyl acetate								
Isopropyl alcohol [67-63-0]	$(H_3C)_2CHOH$	200 see Section XII	500	II(2)			C		44
Isopropylamine [75-31-0]	$H_3C-CH(NH_2)-CH_3$	5	12	I(2)[49]			C		637
Isopropylbenzene	see Cumene								
Isopropyl ether [108-20-3]	$(H_3C)_2CH-O-CH(CH_3)_2$	200	850	I(2)			C		180
Isopropyl glycidyl ether (IGE) [4016-14-2]	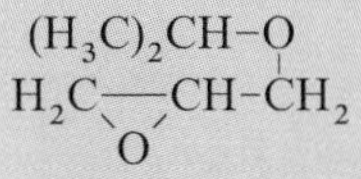	–	–	–		3B	–		
4,4'-Isopropylidene-diphenol	see Bisphenol A								
4,4'-Isopropylidene-diphenol diglycidyl ether	see Bisphenol A diglycidyl ether								
4-Isopropylnitrobenzene	see *p*-Nitrocumene								
Isopropyl oil	Residue of isopropyl alcohol production	–	–	–		3B	–		
4-Isopropylphenyl isocyanate [31027-31-3]	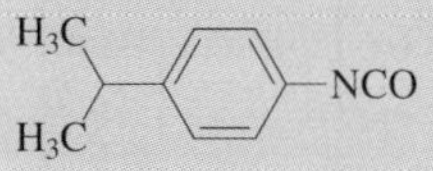	see Section IIb			Sh				
Isotridecanol [27458-92-0]		see Section IIb							

[49] A momentary value of 10 ml/m³ (25 mg/m³) should not be exceeded.

Substance [CAS number]	Formula	MAK ml/m³ (ppm)	MAK mg/m³	Peak limitation	H;S	Carcinogen category	Pregnancy risk group	Germ cell mutagen categ.	Vapour pressure in hPa at 20°C
Isotridecyl alcohol	see Isotridecanol								
Kambala	see Woods, *Chlorophora excelsa*								
Kepone	see Chlordecone								
Ketene [463-51-4]	$H_2C{=}CO$	see Section IIb							
Khaya spp.	see Woods								
Lapacho	see Woods, *Tabebuia avellanedae*								
Laughing gas	see Nitrous oxide								
Lauric acid [143-07-7]	$CH_3{-}(CH_2)_{10}{-}COOH$	see Section Xc		–		3A	–		
Lauryl alcohol	see 1-Dodecanol								
Lead [7439-92-1] and its inorganic compounds (inhalable fraction) except lead arsenate and lead chromate	Pb	see Section XII		–		2	–	3A	
Lead arsenate	see Arsenic								
Lead chromate [7758-97-6] and **Lead chromate oxide** [18454-12-1]	$PbCrO_4$ Pb_2OCrO_4	–	–	–		3B	–		
Limba	see Woods, *Terminalia superba*								
D-Limonene [5989-27-5]	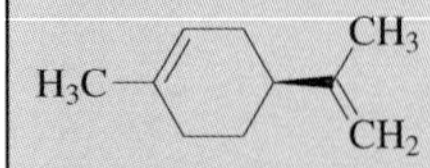	20	110	II(2)	Sh		C		
D,L-Limonene [138-86-3] and similar mixtures	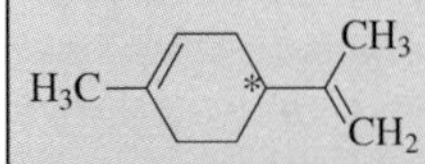	see Section IIb			Sh				
L-Limonene [5989-54-8]	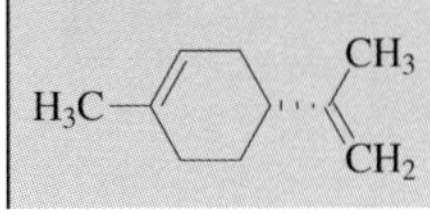	see Section IIb			Sh				

Substance [CAS number]	Formula	MAK ml/m³ (ppm)	MAK mg/m³	Peak limitation	H;S	Carcinogen category	Pregnancy risk group	Germ cell mutagen categ.	Vapour pressure in hPa at 20°C
Lindane [58-89-9]	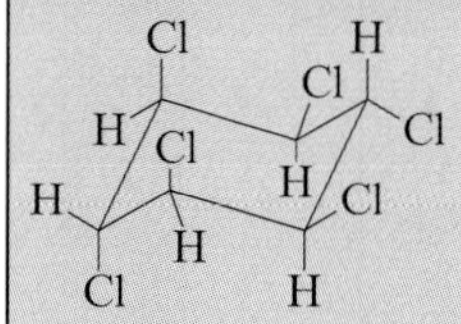	see Section XII	0.1 **I**	II(8)	H	4	C		
Lithium hydride [7580-67-8]	LiH	see Section IIb							
Lubricants		see Section Xd							
Lyral	see 4-(4-Hydroxy-4-methyl pentyl)-3-cyclohexene-1-carboxaldehyde								
Machaerium scleroxylon	see Woods								
★ **Magnesium oxide** [1309-48-4] (inhalable fraction)	MgO	see Section Vf and Vg	4 **I**				C		
★ **Magnesium oxide** [1309-48-4] (respirable fraction)	MgO	see Section Vf and Vg	1.5 **R**				C		
Magnesium oxide fume [1309-48-4]	MgO	see Section IIb and Vh							
Magnesium oxide sulfate [12286-12-3] (fibrous dust)	$MgSO_4 \cdot 5MgO \cdot 8H_2O$	see Section III		–		3B	–		
Mahogany, African	see Woods, *Khaya* spp.								
Mahogany, American	see Woods, *Swietenia* spp.								
Makoré	see Woods, *Tieghemella heckelii*								
Malathion [121-75-5]	$S-PS(OCH_3)_2$ / $CH-COOCH_2-CH_3$ / $CH_2-COOCH_2-CH_3$		15 **I**	II(4)			D		
Maleic anhydride [108-31-6]	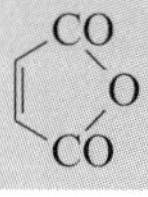	0.1	0.41	I(1)[50]	Sah		C		

[50] A momentary value of 0.2 ml/m³ (0.81 mg/m³) should not be exceeded.

Substance [CAS number]	Formula	MAK ml/m³ (ppm)	MAK mg/m³	Peak limitation	H;S	Carcinogen category	Pregnancy risk group	Germ cell mutagen categ.	Vapour pressure in hPa at 20°C
Manganese [7439-96-5] and its inorganic compounds	Mn	see Section Vg and XII	0.5 **I**	51			C		
Manganese-II, IV-oxide	see Manganese								
Manganous ethylenebis-(dithiocarbamate) (Maneb) [12427-38-2]	$CH_2{-}NH{-}CS{-}S^-$ / $CH_2{-}NH{-}CS{-}S^-$ Mn^{2+}	see Section IV			Sh				
Manganous-manganic oxide	see Manganese								
Man-made mineral fibres (fibrous dust)		see Section III		–			–		
Mansonia altissima	see Woods								
MBT	see 2-Mercaptobenzothiazole								
MDI	see 4,4'-Methylene diphenyl isocyanate								
MDI oligomers	see "Polymeric MDI"								
Mechlorethamine	see *N*-Methyl-bis(2-chloroethyl)-amine								
Medicines, carcinogenic		see Section III		–			–		
Merbromin [129-16-8]	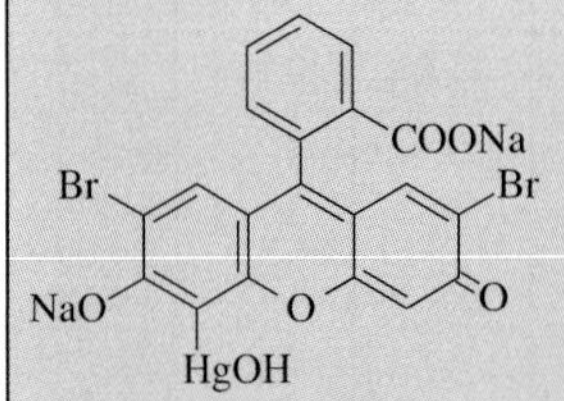	see Section IV			Sh				
2-Mercaptobenzo-thiazole [149-30-4]	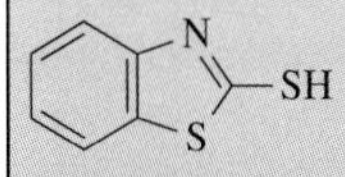	see Section Vf, Vg and Xc	4 **I**		Sh	3B	C		
2-Mercaptoimidazoline	see Ethylene thiourea								

[1] Permanganates: Peak limitation category I(1)

Substance [CAS number]	Formula	MAK ml/m³ (ppm)	MAK mg/m³	Peak limitation	H;S	Carcinogen category	Pregnancy risk group	Germ cell mutagen categ.	Vapour pressure in hPa at 20°C
Mercury (metallic mercury [7439-97-6] and inorganic mercury compounds (as Hg))	Hg		0.1 see Section XII	II (8)	Sh	3B			
Mercury, organic compounds		see Section XII		–	H Sh	3B	–		
Mesitylene (1,3,5-Trimethylbenzene)	see Trimethylbenzene								
Mesityl oxide [141-79-7]	$(H_3C)_2C=CH-CO-CH_3$	5	20	I (2)	H		D		
Metal-working fluids		see Section Xc							
Metal-working fluids which contain nitrite or nitrite-forming compounds and substances which react with nitrite to yield nitrosamines		–	–	–		3B	–		
Methacrylic acid [79-41-4]	$H_2C=C(CH_3)-COOH$	5	18	I (2)			C		0.9
Methacrylic acid ethyl ester [97-63-2]	$H_2C=C(CH_3)-COOCH_2-CH_3$	see Section IV			Sh				
Methacrylic acid 2-hydroxyethyl ester	see 2-Hydroxyethyl methacrylate								
Methacrylic acid 2-hydroxypropyl ester [923-26-2]	$H_2C=C(CH_3)-CO-O-CH_2-\underset{OH}{CH}-CH_3$	see Section IV			Sh				
Methacrylic acid methyl ester [80-62-6]	$H_2C=C(CH_3)-COOCH_3$	50	210	I (2)	Sh		C		47
N,N'-Methanetetraylbiscyclohexanamine	see Dicyclohexylcarbodiimide								
Methanethiol	see Methyl mercaptan								
Methanol [67-56-1]	H_3COH	200 see Section XII	270	II (4)	H		C		128

Substance [CAS number]	Formula	MAK ml/m³ (ppm)	MAK mg/m³	Peak limitation	H;S	Carcinogen category	Pregnancy risk group	Germ cell mutagen categ.	Vapour pressure in hPa at 20°C
★ **Methoxyacetic acid** [625-45-6]	$H_3C{-}O{-}CH_2{-}COOH$	1	3.7	II(8)	H		B		1.8
2-Methoxyaniline, 4-Methoxyaniline	see *o*-Anisidine, *p*-Anisidine								
3-Methoxy-*n*-butyl acetate [4435-53-4]	$CH_3{-}C(=O){-}O{-}(CH_2)_2{-}CH(CH_3){-}O{-}CH_3$	see Section IIb							
Methoxychlor (DMDT) [72-43-5]	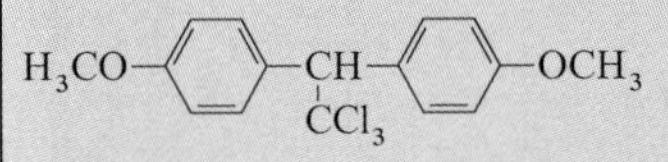		15 **I**	II(8)			D		
2-Methoxyethanol	see Ethylene glycol monomethyl ether								
2-Methoxyethyl acetate	see Ethylene glycol monomethyl ether acetate								
2-Methoxy-5-methyl-aniline	see 5-Methyl-*o*-anisidine								
2-Methoxy-2-methyl-propane	see *tert*-Butyl methyl ether								
1-Methoxy-2-nitro-benzene	see 2-Nitroanisole								
1-Methoxy-2-propanol	see Propylene glycol 1-methyl ether								
2-Methoxy-1-propanol	see Propylene glycol 2-methyl ether								
2-Methoxy-4-(1-propenyl)phenol	see Isoeugenol								
2-Methoxy-4-(2-propenyl)phenol	see Eugenol								
1-Methoxypropyl-2-acetate	see Propylene glycol 1-methyl ether-2-acetate								
2-Methoxypropyl-1-acetate	see Propylene glycol 2-methyl ether-1-acetate								
Methyl acetate [79-20-9]	$H_3C{-}COOCH_3$	100	310	I(4)			C		220
Methyl acetylene [74-99-7]	$H_3C{-}C{\equiv}CH$	see Section IIb							
Methyl acrylate	see Acrylic acid methyl ester								

Substance [CAS number]	Formula	MAK ml/m³ (ppm)	MAK mg/m³	Peak limitation	H;S	Carcinogen category	Pregnancy risk group	Germ cell mutagen categ.	Vapour pressure in hPa at 20°C
Methylal	see Dimethoxymethane								
Methyl alcohol	see Methanol								
2-Methylallyl chloride	see 3-Chloro-2-methylpropene								
Methylamine [74-89-5]	$H_3C{-}NH_2$	10	13	I(1)[52]			D		
1-Methyl-2-amino-5-chlorobenzene	see 4-Chloro-*o*-toluidine								
4-Methylaniline	see *p*-Toluidine								
***N*-Methylaniline** [53] [100-61-8]	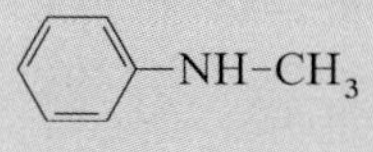	0.5	2.2	II(2)	H		D		
5-Methyl-*o*-anisidine [120-71-8]	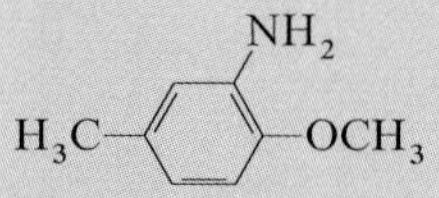	–	–	–		2	–		
Methyl benzimidazol-2-ylcarbamate	see Carbendazim								
Methyl-1*H*-benzotriazole [29385-43-1]	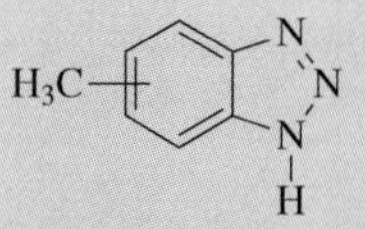	see Section IIb							
***N*-Methyl-bis(2-chloro-ethyl)amine** (nitrogen mustard) [51-75-2]	$(ClH_2C{-}CH_2)_2N{-}CH_3$	–	–	–	H Sh	1	–	2	
Methyl bromide [74-83-9]	CH_3Br	see Section XII		–	H	3B	–		
2-Methyl-1,3-butadiene	see Isoprene								
1-Methylbutyl acetate	see Amyl acetate								
2-Methylbutyl acetate	see Amyl acetate								
3-Methylbutyl acetate	see Amyl acetate								
Methyl-*tert*-butyl ether	see *tert*-Butyl methyl ether								
Methyl butyl ketone	see 2-Hexanone								

[52] A momentary value of 10 ml/m³ (13 mg/m³) should not be exceeded.
[53] Reaction with nitrosating agents can result in the formation of carcinogenic *N*-nitrosomethylaniline, see Section III "Amines which form carcinogenic nitrosamines on nitrosation", p. 147.

Substance [CAS number]	Formula	MAK ml/m³ (ppm)	MAK mg/m³	Peak limitation	H;S	Carcinogen category	Pregnancy risk group	Germ cell mutagen categ.	Vapour pressure in hPa at 20°C
Methyl chloride [74-87-3]	CH_3Cl	50	100	II (2)	H	3B	B		
Methyl chloroacetate	see Chloroacetic acid methyl ester								
Methyl chloroform	see 1,1,1-Trichloroethane								
Methyl chloroformate	see Chloroformic acid methyl ester								
Methyl 2-cyanoacrylate [137-05-3]	$H_2C{=}CCN{-}CO{-}OCH_3$	2	9.2	I (1)			D		
Methylcyclohexane [108-87-2]	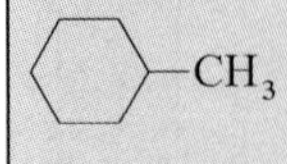	200	810	II (2)			D		48
Methylcyclohexanol (all isomers) [25639-42-3]	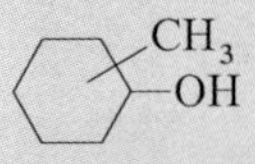	see Section II b							
1-Methylcyclohexan-2-one [583-60-8]	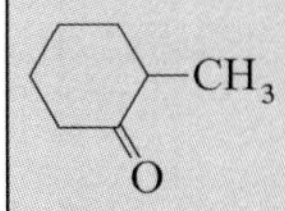	see Section II b							
Methyl demeton	see Demeton-methyl								
Methyldiethanolamine [105-59-9]	$H_3C{-}N(CH_2{-}CH_2OH)_2$	see Section II b							
4,4'-Methylene-bis(2-chloroaniline) [101-14-4]	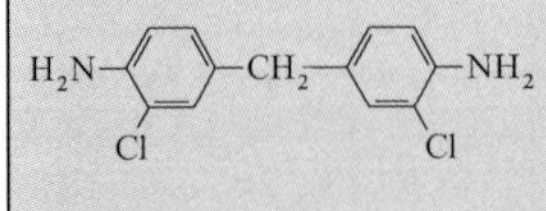	–	–	–	H	2	–		
4,4'-Methylene-bis(*N,N*-dimethylaniline) [101-61-1]	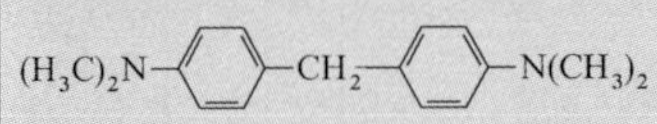	–	–	–		2	–		
4,4'-Methylene-bis(*N,N*-dimethyl)benzenamine	see 4,4'-Methylene-bis(*N,N*-dimethylaniline)								
4,4'-Methylene-bis(2-methylaniline) [838-88-0]	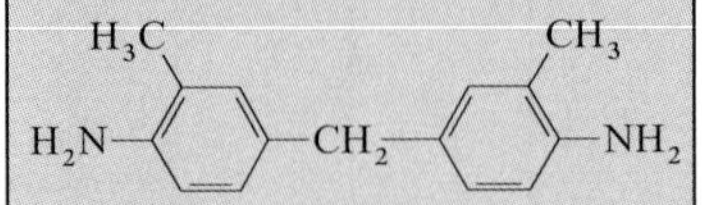	–	–	–	H	2	–	–	
***N,N'*-Methylene-bis(5-methyloxazolidine)** [66204-44-2]	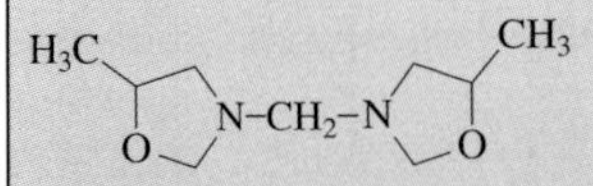	see Section II b			Sh				
Methylene chloride	see Dichloromethane								
4,4'-Methylene dianiline	see 4,4'-Diaminodiphenylmethane								

Substance [CAS number]	Formula	MAK ml/m³ (ppm)	MAK mg/m³	Peak limitation	H;S	Carcinogen category	Pregnancy risk group	Germ cell mutagen categ.	Vapour pressure in hPa at 20°C
4,4'-Methylenedimorpholine [17] [5625-90-1]	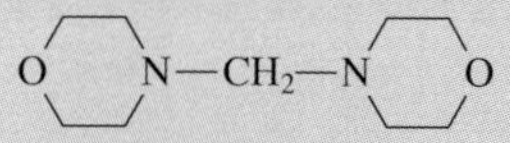	see Section IIb							
4,4'-Methylene diphenyl diisocyanate (MDI) [101-68-8] (inhalable fraction) see also "polymeric MDI"	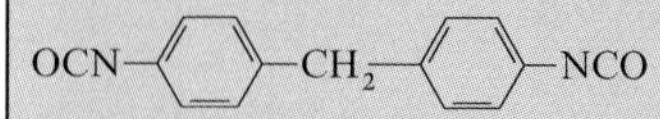	see Section XII	0.05 **I**	I(1)[54]	HSah	4	C		
Methyl ether	see Dimethyl ether								
2-(1-Methylethoxy)-ethanol	see 2-Isopropoxyethanol								
4,4'-(1-Methylethylidene)bisphenol	see Bisphenol A								
Methyl ethyl ketone	see 2-Butanone								
Methyl ethyl ketone peroxide [1338-23-4]	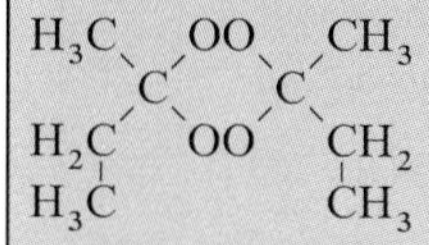	see Section Xa							
Methyl ethyl ketoxime	see Butanone oxime								
1-(1-Methylethyl)-4-nitrobenzene	see *p*-Nitrocumene								
N,N-Methylethylnitrosoamine	see *N*-Nitrosomethylethylamine								
Methyl formate	see Formic acid methyl ester								
Methyl glycol	see Ethylene glycol monomethyl ether								
Methyl glycol acetate	see Ethylene glycol monomethyl ether acetate								
5-Methyl-3-heptanone [541-85-5]	$CH_3–CH_2–CO–CH_2–CH(CH_3)–CH_2–CH_3$	10	53	I(2)			D		2.4
Methyl-2-hexanone [110-12-3]	$CH_3–CO–CH_2–CH_2–CH_2(CH_3)_2$	10	47	I(2)			D		6
Methyl iodide [74-88-4]	$H_3C\ I$	–	–	–	H	2	–		438

17 releases formaldehyde

54 A momentary value of 0.1 mg/m³ should not be exceeded.

Substance [CAS number]	Formula	MAK ml/m³ (ppm)	MAK mg/m³	Peak limitation	H;S	Carcinogen category	Pregnancy risk group	Germ cell mutagen categ.	Vapour pressure in hPa at 20°C
Methyl isobutyl carbinol	see 4-Methyl-2-pentanol								
Methyl isobutyl ketone	see Hexone								
Methyl isocyanate [624-83-9]	$H_3C{-}NCO$	0.01	0.024	I(1)			D		513
Methyl mercaptan [74-93-1]	H_3CSH	0.5	1.0	II(2)			D		1710
Methyl mercury	see Mercury, organic compounds								
Methyl methacrylate	see Methacrylic acid methyl ester								
2-Methyl-4-[(2-methylphenyl)azo]benzenamine	see *o*-Aminoazotoluene								
1-Methyl-3-nitrobenzene	see 3-Nitrotoluene								
1-Methyl-4-nitrobenzene	see 4-Nitrotoluene								
2,2'-[[3-Methyl-4-[(4-nitrophenyl)azo]phenyl]imino]bisethanol	see Disperse Red 17								
N-Methyl-*N*-nitrosoaniline	see *N*-Nitrosomethylphenylamine								
(*Z*)-*N*-Methyl-*N*-(1-oxo-9-octadecenyl)glycine	see Oleoyl sarcosine								
2-Methylpentane	see Hexane (all isomers except *n*-Hexane)								
3-Methylpentane	see Hexane (all isomers except *n*-Hexane)								
2-Methyl-2,4-pentanediol	see Hexylene glycol								
4-Methyl-2-pentanol [108-11-2]	$(H_3C)_2CH{-}CH_2{-}CHOH{-}CH_3$	20	85	I(1)			D		7
4-Methyl-2-pentanone	see Hexone								
2-Methyl-2-penten-4-one	see Mesityl oxide								
4-Methylphenyl diiodomethyl sulfone	see 4-(Diiodomethylsulfonyl)-toluene								
Methylphenyl diphenyl phosphate	see Diphenyl cresyl phosphate								

Substance [CAS number]	Formula	MAK ml/m³ (ppm)	MAK mg/m³	Peak limitation	H;S	Carcinogen category	Pregnancy risk group	Germ cell mutagen categ.	Vapour pressure in hPa at 20°C
2-Methyl-1-propanamine	see Isobutylamine								
2-Methyl-2-propenoic acid 1,2-ethanediyl ester	see Ethylene glycol dimethacrylate								
2-Methyl-2-propenoic acid 2-hydroxyethyl ester	see 2-Hydroxyethyl methacrylate								
2-Methyl-2-propenoic acid 2-hydroxypropyl ester	see Methacrylic acid 2-hydroxypropyl ester								
Methyl propyl ketone	see 2-Pentanone								
1-Methylpyrene [2381-21-7]	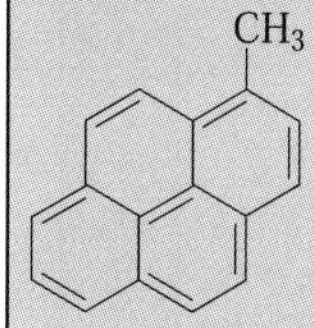	see Section III pyrolysis products of organic materials		–	H	2	–		
***N*-Methyl-2-pyrrolidone** [872-50-4] (vapour)	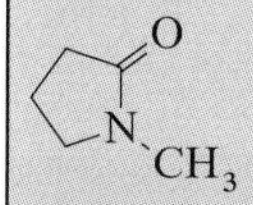	20 see Section XII	82	II(2)	H		C		0.3
α-Methyl styrene [98-83-9]	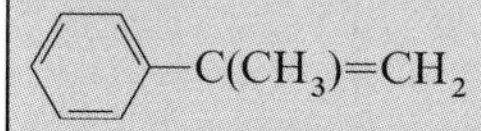	50	250	I(2)			D		3
Methyl styrene (all isomers) [25013-15-4]	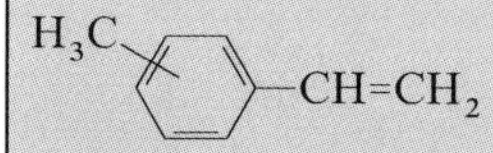	100	490	I(2)					
Methyltetrahydrophthalic anhydride [11070-44-3]	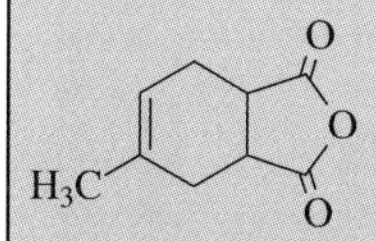	see Section IV			Sa				
***N*-Methyl-*N*,2,4,6-tetranitroaniline** [479-45-8]	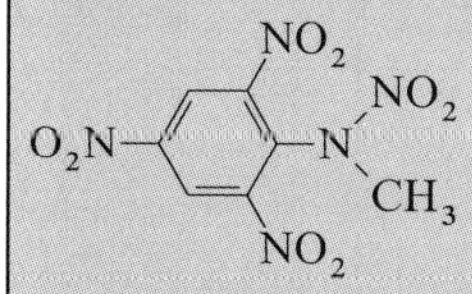	–	–	–	H Sh	3B	–		
Methyl tribromide	see Tribromomethane								
Methyl vinyl ketone [78-94-4]	$H_2C{=}CH{-}\overset{\overset{O}{\parallel}}{C}{-}CH_3$	see Section IIb			H Sh				
Mevinphos [7786-34-7]	$(H_3CO)_2PO{-}O{-}C{-}CH_3$ ‖ $H_3CO{-}CO{-}CH$	0.01	0.093	II(2)	H				

Substance [CAS number]	Formula	MAK ml/m³ (ppm)	MAK mg/m³	Peak limitation	H;S	Carcinogen category	Pregnancy risk group	Germ cell mutagen categ.	Vapour pressure in hPa at 20°C
Michler's ketone [90-94-8]	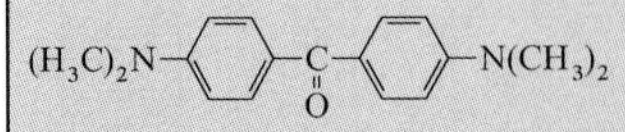	–	–	–		2	–		
Mist		see Section V							
Molybdenum [7439-98-7] and its compounds apart from molybdenum trioxide	Mo	see Section IIb and XII							
Molybdenum(IV) oxide	see Molybdenum trioxide								
Molybdenum trioxide [1313-27-5]	MoO_3	–	–	–		3B	–		
Molybdic anhydride	see Molybdenum trioxide								
Molybdic trioxide	see Molybdenum trioxide								
Molybdocene dichloride	see Molybdenum and its compounds								
Monochloroacetic acid	see Chloroacetic acid								
Monochlorodifluoromethane	see Chlorodifluoromethane								
Monochlorodimethyl ether [55] [107-30-2]	$H_3C{-}O{-}CH_2Cl$	–	–	–		1	–		213
Monochloronaphthalenes	see Chlorinated naphthalenes								
Monocyclic aromatic amino and nitro compounds		see Section III							
Monoisopropanolamine	see 1-Amino-2-propanol								
Monomethylhydrazine [60-34-4]	$H_3C{-}NH{-}NH_2$	see Section IIb			H Sh				
Mono-*n*-octyltin compounds	see *n*-Octyltin compounds								

55 The classification in Category 1 applies to technical monochlorodimethyl ether which can be contaminated with up to 7% bis-chloromethyl ether.

Substance [CAS number]	Formula	MAK ml/m³ (ppm)	MAK mg/m³	Peak limi-tation	H;S	Car-cino-gen cate-gory	Preg-nancy risk group	Germ cell muta-gen categ.	Vapour pres-sure in hPa at 20°C
Morpholine [18,56] [110-91-8]	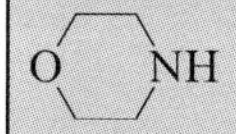	10	36	I(2)			D		10
Morpholinyl carbonyl chloride	see *N*-Chloroformylmorpholine								
Myristic acid [544-63-8]	$CH_3-(CH_2)_{12}-COOH$	see Section IIb							
Naled [300-76-5]	$(H_3CO)_2PO-O-CHBr-CBrCl_2$		1 **I**	II(2)	H Sh		C		
Naphthalene [91-20-3]	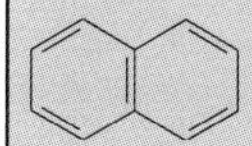	see Section III pyrolysis products of organic materials		–	H	2	–	3B	
1,8-Naphthalic anhydride [81-84-5]	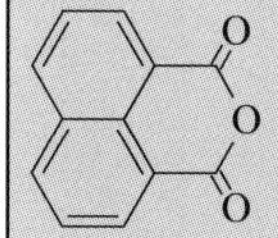	see Section IV			Sh				
2-Naphthylamine [91-59-8]	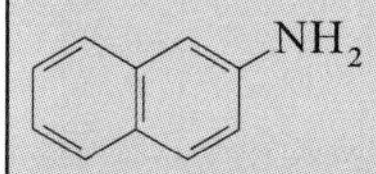	see Section XII		–	H	1	–		
1,5-Naphthylene diisocyanate [3173-72-6]	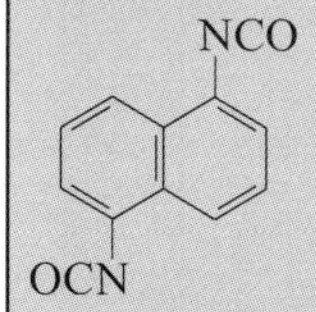	– see Section XII	–	–	Sa	3B	–		
1-Naphthylthiourea [86-88-4]	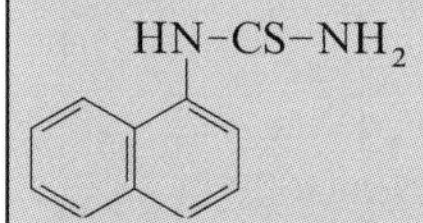		0.3 **I**	II(2)					
Natural latex	see Natural rubber latex								
Natural rubber	see Natural rubber latex								
Natural rubber latex [9006-04-6]		see Section IV			Sah				
Nemalite [1317-43-7] (fibrous dust)	$Mg(OH)_2$	see Section III		–		3B	–		

18 Use in metal-working fluids is not permitted: see TRGS 611.

56 Reaction with nitrosating agents can result in the formation of carcinogenic *N*-nitrosomorpholine, see Section III "Amines which form carcinogenic nitrosamines on nitrosation", p. 147.

Substance [CAS number]	Formula	MAK ml/m³ (ppm)	MAK mg/m³	Peak limitation	H;S	Carcinogen category	Pregnancy risk group	Germ cell mutagen categ.	Vapour pressure in hPa at 20°C
Nickel and nickel compounds (inhalable fraction):[57]		see Section XIII		–	Sah	1	–		
Metallic nickel [7440-02-0],	Ni								
Nickel acetate [373-02-4] and similar soluble salts,	$Ni(OOC{-}CH_3)_2$								
Nickel carbonate [3333-67-3],	$NiCO_3$								
Nickel chloride [7718-54-9],	$NiCl_2$								
Nickel dioxide [12035-36-8],	NiO_2								
Nickel hydroxide [12054-48-7],	$Ni(OH)_2$								
Nickel monoxide [1313-99-1],	NiO								
Nickel sesquioxide [1314-06-3],	Ni_2O_3								
Nickel subsulfide [12035-72-2],	Ni_3S_2								
Nickel sulfate [7786-81-4],	$NiSO_4$								
Nickel sulfide [16812-54-7]	NiS								
★ **Nickel alloys**					[58]				
Nickel titanic yellow pigment [8007-18-9]	$(Ti,Sb,Ni)O_2$	see Section II b							
Nicotine [54-11-5]	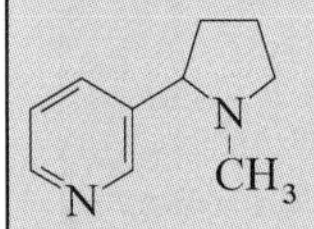	see Section II b			H				0.057
Nitric acid [7697-37-2]	HNO_3	see Section II b							
Nitrilotriacetic acid [139-13-9] and its sodium salts[59]	$N(CH_2OOH)_3$	–	–	–		3A	–	–	

57 Regarding compounds which have been found to be unequivocally carcinogenic in man, see *Toxikologisch-arbeitsmedizinische Begründung von MAK-Werten*, available from the publisher: WILEY-VCH, D-69451 Weinheim.
58 For nickel alloys containing bio-available nickel see Nickel and nickel compounds.
59 Avoid simultaneous exposure to iron compounds (formation of FeNTA)

Substance [CAS number]	Formula	MAK ml/m³ (ppm)	MAK mg/m³	Peak limitation	H;S	Carcinogen category	Pregnancy risk group	Germ cell mutagen categ.	Vapour pressure in hPa at 20°C
5-Nitroacenaphthene [602-87-9]	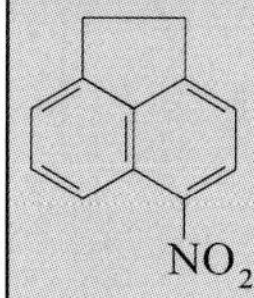	–	–	–		2	–		
4-Nitro-4'-aminodiphenylamine-2-sulfonic acid [91-29-2]	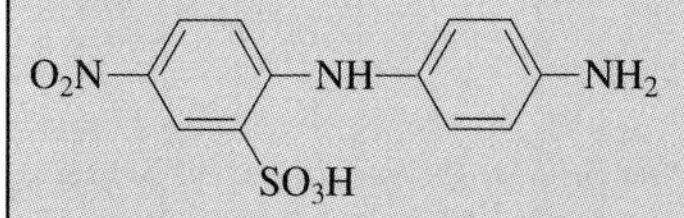	see Section IV			Sh				
2-Nitro-4-aminophenol [119-34-6]	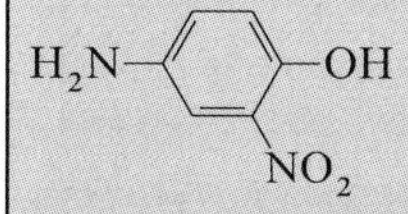	–	–	–	H	3B	–		
4-Nitro-2-aminotoluene	see 5-Nitro-*o*-toluidine								
4-Nitroaniline [100-01-6]	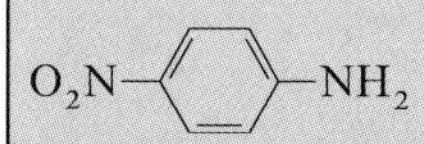	–	–	–	H	3A	–		
2-Nitroanisole [91-23-6]	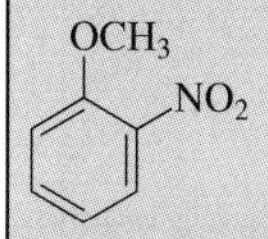	–	–	–		2	–		0.04
Nitrobenzene [98-95-3]	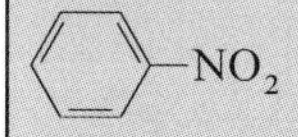	see Section XII		–	H	3B	–		
2-Nitro-1,4-benzenediamine	see 2-Nitro-*p*-phenylenediamine								
4-Nitrobiphenyl [92-93-3]	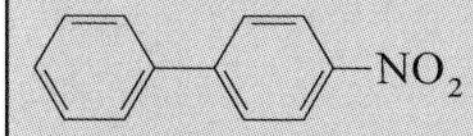	–	–	–	H	2	–		
4-(2-Nitrobutyl)-morpholine (70% w/w) [2224-44-4] **and 4,4'-(2-Ethyl-2-nitro-1,3-propanediyl)bis-morpholine** (20% w/w) [1854-23-5] (mixture) [60, 18]	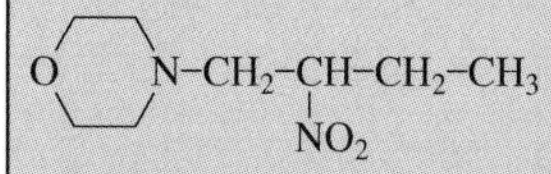 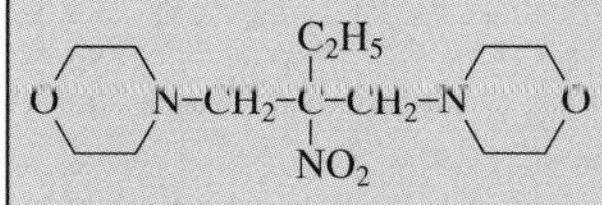	0.5 see Section Xc	4.2	I(2)	Sh		D		
o-Nitrochlorobenzene	see *o*-Chloronitrobenzene								
p-Nitrochlorobenzene	see *p*-Chloronitrobenzene								

[60] In this mixture formaldehyde can be released and nitrosamines formed.
[18] Use in metal-working fluids is not permitted: see TRGS 611.

Substance [CAS number]	Formula	MAK ml/m³ (ppm)	MAK mg/m³	Peak limitation	H;S	Carcinogen category	Pregnancy risk group	Germ cell mutagen categ.	Vapour pressure in hPa at 20°C
***p*-Nitrocumene** [1817-47-6]	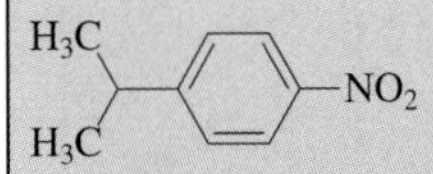	see Section IV			Sh				
4-Nitrodiphenyl	see 4-Nitrobiphenyl								
Nitroethane [79-24-3]	$H_3C{-}CH_2{-}NO_2$	100	310	II(4)			D		20.8
4-Nitro-4'-[*N*-ethyl-*N*-(2-hydroxyethyl)-amino]-azobenzene	see Disperse Red 1								
Nitrogen dioxide [10102-44-0]	NO_2	–	–	–		3B	–		960
Nitrogen oxide	see Nitrous oxide								
Nitroglycerin [55-63-0]	$H_2C{-}ONO_2$ $HC{-}ONO_2$ $H_2C{-}ONO_2$	see Section XII		–	H	3B	–		
Nitroglycol	see Ethylene glycol dinitrate								
Nitromethane [75-52-5]	$H_3C{-}NO_2$	–	–	–	H	3B	–		37
1-Nitronaphthalene [86-57-7]	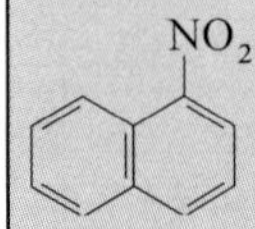	–	–	–		3B	–		
2-Nitronaphthalene [581-89-5]	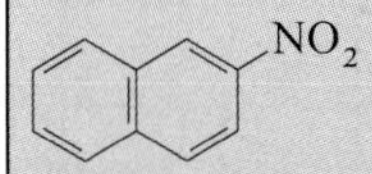	–	–	–		2	–		
4-(4-Nitrophenylazo)aniline	see Disperse Orange 3								
2-Nitro-*p*-phenylene-diamine [5307-14-2]	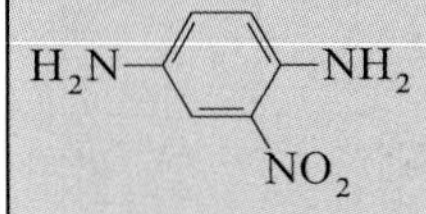	–	–	–	H Sh	3B	–		
1-Nitropropane [61] [108-03-2]	$H_3C{-}(CH_2)_2{-}NO_2$	25	92	I(4)			D		
2-Nitropropane [79-46-9]	$(H_3C)_2CH{-}NO_2$	–	–	–	H	2	–		17

[61] Technical products measurably contaminated with 2-nitropropane, see 2-Nitropropane.

Substance [CAS number]	Formula	MAK ml/m³ (ppm)	MAK mg/m³	Peak limitation	H;S	Carcinogen category	Pregnancy risk group	Germ cell mutagen categ.	Vapour pressure in hPa at 20°C
Nitropyrenes (Mono-, Di-, Tri-, Tetra-) (isomers)	$C_{16}H_{10-n}(NO_2)_n$; n = 1–4	–	–	–		3B	–		
Nitrosamines (formed from amines)		see Section III							
N-Nitroso-bis(2–hydroxyethyl)amine	see *N*-Nitrosodiethanolamine								
***N*-Nitrosodi-*n*-butylamine** [924-16-3]	$O{=}N{-}N{<}^{CH_2-CH_2-CH_2-CH_3}_{CH_2-CH_2-CH_2-CH_3}$	–	–	–	H	2	–		
***N*-Nitrosodiethanolamine** [1116-54-7]	$O{=}N{-}N{<}^{CH_2-CH_2OH}_{CH_2-CH_2OH}$	–	–	–	H	2	–		
***N*-Nitrosodiethylamine** [55-18-5]	$O{=}N{-}N{<}^{CH_2-CH_3}_{CH_2-CH_3}$	–	–	–	H	2	–		
***N*-Nitrosodiisopropylamine** [601-77-4]	$O{=}N{-}N{<}^{CH(CH_3)_2}_{CH(CH_3)_2}$	–	–	–	H	2	–		
***N*-Nitrosodimethylamine** [62-75-9]	$O{=}N{-}N{<}^{CH_3}_{CH_3}$	–	–	–	H	2	–		
***N*-Nitrosodiphenylamine** [86-30-6]	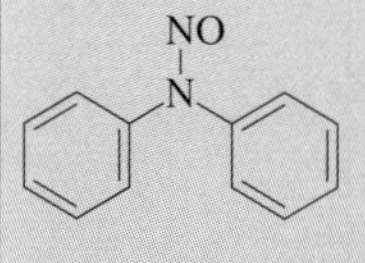	–	–	–		3B	–		
***N*-Nitrosodi-*n*-propylamine** [621-64-7]	$O{=}N{-}N{<}^{CH_2-CH_2-CH_3}_{CH_2-CH_2-CH_3}$	–	–	–	H	2	–		
Nitrosoethylaniline	see *N*-Nitrosoethylphenylamine								
***N*-Nitrosoethylphenylamine** [612-64-6]	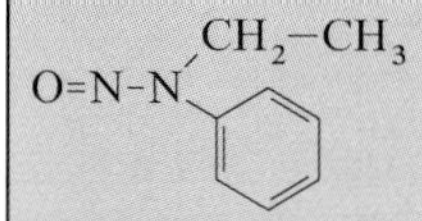	–	–	–	H	2	–		
Nitrosomethylaniline	see *N*-Nitrosomethylphenylamine								
***N*-Nitrosomethylethylamine** [10595-95-6]	$O{=}N{-}N{<}^{CH_3}_{CH_2-CH_3}$	–	–	–	H	2	–		

Substance [CAS number]	Formula	MAK ml/m³ (ppm)	MAK mg/m³	Peak limitation	H;S	Carcinogen category	Pregnancy risk group	Germ cell mutagen categ.	Vapour pressure in hPa at 20°C
***N*-Nitrosomethylphenylamine** [614-00-6]	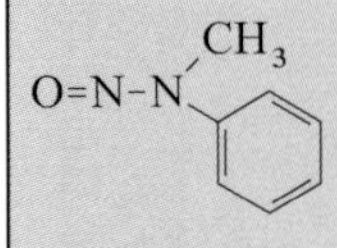	–	–	–	H	2	–		
***N*-Nitrosomorpholine** [59-89-2]	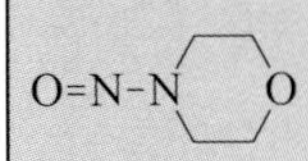	–	–	–	H	2	–		
4-Nitrosophenol [104-91-6]	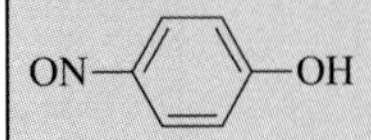	see Section IV			–				
p-Nitrosophenol	see 4-Nitrosophenol								
N-Nitroso-*N*-phenylaniline	see *N*-Nitrosodiphenylamine								
***N*-Nitrosopiperidine** [100-75-4]	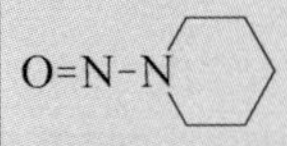	–	–	–	H	2	–		
***N*-Nitrosopyrrolidine** [930-55-2]	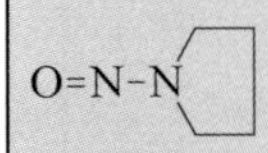	–	–	–	H	2	–		
2-Nitrotoluene [88-72-2]	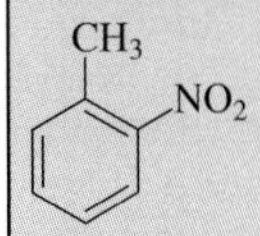	–	–	–	H	2	–	3B	
3-Nitrotoluene [99-08-1]	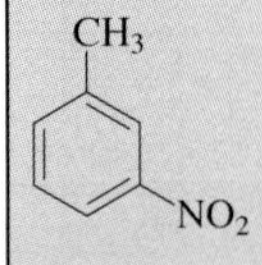	–	–	–	H	3B	–		
4-Nitrotoluene [99-99-0]	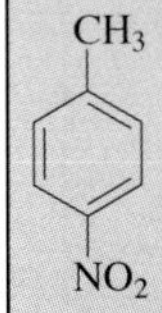	–	–	–	H	3B	–		
5-Nitro-*o*-toluidine [99-55-8]	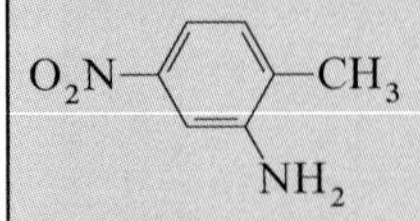	–	–	–		2	–		
Nitrous oxide [10024-97-2]	N_2O	100	180	II(2)			C		
3,3,4,4,5,5,6,6,6-Nonafluoro-1-hexene	see 1*H*,1*H*,2*H*-Perfluorohexene								
Oak	see Woods, *Quercus* spp.								
Oakmoss extracts		see Section IV			Sh				

Substance [CAS number]	Formula	MAK ml/m³ (ppm)	MAK mg/m³	Peak limitation	H;S	Carcinogen category	Pregnancy risk group	Germ cell mutagen categ.	Vapour pressure in hPa at 20°C
Oak wood dust		–	–	–		1	–		
Obeche	see Woods, *Triplochiton scleroxylon*								
Ochratoxin A [303-47-9]	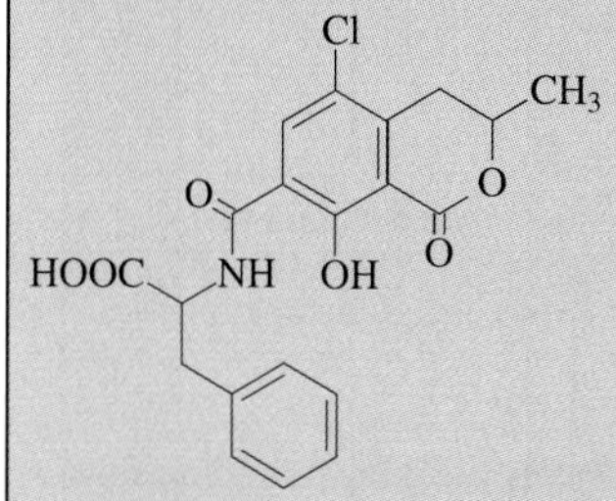	–	–	–		2	–	3B	$4.4 \cdot 10^{-1}$
Octadecanoic acid	see Stearic acid								
1-Octadecanol [112-92-5]	$HO-(CH_2)_{17}-CH_3$	see Section IIb[35]							
9-Octadecenoic acid	see Oleic acid								
9-Octadecenoic acid decyl ester	see Decyl oleate								
Octane (all isomers except trimethylpentane isomers)	$H_3C-C_6H_{12}-CH_3$	500	2400	II(2)			D		15
1-Octanol [111-87-5]	$CH_3-(CH_2)_6-CH_2OH$	see Section IIb							
n-Octanol	see 1-Octanol								
Octyl alcohol	see 1-Octanol								
2-Octyl-1-dodecanol [5333-42-6]	$CH_3-(CH_2)_9-CH(C_8H_{17})-CH_2OH$	see Section IIb[35]							
2-Octyldodecyl alcohol	see 2-Octyl-1-dodecanol								
2-Octyl-4-isothiazolin-3-one [26530-20-1]	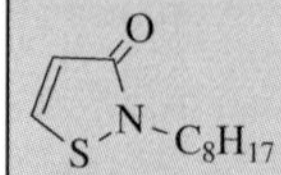	see Section Xc	0.05 **I**	I(2)	H Sh		C		
2-Octyl-3(2*H*)-isothiazol-one	see 2-Octyl-4-isothiazolin-3-one								

[35] Provided the technical exposure limit of 10 mg/m³ I for metal-working fluids is observed, adverse effects on health are not to be expected.

Substance [CAS number]	Formula	MAK ml/m³ (ppm)	MAK mg/m³	Peak limitation	H;S	Carcinogen category	Pregnancy risk group	Germ cell mutagen categ.	Vapour pressure in hPa at 20°C
4-Octyl-*N*-(4-octylphenyl)benzenamine	see 4,4'-Dioctyldiphenylamine								
★ ***n*-Octyltin compounds** (as Sn [7440-31-5])		0.004	0.02	I(1)	H [62]	4	C		
Olaquindox (*N*-(2-Hydroxyethyl)-3-methyl-2-quinoxalinecarboxamide 1,4-dioxide) [23696-28-8]	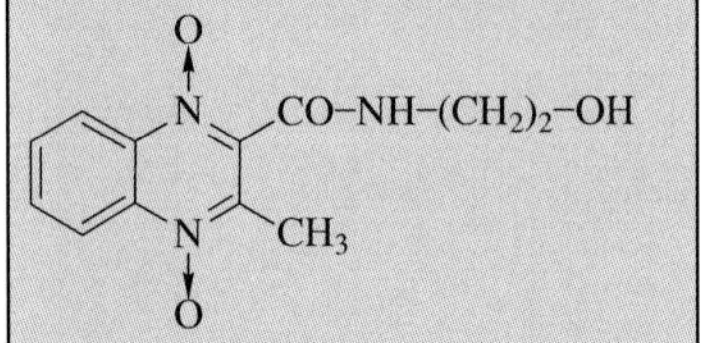	–	–	–	SP	3B	–	2	
Oleic acid [112-80-1]	CH_3–$(CH_2)_7$–CH=CH–$(CH_2)_7$–COOH	see Section Xc				3A			
Oleic acid decyl ester	see Decyl oleate								
Oleoyl sarcosine [110-25-8]	H_3C–$(CH_2)_7$–CH=CH–$(CH_2)_7$–CO–N(CH_3)–CH_2–COOH	see Section IIb							
Oleyl alcohol [143-28-2]	HO–$(CH_2)_8$–CH=CH–$(CH_2)_7$–CH_3	see Section IIb							
Organomercury compounds	see Mercury, organic compounds								
Organotin compounds	see Tin compounds, organic								
Orthoarsenic acid	see Arsenic								
Orthophosphoric acid	see Phosphoric acid								
Osmium tetroxide [20816-12-0]	OsO_4	see Section IIb							
Oxacyclopentadiene	see Furan								
Oxalaldehyde	see Glyoxal								
3-Oxapentane-1,5-diol	see Diethylene glycol								
Oxirane	see Ethylene oxide								
1,1-Oxybis(2-methoxyethane)	see Diethylene glycol dimethyl ether								
Oxybispropanol	see Dipropylene glycol								

[62] For n-octyltin compounds whose organic ligands are already designated with "Sa" or "Sh", these designations also apply.

Substance [CAS number]	Formula	MAK ml/m³ (ppm)	MAK mg/m³	Peak limitation	H;S	Carcinogen category	Pregnancy risk group	Germ cell mutagen categ.	Vapour pressure in hPa at 20°C
4,4'-Oxydianiline [101-80-4]	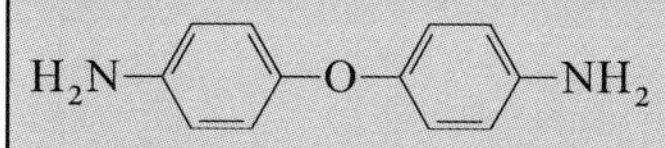	–	–	–		2	–		
2,2'-Oxydiethanol	see Diethylene glycol								
Ozone [10028-15-6]	O_3	–	–	–		3B	–		
PAH	see Polycyclic aromatic hydrocarbons and Pyrolysis products of organic materials								
Palladium and palladium compounds		see Section IIb							
Metallic palladium [7440-05-3]	Pd				–				
Palladium chloride [7647-10-1] and other bioavailable palladium(II) compounds	$PdCl_2$				Sh				
Palmitic acid [57-10-3]	CH_3–$(CH_2)_{14}$–COOH	see Section IIb							
Palygorskite (fibrous dust)	see Attapulgite								
Pao ferro	see Woods, *Machaerium scleroxylon*								
Papain [9001-73-4]		see Section IV			Sa				
Paraquat [1910-42-5]	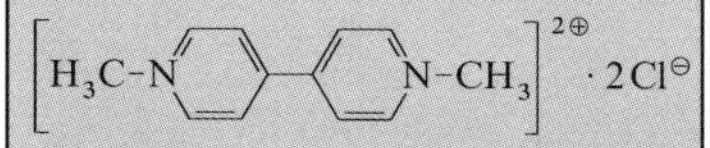		0.1 **I**	I(1)	H				
Paratecoma peroba	see Woods								
Parathion° [56-38-2]	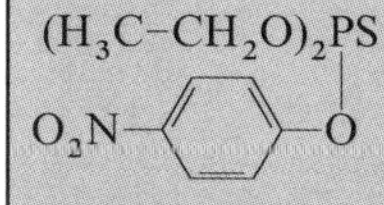		0.1 **I** see Section XII	II(8)	H		D		
Passive smoking	see Sidestream smoke								
PCBs	see Chlorinated biphenyls								
PCP	see Pentachlorophenol								
PEG	see Polyethylene glycol								
Pencil cedar	see Woods, *Calocedrus decurrens*								

Substance [CAS number]	Formula	MAK ml/m³ (ppm)	MAK mg/m³	Peak limitation	H;S	Carcinogen category	Pregnancy risk group	Germ cell mutagen categ.	Vapour pressure in hPa at 20°C
Pentaborane [19624-22-7]	B_5H_9	0.005	0.013	II(2)					213
Pentachloroethane [76-01-7]	$Cl_2HC-CCl_3$	5	42	II(2)					
Pentachloronaphthalenes	see Chlorinated naphthalenes								
Pentachlorophenol [87-86-5]	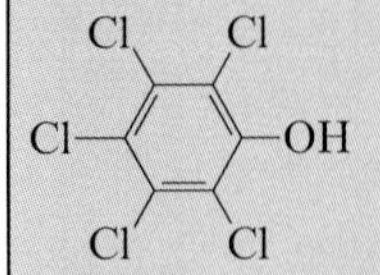	see Section XIII		–	H	2	–		
Pentadecafluorooctanoic acid	see Perfluorooctanoic acid								
Pentaerythritol triacrylate [3524-68-3]	$HO-CH_2-C(CH_2-O-OC-CH=CH_2)_3$	see Section IV			Sh				
Pentane (all isomers): Isopentane [78-78-4], *n*-Pentane [109-66-0], *tert*-Pentane [463-82-1]	 $(H_3C)_2CH-CH_2-CH_3$ $H_3C-(CH_2)_3-CH_3$ $C(CH_3)_4$	1000	3000	II(2)			C		573
1,5-Pentanedial	see Glutaraldehyde								
2,4-Pentanedione [123-54-6]	$CH_3-CO-CH_2-CO-CH_3$	20	83	II(2)	H		C		
Pentanol (isomers) [30899-19-5; 94624-12-1] 1-Pentanol [71-41-0] 2-Pentanol [6032-29-7] 3-Pentanol [584-02-1] 2-Methyl-1-butanol [137-32-6] 3-Methyl-1-butanol [123-51-3] 3-Methyl-2-butanol [598-75-4] 2-Methyl-2-butanol [75-85-4] 2,2-Dimethyl-1-propanol [75-84-3]	$C_5H_{11}OH$	20	73	I(4)			C		

Substance [CAS number]	Formula	MAK ml/m³ (ppm)	MAK mg/m³	Peak limitation	H;S	Carcinogen category	Pregnancy risk group	Germ cell mutagen categ.	Vapour pressure in hPa at 20°C
2-Pentanone [107-87-9]	$H_3C{-}(CH_2)_2{-}CO{-}CH_3$	see Section II b							16
Pentyl acetate	see Amyl acetate								
1-Pentyl acetate	see Amyl acetate								
3-Pentyl acetate	see Amyl acetate								
2-Pentyl-3-phenyl-propenoic aldehyde	see α-Amylcinnamaldehyde								
Peracetic acid [79-21-0]	$H_3C{-}CO{-}OOH$	see Section Xa		–		3B	–		
Perchloroethylene	see Tetrachloroethylene								
Perchloromethyl mercaptan [594-42-3]	$Cl_3C{-}S{-}Cl$	see Section II b							
***1H,1H,2H*-Perfluoro-hexene** [19430-93-4]	$H_2C{=}CH{-}(CF_2)_3{-}CF_3$	see Section II b							
Perfluorooctanoic acid [335-67-1] and its inorganic salts	$F_3C(CF_2)_6COOR$ R = Ag, H, K, NH_4, Na	see Section XII	0.005 **I**	II(8)	H	4	C		
Peroxydisulfuric acid diammonium salt	see Ammonium persulfate								
PHC	see Propoxur								
Phenanthrene [85-01-8]	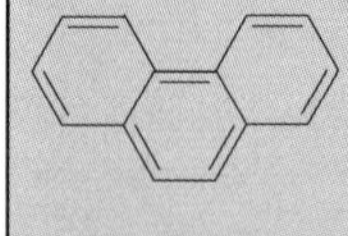	see Section III pyrolysis products of organic materials			H				
Phenol [108-95-2]	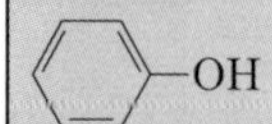	see Section XII		–	H	3B			
Phenol	see also Formaldehyde condensation products with phenol								
★ **Phenothiazine**[63] [92-84-2]	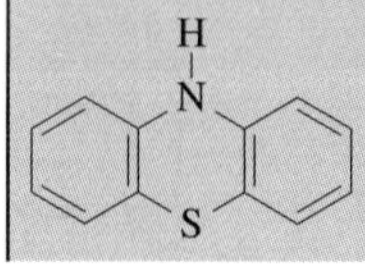	see Section II b and Xc							

[63] phototoxic effect

Substance [CAS number]	Formula	MAK ml/m³ (ppm)	MAK mg/m³	Peak limitation	H;S	Carcinogen category	Pregnancy risk group	Germ cell mutagen categ.	Vapour pressure in hPa at 20°C
2-Phenoxyethanol [122-99-6]	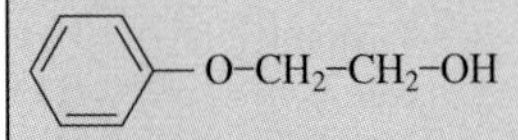	20 see Section Xc	110	I(2)	H		C		0.04
1-Phenoxy-2-propanol [770-35-4]	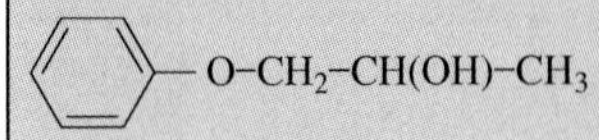	see Section IIb							
Phenylacrolein	see Cinnamaldehyde								
γ-Phenylallyl alcohol	see Cinnamyl alcohol								
Phenylbenzene	see Biphenyl								
Phenyl Cellosolve	see 2-Phenoxyethanol								
***o*-Phenylenediamine** [95-54-5]	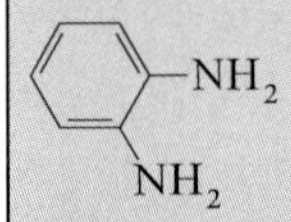	–	–	–	Sh	3B	–		
★ ***m*-Phenylenediamine** [108-45-2]	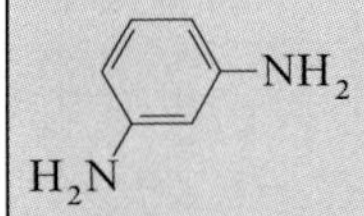	–	–	–	H Sh	3B	–		
***p*-Phenylenediamine** [106-50-3]			0.1 **I**	II(2)	H Sh[64]	3B	C		
Phenyl ether	see Diphenyl ether								
Phenyl glycidyl ether (PGE) [122-60-1]	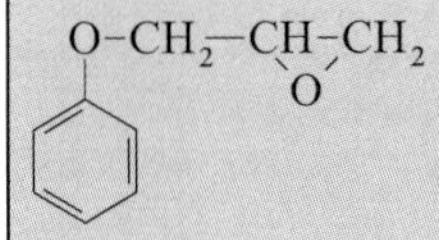	–	–	–	H Sh	2	–		
Phenylhydrazine [100-63-0]	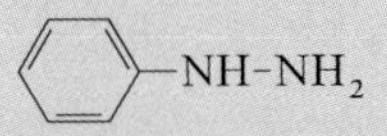	–	–	–	H Sh	3B	–		0.13
Phenyl isocyanate [103-71-9]	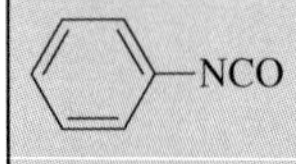	see Section IV			Sah				
Phenyl mercury	see Mercury, organic compounds								
Phenylmethanal	see Benzaldehyde								
2-(Phenylmethylene)-heptanal	see α-Amylcinnamaldehyde								

[64] The "Ursol-Asthma" which used to be observed frequently, especially in persons dyeing furs with *p*-phenylenediamine, has not been demonstrated unequivocally to involve respiratory allergy to *p*-phenylenediamine; see *Toxikologisch-arbeitsmedizinische Begründung von MAK-Werten* (18th issue, 1992) and in English translation in *Occupational Toxicants* Volume 6, VCH-Verlagsgesellschaft mbH, Weinheim 1994

Substance [CAS number]	Formula	MAK ml/m³ (ppm)	MAK mg/m³	Peak limitation	H;S	Carcinogen category	Pregnancy risk group	Germ cell mutagen categ.	Vapour pressure in hPa at 20°C
★ ***N*-Phenyl-1-naphthylamine** [90-30-2]	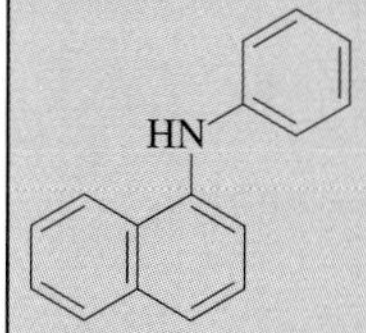	see Section IIb and Xc			Sh			–	
***N*-Phenyl-2-naphthylamine** [135-88-6]	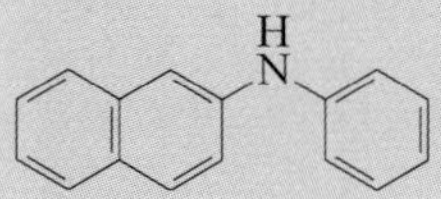	–	–	–		3B	–		
4-Phenylnitrobenzene	see 4-Nitrobiphenyl								
***o*-Phenylphenol** [90-43-7] and Sodium *o*-phenylphenol [132-27-4]	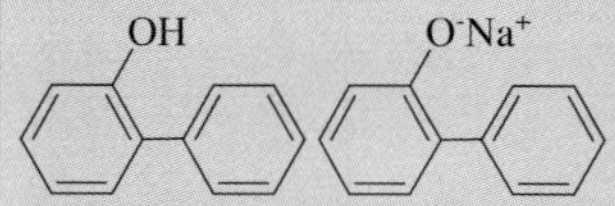	see Section IIb							
3-Phenyl-2-propenal	see Cinnamaldehyde								
2-Phenylpropene	see α-Methyl styrene								
3-Phenyl-2-propen-1-ol	see Cinnamyl alcohol								
Phosgene [75-44-5]	$COCl_2$	0.1	0.41	I(2)			C		
Phosphine [7803-51-2]	PH_3	0.1	0.14	I(1)			D		
Phosphomolybdic acid	see Molybdenum and its compounds								
Phosphoric acid [7664-38-2]	H_3PO_4		2 **I**	I(2)			C		
Phosphoric acid methylphenyl diphenyl ester	see Diphenyl cresyl phosphate								
Phosphoric acid tributyl ester	see Tributyl phosphate								
Phosphoric acid triisobutyl ester	see Triisobutyl phosphate								
Phosphorus, red [7723-14-0]	P_4	see Section IIb							
Phosphorus, white/yellow [7723-14-0; 12185-10-3]	P_4		0.05 **I**	II(2)			C		

Substance [CAS number]	Formula	MAK ml/m³ (ppm)	MAK mg/m³	Peak limitation	H;S	Carcinogen category	Pregnancy risk group	Germ cell mutagen categ.	Vapour pressure in hPa at 20°C
Phosphorus oxychloride [10025-87-3]	$POCl_3$	0.2	1.3	I(1)			C		36
Phosphorus pentachloride [10026-13-8]	PCl_5		1 **I**	I(1)			C		
Phosphorus pentasulfide [1314-80-3]	P_2S_5	see Section IIb							
Phosphorus pentoxide [1314-56-3]	P_2O_5		2 **I**	I(2)			C		
Phosphorus trichloride [7719-12-2]	PCl_3	0.5	2.8	I(1)			C		127
Phosphoryl chloride	see Phosphorus oxychloride								
***o*-Phthalic acid** [88-99-3]	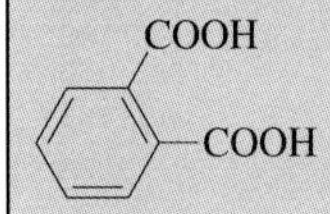	see Section IIb							
***m*-Phthalic acid** [121-91-5]	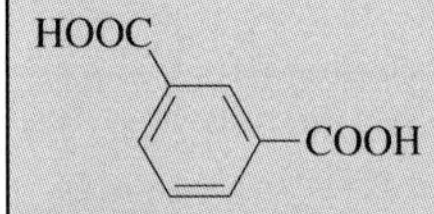		2 **I**	I(2)			C		
***p*-Phthalic acid** [100-21-0]	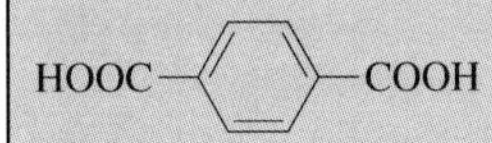		0.1 **I**	I(2)			C		
Phthalic acid diallyl ester	see Diallyl phthalate								
Phthalic anhydride [85-44-9]	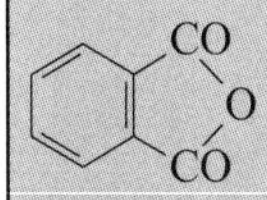	see Section IIb			Sa				
Phytases		see Section IV			Sa				
Picric acid [88-89-1]	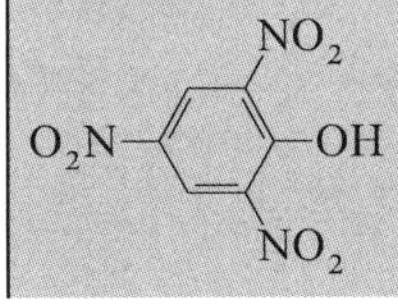	–	–	–	H Sh	3B	–		

Substance [CAS number]	Formula	MAK ml/m³ (ppm)	MAK mg/m³	Peak limitation	H;S	Carcinogen category	Pregnancy risk group	Germ cell mutagen categ.	Vapour pressure in hPa at 20°C
Picryl chloride [88-88-0]	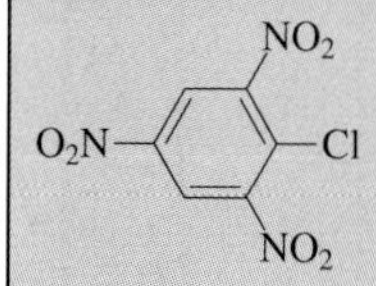	see Section IV			Sh				
Piperazine [65, 66] [110-85-0]	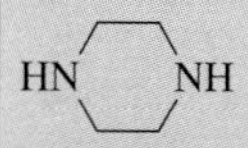	see Section IIb			Sah				
Plant or animal proteins		see Section IVe							
Plants containing sesquiterpene lactones	see Sesquiterpene lactone								
Platinum compounds (Chloroplatinates)		see Section IIb [67]			Sah				
pMDI	see "polymeric MDI"								
Polychlorinated biphenyls	see Chlorinated biphenyls								
Polycyclic aromatic hydrocarbons (PAH)		see Section III pyrolysis products of organic materials							
Polydimethyl siloxanes, linear [63148-62-9; 9006-65-9; 9016-00-6]	$(CH_3)_3Si–[O–Si(CH_3)_2]_n–O–Si(CH_3)_3$ $n > 14$	see Section IIb							
Polyethylene glycol (average molecular weight 200–600) [68]	$HO(CH_2–CH_2–O)_xH$; $x \geq 4$	see Section Xc	1000 **I**	II(8)			C		<0.1
Polyethylene glycol (average molecular weight > 600)		see Section IIb							

65 Reaction with nitrosating agents can result in the formation of carcinogenic *N,N'*-dinitrosopiperazine, see Section III "Amines which form carcinogenic nitrosamines on nitrosation", p. 147.
66 Use in metal-working fluids is restricted: see TRGS 611.
67 A peak concentration of 2 µg/m³ should not be exceeded.
68 Because formation of a mist is possible, exposure should be minimized for reasons of occupational safety and hygiene.

Substance [CAS number]	Formula	MAK ml/m³ (ppm)	MAK mg/m³	Peak limitation	H;S	Carcinogen category	Pregnancy risk group	Germ cell mutagen categ.	Vapour pressure in hPa at 20°C
"polymeric MDI"[69] [9016-87-9] (inhalable fraction) see also 4,4'-Methylene diphenyl diisocyanate (MDI)	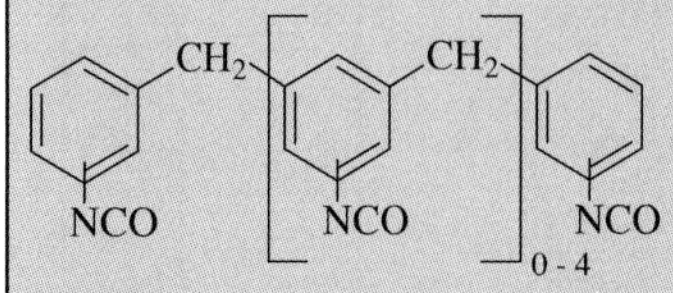		0.05 **I**	I(1)[54]	HSah	4	C		
Poly(oxy-1,2-ethanediyl)-ω-alkoxy-α-acetic acid	see Alkyl ether carboxylic acids								
Poly(oxy-1,2-propanediyl)-ω-alkoxy-α-acetic acid	see Alkyl ether carboxylic acids								
Polypropylene glycol (PPG) [25322-69-4]	$HO{-}(CH_2{-}CH(CH_3){-}O)_x{-}H$ x = 3 – 70	see Section II b							
Polyvinyl chloride	see PVC								
Portland cement [65997-15-1]		see Section V	5 **I**		[70]				
Potassium citrate	see Citric acid								
Potassium cyanide [151-50-8]	KCN		5.0 **I**	II(1)	H		C		
Potassium metabisulfite	see Sulfites								
Potassium perfluorooctanoate	see Perfluorooctanoic acid								
Potassium persulfate	see Alkali persulfates								
Potassium titanates (fibrous dust), several CAS Nos and formulas, e. g. [12030-97-6] [12056-46-1] [12056-49-4] [12056-51-8] [59766-31-3]	K_2TiO_3 $K_2Ti_2O_5$ $K_2Ti_4O_9$ $K_2Ti_6O_{13}$ $K_2Ti_8O_{17}$	see Section III		–		2	–		
Propane [74-98-6]	$H_3C{-}CH_2{-}CH_3$	1000	1800	II(4)			D		

69 "polymeric MDI" (pMDI) is a technical grade MDI, containing 30% – 80% w/w 4,4'-methylene diphenyl isocyanate (MDI); the remainder consists of MDI oligomers and MDI homologues.
54 A momentary value of 0.1 mg/m³ should not be exceeded.
70 For cements containing chromate see Chromium(VI) compounds.

Substance [CAS number]	Formula	MAK ml/m³ (ppm)	MAK mg/m³	Peak limitation	H;S	Carcinogen category	Pregnancy risk group	Germ cell mutagen categ.	Vapour pressure in hPa at 20°C
1,2-Propanediol	see Propylene glycol								
1,3-Propane sultone [1120-71-4]	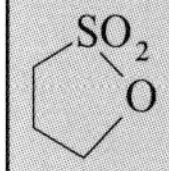	–	–	–	H	2	–		
1,2,3-Propanetriol	see Glycerin								
2-Propanol	see Isopropyl alcohol								
Propargyl alcohol [107-19-7]	$HC{\equiv}C{-}CH_2OH$	2	4.7	I(2)	H		D		11.6
2-Propenal	see Acrolein								
2-Propenoic acid 1,4-butanediyl ester	see 1,4-Butanediol diacrylate								
2-Propenoic acid 1,2-ethanediylbis(oxy-2,1-ethanediyl)ester	see Triethylene glycol diacrylate								
2-Propenoic acid homopolymer	see Acrylic acid polymer								
2-Propenoic acid 2-hydroxyethyl ester	see Acrylic acid 2-hydroxyethyl ester								
2-Propenoic acid 2-(hydroxymethyl)-2-(((1-oxo-2-propenyl)oxy)-methyl)-1,3-propanediyl ester	see Pentaerythritol triacrylate								
2-Propenoic acid hydroxypropyl ester	see Acrylic acid hydroxypropyl ester								
2-Propenoic acid oxydi-2,1-ethanediyl ester	see Diethylene glycol diacrylate								
2-Propen-1-ol	see Allyl alcohol								
4-Propenyl-2-methoxyphenol	see Isoeugenol								
β-Propiolactone [57-57-8]	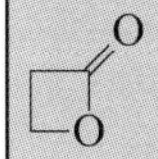	–	–	–	H	2	–		
Propionic acid [79-09-4]	$H_3C{-}CH_2{-}COOH$	see Section IIb							

Substance [CAS number]	Formula	MAK ml/m³ (ppm)	MAK mg/m³	Peak limitation	H;S	Carcinogen category	Pregnancy risk group	Germ cell mutagen categ.	Vapour pressure in hPa at 20°C
Propoxur [114-26-1]	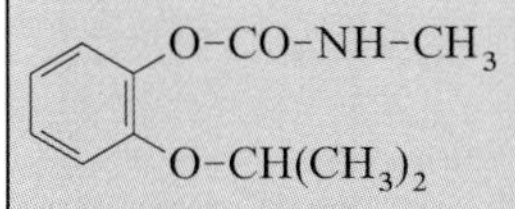		2 **I**	II(8)					
2-Propoxyethanol	see Ethylene glycol mono-*n*-propyl ether								
2-Propoxyethanol acetate	see Ethylene glycol monopropyl ether acetate								
2-Propoxyethyl acetate	see Ethylene glycol monopropyl ether acetate								
Propyl acetate:		100	420	I(2)					33
n-Propyl acetate [109-60-4],	$H_3C-COOCH_2-CH_2-CH_3$						D		
Isopropyl acetate [108-21-4]	$H_3C-COOCH(CH_3)_2$						C		
Propyl allyl disulfide	see Allyl propyl disulfide								
Propyl Cellosolve	see Ethylene glycol mono-*n*-propyl ether								
Propylene dichloride	see 1,2-Dichloropropane								
Propylene glycol [57-55-6]	$CH_3-CH(OH)-CH_2OH$	see Section IIb							
Propylene glycol dinitrate [39] [6423-43-4]	CH_2-ONO_2 / $CH-ONO_2$ / CH_3	0.05	0.34	II(1)	H				
Propylene glycol 1-methyl ether [107-98-2]	$H_3C-CHOH-CH_2OCH_3$	100 see Section XII	370	I(2)			C		12
Propylene glycol 2-methyl ether [1589-47-5]	$H_3C-CH(OCH_3)-CH_2OH$	5	19	II(8)	H		B		6
Propylene glycol 1-methyl ether-2-acetate [108-65-6]	$H_3C-O-CH_2-CH(O-C(=O)-CH_3)-CH_3$	50	270	I(1)			C		
Propylene glycol 2-methyl ether-1-acetate [70657-70-4]	$H_3C-CH(OCH_3)-CH_2OOC-CH_3$	5	28	II(8)	H		B		

only applies for work areas where skin contact with the substance does not occur

Substance [CAS number]	Formula	MAK ml/m³ (ppm)	MAK mg/m³	Peak limitation	H;S	Carcinogen category	Pregnancy risk group	Germ cell mutagen categ.	Vapour pressure in hPa at 20°C
Propylene glycol monoacrylate	see Acrylic acid hydroxypropyl ester								
Propylene glycol monoethyl ether	see 1-Ethoxy-2-propanol								
Propylene imine [75-55-8]	$H_3C-CH(NH)CH_2$ (H₃C–CH–CH₂ bridged by NH)	–	–	–	H	2	–	3B	
Propylene oxide [75-56-9]	$H_3C-CH(O)CH_2$ (H₃C–CH–CH₂ bridged by O)	–	–	–	H	2	–		
***n*-Propyl nitrate** [627-13-4]	$H_3C-(CH_2)_2-ONO_2$	25	110	II(2)					
Propyne	see Methyl acetylene								
Pruno	see Woods, *Mansonia altissima*								
Pseudocumene (1,2,4-Trimethylbenzene)	see Trimethylbenzene								
PTBBA (*p-tert*-Butylbenzoic acid)	see 4-*tert*-Butylbenzoic acid								
★ **PVC** [9002-86-2]	$(-CH_2-CHCl-)_n$ n = 500–2000		1.5 **R** see Section Vf and Vg				C		
Pyrene [129-00-0]	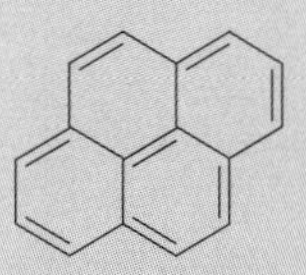	see Section III pyrolysis products of organic materials			H				
Pyrethrum [8003-34-7]	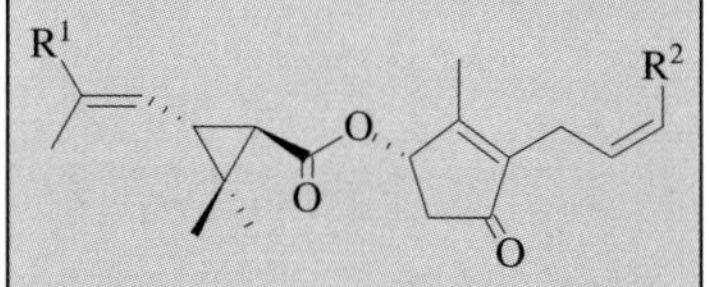	see Section IIb and XII			Sh[71]				
★ **Pyridine** [110-86-1]	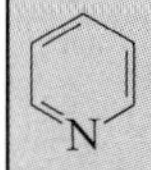	–	–	–	H	3B	–	–	20
Pyrolysis products of organic materials		see Section III		–			–		

[71] does not apply for the constituents of insecticides (pyrethrins and cinerins) or for synthetic derivatives (pyrethroids) but only for th constituents of the plant drug and its crude extracts, including α-methylene sesquiterpene lactones (e.g. pyrethrosin)

Substance [CAS number]	Formula	MAK ml/m³ (ppm)	MAK mg/m³	Peak limitation	H;S	Carcinogen category	Pregnancy risk group	Germ cell mutagen categ.	Vapour pressure in hPa at 20°C
Pyrrolidine [72] [123-75-1]	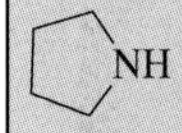	see Section IIb			H				
Quartz	see Silica, crystalline								
Quartz glass	see Silica, amorphous								
Quercus spp.	see Woods								
Quinone [106-51-4]	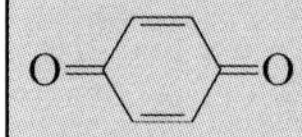	–	–	–	Sh	3B	–	3B	0.12
Quinone oxime	see 4-Nitrosophenol								
Ramin	see Woods, *Gonystylus bancanus*								
Refrigerant 134a	see 1,1,1,2-Tetrafluoroethane								
Resorcinol [108-46-3]	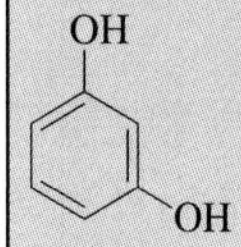	see Section IIb			Sh				
Resorcinol bis(2,3-epoxypropyl)ether	see Diglycidyl resorcinol ether								
Resorcinol diglycidyl ether	see Diglycidyl resorcinol ether								
Rhodium [7440-16-6] and its inorganic compounds	Rh	–	–	–		3B	–		
Ricinus protein		see Section IV			Sa				
Rock wool (fibrous dust)		see Section III		–		2	–		
Rosewood	see Woods, *Dalbergia* spp.								
Rosin (colophony) [8050-09-7]		see Section IV			Sh[73]				

[72] Reaction with nitrosating agents can result in the formation of carcinogenic *N*-nitrosopyrrolidine, see Section III "Amines which form carcinogenic nitrosamines on nitrosation", p. 147.

[73] An immunological genesis of the asthma often seen in persons working with materials containing rosin has not been proved.

Substance [CAS number]	Formula	MAK ml/m³ (ppm)	MAK mg/m³	Peak limitation	H;S	Carcinogen category	Pregnancy risk group	Germ cell mutagen categ.	Vapour pressure in hPa at 20°C
Rotenone [83-79-4]	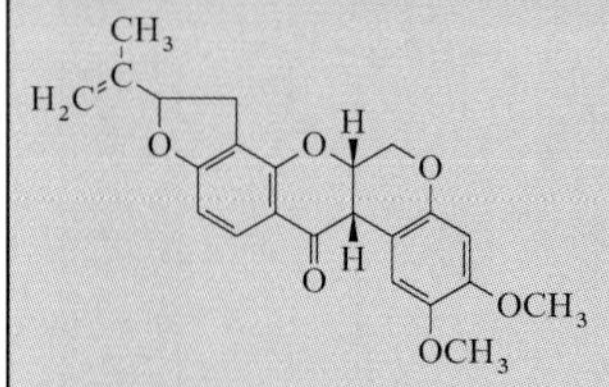	see Section II b			H				
Rubber components:		see Section IV							
Dithiocarbamates					Sh				
p-Phenylenediamine compounds					Sh				
Thiazoles					Sh				
Thiurams					Sh				
Rye	see Cereal flour dusts								
Santos rosewood	see Woods, *Machaerium scleroxylon*								
Sapele	see Woods, *Entandrophragma* spp.								
Sapupira, (black) sucupira	see Woods, *Bowdichia nitida*								
Selenium [7782-49-2] and its inorganic compounds (as Se)	Se		0.05 **I**	II(4)		3B	C		
Sepiolite (fibrous dust), several CAS Nos and formulas, e.g. [18307-23-8] [15501-74-3]	$Mg_9H_6(SiO_3)_{12} \cdot 10\ H_2O$ $Mg_2H_2(SiO_3)_3 \cdot H_2O$	see Section III		–		3B	–		
Sesquiterpene lactones		see Section IV			Sh				
Alantolactone [546-43-0]									
Anthecotulide [23971-84-8]									
Arteglasin A [33204-39-6]									
Carabrone [1748-81-8]									
Costunolide [553-21-9]									
Dehydrocostus lactone [477-43-0]									
(+)-Frullanolide and (−)-Frullanolide [40776-40-7; 27579-97-1]									

Substance [CAS number]	Formula	MAK ml/m³ (ppm)	MAK mg/m³	Peak limitation	H;S	Carcinogen category	Pregnancy risk group	Germ cell mutagen categ.	Vapour pressure in hPa at 20°C
Helenalin [6754-13-8]									
Isoalantolactone [470-17-7]									
Lactucin [1891-29-8]									
Laurenobiolide [35001-25-3]									
Parthenin [508-59-8]									
Parthenolide [20554-84-1]									
α-Peroxyachifolide [134954-21-5]									
Pyrethrosin [28272-18-6]									
Sidestream smoke (passive smoking at the workplace)		–	–	–		1	–		
Silica, amorphous [7631-86-9]									
a) colloidal amorphous silica including pyrogenic and wet process silica and diatomaceous earth (uncalcined) [61790-53-2]		see Section V	4 **I**				C		
b) quartz glass [60676-86-0], fused silica [7699-41-4], silica fume, calcined diatomaceous earth [68855-54-9]		see Section V	0.3 **R**				C		
Silica, crystalline (respirable fraction): Quartz [14808-60-7], Cristobalite [14464-46-1], Tridymite [15468-32-3]		–	–	–		1	–		
Silicic acid tetraethyl ester [78-10-4]	$Si(OCH_2{-}CH_3)_4$	10	86	I(1)			D		~2

Substance [CAS number]	Formula	MAK ml/m³ (ppm)	MAK mg/m³	Peak limitation	H;S	Carcinogen category	Pregnancy risk group	Germ cell mutagen categ.	Vapour pressure in hPa at 20°C
Silicon carbide [409-21-2] (fibrous dust)	SiC	see Section III		–		2	–		
★ **Silicon carbide** [409-21-2] (without fibres)	SiC	see Section Vf and Vg	1.5 **R**				C		
Silicon dioxide	see Silica								
Silicone	see Polydimethyl siloxanes								
Silicone oil	see Polydimethyl siloxanes								
Silver [7440-22-4]	Ag		0.1 **I**	II(8)			D		
Silver perfluorooctanoate	see Perfluorooctanoic acid								
Silver salts (as Ag [7440-22-4])			0.01 **I**	I(2)			D		
Slag wool (fibrous dust)		see Section III		–		3B	–		
Sodium azide [26628-22-8]	N_3Na		0.2 **I**	I(2)			D		
Sodium bisulfite	see Sulfites								
Sodium citrate	see Citric acid								
Sodium cyanide [143-33-9]	NaCN		3.8 **I**	II(1)	H		C		
Sodium diethyldithiocarbamate [29] [148-18-5]	$(CH_3{-}CH_2)_2N{-}C({=}S){-}SNa$	see Section Xc	2 **I**	II(2)	Sh		D		
Sodium ethylmercurithiosalicylate	see Thimerosal								
Sodium fluoroacetate° [62-74-8]	$FCH_2{-}COO^{\ominus}\ Na^{\oplus}$		0.05 **I**	II(4)	H		C		
Sodium hydroxide [1310-73-2]	NaOH	see Section IIb							
Sodium metabisulfite	see Sulfites								

[29] Reaction with nitrosating agents can result in the formation of carcinogenic *N*-nitrosodiethylamine, see Section III "Amines whic form carcinogenic nitrosamines on nitrosation", p. 147.

Substance [CAS number]	Formula	MAK ml/m³ (ppm)	MAK mg/m³	Peak limitation	H;S	Carcinogen category	Pregnancy risk group	Germ cell mutagen categ.	Vapour pressure in hPa at 20°C
Sodium molybdate	see Molybdenum and its compounds								
Sodium perfluorooctanoate	see Perfluorooctanoic acid								
Sodium persulfate	see Alkali persulfates								
Sodium pyridinethione	see Sodium pyrithione								
Sodium pyrithione [3811-73-2; 15922-78-8]	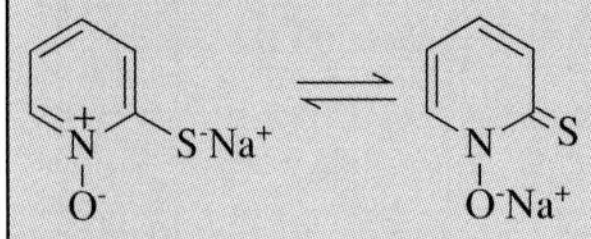	see Section Xc	1 **I**	II(2)	H		C		
Soot	see Carbon black								
Soya bean constituents		see Section IV			Sa				
Stearic acid [57-11-4]	$CH_3{-}(CH_2)_{16}{-}COOH$	see Section IIb							
Stibine [7803-52-3]	SbH_3	see Section IIb							
Strontium [7440-24-6] and its inorganic compounds	Sr	see Section IIb							
Strontium chromate	see Chromium(VI) compounds								
Strychnine° [57-24-9]	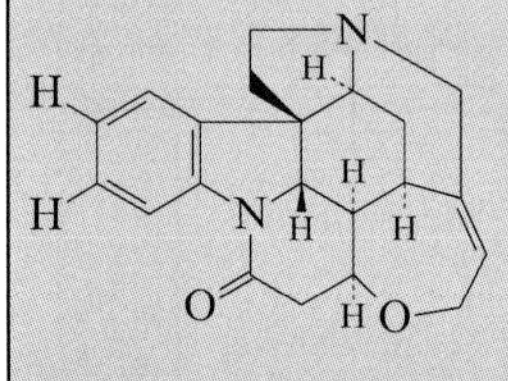	see Section IIb							
Styrene [100-42-5]	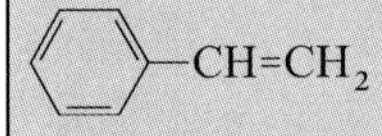	20 see Section XII	86	II(2)		5	C		6
Subtilisins		see Section IV			Sa				
Sulfites [74]		see Section IV			–				
Sulfotep	see TEDP								
Sulfur dioxide [7446-09-5]	SO_2	0.5	1.3	I(1)[75]			C		

[74] cause pseudoallergic reactions, see *Toxikologisch-arbeitsmedizinische Begründung von MAK-Werten* (26th issue 1998)
[75] A momentary value of 1 ml/m³ (2.7 mg/m³) should not be exceeded.

Substance [CAS number]	Formula	MAK ml/m³ (ppm)	MAK mg/m³	Peak limitation	H;S	Carcinogen category	Pregnancy risk group	Germ cell mutagen categ.	Vapour pressure in hPa at 20°C
Sulfur hexafluoride [2551-62-4]	SF_6	1000	6100	II(8)			D		
Sulfuric acid [7664-93-9]	H_2SO_4		0.1 **I**	I(1)[76]		4	C		
Sulfur monochloride [10025-67-9]	S_2Cl_2	see Section IIb							
Sulfur pentafluoride [5714-22-7]	S_2F_{10}	see Section IIb							
Swietenia spp.	see Woods								
Sylvic acid	see Abietic acid								
2,4,5-T	see 2,4,5-Trichlorophenoxyacetic acid								
Tabebuia spp.	see Woods								
Talc [14807-96-6] (without asbestos fibres) (respirable fraction)	$Mg_3(OH)_2Si_4O_{10}$	–	–	–		3B	–		
Talleol	see Talloil, distilled								
Tall oil derivatives	see Abietic acid, Oleic acid								
★ **Tall oil, distilled** [8002-26-4]		see Section Xc			Sh[77]	3A			
Tall oil rosin and fatty acids	see Tall oil, distilled								
★ **Tantalum** [7440-25-7] (inhalable fraction)	Ta	see Section Vf and Vg	4 **I**				C		
★ **Tantalum** [7440-25-7] (respirable fraction)	Ta	see Section Vf and Vg	1.5 **R**				C		
TBTO	see *n*-Butyltin compounds								
TCDD	see 2,3,7,8-Tetrachlorodibenzo-*p*-dioxin								

[76] A momentary value of 0.2 mg/m³ should not be exceeded.

[77] only applies to tall oil distillates containing abietic acid, see also *Toxikologisch-arbeitsmedizinische Begründung von MAK-Werte[n]* (34th issue 2002)

Substance [CAS number]	Formula	MAK ml/m³ (ppm)	MAK mg/m³	Peak limitation	H;S	Carcinogen category	Pregnancy risk group	Germ cell mutagen categ.	Vapour pressure in hPa at 20°C
Teak	see Woods, *Tectona grandis*								
Tectona grandis	see Woods								
TEDP [3689-24-5]	$[(H_3C{-}CH_2{-}O)_2PS]_2O$	0.0075	0.1	II(2)	H		C		
Tellurium [13494-80-9] and its inorganic compounds	Te	see Section II b							
TEPP [107-49-3]	$[(H_3C{-}CH_2{-}O)_2PO]_2O$	0.005	0.060	II(2)	H				
Terminalia spp.	see Woods								
3,3',4,4'-Tetraamino-biphenyl	see 3,3'-Diaminobenzidine								
1,1,2,2-Tetrabromo-ethane [79-27-6]	$Br_2HC{-}CHBr_2$	see Section II b							
2,4,5,6-Tetrachloro-1,3-benzenedicarbonitrile	see Chlorothalonil								
2,3,7,8-Tetrachloro-dibenzo-*p*-dioxin [1746-01-6]	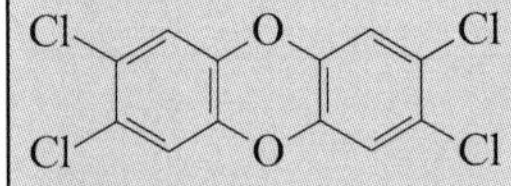		$1.0 \cdot 10^{-8}$ **I**	II(8)	H	4	C		
1,1,1,2-Tetrachloro-2,2-difluoroethane (FC-112a) [76-11-9]	$ClF_2C{-}CCl_3$	200	1700	II(2)			D		
1,1,2,2-Tetrachloro-1,2-difluoroethane (FC-112) [76-12-0]	$Cl_2FC{-}CCl_2F$	200	1700	II(2)			D		
1,1,2,2-Tetrachloro-ethane [79-34-5]	$Cl_2HC{-}CHCl_2$	1	7.0	II(2)	H	3B	D		7
Tetrachloroethylene [127-18-4]	$Cl_2C{=}CCl_2$	see Section XIII		–	H	3B	–		19
Tetrachloroisophthalo-nitrile	see Chlorothalonil								
Tetrachloromethane	see Carbon tetrachloride								
Tetrachloronaphthalenes	see Chlorinated naphthalenes								

Substance [CAS number]	Formula	MAK ml/m³ (ppm)	MAK mg/m³	Peak limitation	H;S	Carcinogen category	Pregnancy risk group	Germ cell mutagen categ.	Vapour pressure in hPa at 20°C
α,α,α,4-Tetrachlorotoluene	see *p*-Chlorobenzotrichloride								
Tetradecanoic acid	see Myristic acid								
1-Tetradecanol [112-72-1]	$HO-(CH_2)_3-CH_3$	see Section IIb							
Tetraethylene glycol diacrylate [17831-71-9]	$O-(CH_2-CH_2-O)_2-OC-CH=CH_2$ $(CH_2-CH_2-O)_2-OC-CH=CH_2$	see Section IV			Sh				
Tetraethylene glycol dimethacrylate [109-17-1]	$O-(CH_2-CH_2-O)_2-OC-C(CH_3)=CH_2$ $(CH_2-CH_2-O)_2-OC-C(CH_3)=CH_2$	see Section IV			Sh				
★ **Tetraethyllead** [78-00-2] (as Pb)	$Pb(C_2H_5)_4$	see Section XII	0.05	II(2)	H		B		
Tetraethyl silicate	see Silicic acid tetraethyl ester								
1,1,1,2-Tetrafluoroethane [811-97-2]	F_3C-CH_2F	1000	4200	II(8)			C		5700
Tetrafluoroethene [116-14-3]	$F_2C=CF_2$	–	–	–		2	–		
Tetrahydrobenzotriazole [6789-99-7]	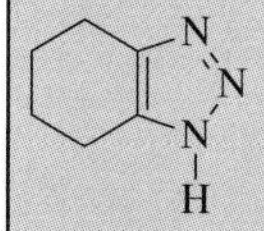	see Section IIb							
Tetrahydrofuran [109-99-9]		50 see Section XII	150	I(2)	H	4	C		200
Tetrahydrofurfuryl methacrylate [2455-24-5]	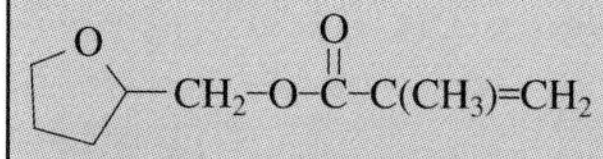	see Section IV			Sh				
3a,4,7,7a-Tetrahydro-4,7-methanoindene	see Dicyclopentadiene								
Tetrahydromethyl-1,3-isobenzofurandione	see Methyltetrahydrophthalic anhydride								
Tetrahydrothiophene (THT) [110-01-0]	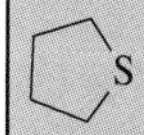	50	180	I(1)			C		
Tetramethyl diaminobenzophenone	see Michler's ketone								

Substance [CAS number]	Formula	MAK ml/m³ (ppm)	MAK mg/m³	Peak limitation	H;S	Carcinogen category	Pregnancy risk group	Germ cell mutagen categ.	Vapour pressure in hPa at 20°C
Tetramethyl diamino-diphenylacetimine	see Auramine								
Tetramethyl diamino-diphenylacetimine hydrochloride	see Auramine								
N,N,N',N'-Tetramethyl-4,4'-diaminodiphenyl-methane	see 4,4'-Methylene-bis(*N,N*-dimethylaniline)								
★ **Tetramethyllead** [75-74-1] (as Pb)	$Pb(CH_3)_4$		0.05 see Section XII	II(2)	H		B		30
Tetramethyl succino-nitrile [3333-52-6]	$NC{-}C(CH_3)_2{-}C(CH_3)_2{-}CN$	see Section II b			H				
Tetramethylthiuram disulfide	see Thiram								
Tetramethyl urea (TMU) [632-22-4]	$((CH_3)_2N)_2CO$	see Section II b							
Tetranitromethane [509-14-8]	$C(NO_2)_4$	–	–	–	H	2	–		11
Tetryl	see *N*-Methyl-*N*,2,4,6-tetranitro-aniline								
Thallium, soluble compounds		see Section II b							
★ **Thiabendazole** [148-79-8]	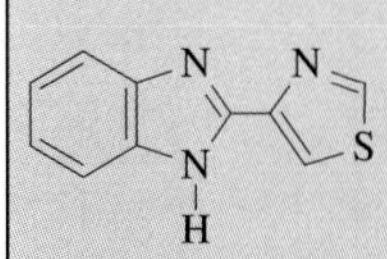		20 **I** see Section Xc	II(2)			C	5	
2-(4'-Thiazolyl)benz-imidazole	see Thiabendazole								
Thimerosal [54-64-8]	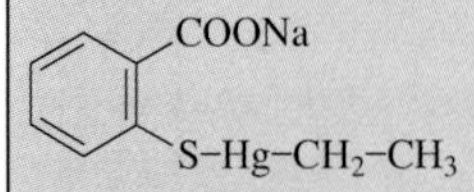	see Section IV			Sh				
2,2'-Thiobis(4,6-di-chlorophenol)	see Bithionol								
Thiocarbamide	see Thiourea								

Substance [CAS number]	Formula	MAK ml/m³ (ppm)	MAK mg/m³	Peak limitation	H;S	Carcinogen category	Pregnancy risk group	Germ cell mutagen categ.	Vapour pressure in hPa at 20°C
4,4'-Thiodianiline [139-65-1]	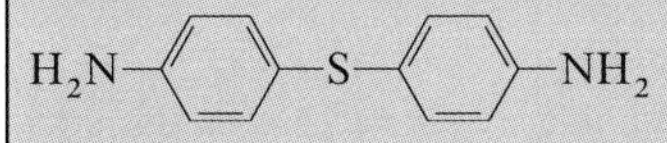	–	–	–		2	–		
p,p'-Thiodianiline	see 4,4'-Thiodianiline								
Thioglycolic acid monoglyceryl ester	see Glyceryl monothioglycolate								
Thiomersal	see Thimerosal								
Thiomersalate	see Thimerosal								
Thiourea [62-56-6]	$H_2N{-}CS{-}NH_2$	–	–	–	Sh SP	3B	–		
Thiram[32] [137-26-8]	$[(H_3C)_2N{-}CS]_2S_2$		1 **I**	II(2)	Sh		C		
THU	see Thiourea								
Thuja spp.	see Woods								
Tieghemella spp.	see Woods								
Tin [7440-31-5] and its inorganic compounds	Sn	see Section IIb							
Tin compounds, organic (as Sn [7440-31-5])	see also *n*-Butyltin compounds and *n*-Octyltin compounds		0.1 **I**	II(2)	H		D		
★ **Titanium dioxide** [13463-67-7] (inhalable fraction)[78]	TiO_2	–	–	–		3A	–		
TNT	see 2,4,6-Trinitrotoluene								
o-Tolidine	see 3,3'-Dimethylbenzidine								
Toluene (Toluol) [108-88-3]	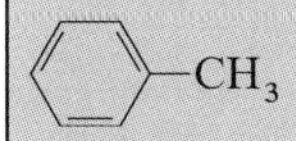	50	190	II(4)	H		C		29
		see Section XII							
Toluene-2,4-diamine [95-80-7]	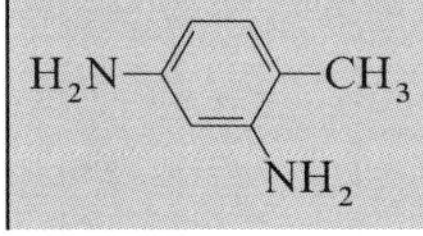	see Section XIII		–	H Sh	2	–		

[32] Reaction with nitrosating agents can result in the formation of carcinogenic *N*-nitrosodimethylamine, see Section III "Amines which form carcinogenic nitrosamines on nitrosation", p. 147.

[78] except for ultrafine particles

Substance [CAS number]	Formula	MAK ml/m³ (ppm)	MAK mg/m³	Peak limitation	H;S	Carcinogen category	Pregnancy risk group	Germ cell mutagen categ.	Vapour pressure in hPa at 20°C
Toluene-2,5-diamine [95-70-5]	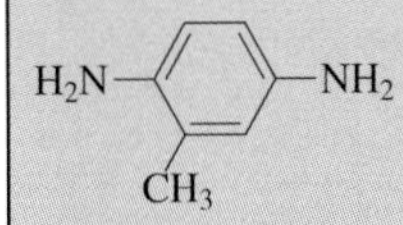	see Section IV			Sh				
Toluenediisocyanate: Toluene-2,4-diisocyanate [584-84-9], Toluene-2,6-diisocyanate [91-08-7]	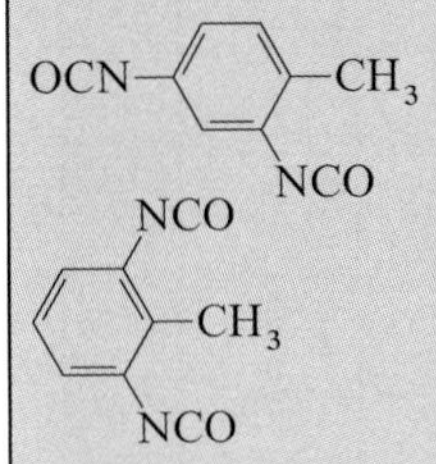	–	–	–	Sa	3A	–		
***o*-Toluidine** [95-53-4]	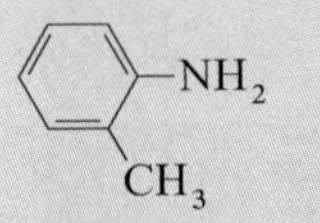	–	–	–	H	1	–	3A	
***p*-Toluidine** [106-49-0]	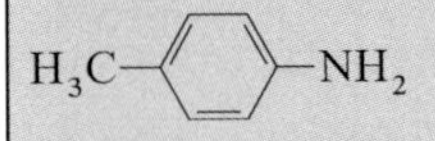	–	–	–	H Sh	3B	–		
2,4-Toluylenediamine	see Toluene-2,4-diamine								
Tolyl diiodomethyl sulfone	see 4-(Diiodomethylsulfonyl)-toluene								
Tremolite (fibrous dust)	see Asbestos								
Triazinetriyltriiminotrishexanoic acid [80584-91-4]	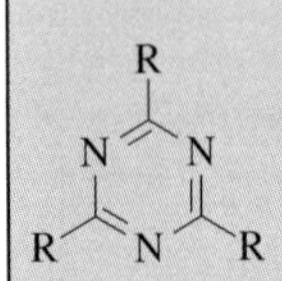 R = NH–C_5H_{10}COOH	see Section II b[35]							
Tribromomethane [75-25-2]	$CHBr_3$	–	–	–		3B	–		7
Tri-n-butylamine[79] [102-82-9]	$N(CH_2{-}CH_2{-}CH_2{-}CH_3)_3$	see Section II b							
Tributyl phosphate [126-73-8]	$O{=}P(O{-}(CH_2)_3{-}CH_3)_3$	1	11	II(4)	H	4	C		0.008
Tri-*n*-butyltin compounds	see *n*-Butyltin compounds								

35 Provided the technical exposure limit of 10 mg/m³ I for metal-working fluids is observed, adverse effects on health are not to be expected.

79 Reaction with nitrosating agents can result in the formation of carcinogenic *N*-Nitrosodi-*n*-butylamine, see Section III "Amines which form carcinogenic nitrosamines on nitrosation", p. 147.

Substance [CAS number]	Formula	MAK ml/m³ (ppm)	MAK mg/m³	Peak limitation	H;S	Carcinogen category	Pregnancy risk group	Germ cell mutagen categ.	Vapour pressure in hPa at 20°C
Trichloroacetic acid [76-03-9]	$Cl_3C-COOH$	see Section II b							
1,2,3-Trichlorobenzene [87-61-6]	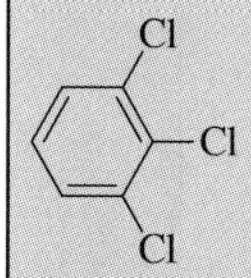	5	38	II (2)	H		C		
1,2,4-Trichlorobenzene [120-82-1]	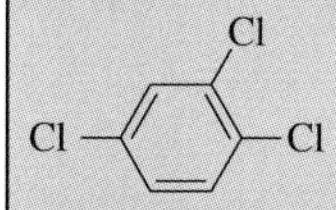	–	–	–	H	3B	–		0.21
1,3,5-Trichlorobenzene [108-70-3]	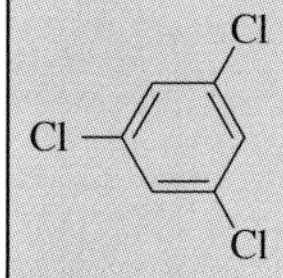	5	38	II (2)	H		C		
2,3,4-Trichloro-1-butene [2431-50-7]	$ClCH_2-CHCl-CCl{=}CH_2$	–	–	–	H	2	–		
1,1,1-Trichloroethane [71-55-6]	H_3C-CCl_3	200 see Section XII	1100	II (1)	H		C		133
1,1,2-Trichloroethane [79-00-5]	$ClH_2C-CHCl_2$	10	55	II (2)	H	3B			25
Trichloroethylene [79-01-6]	$ClHC{=}CCl_2$	see Section XIII		–	H	1	–	3B	77
Trichlorofluoromethane (FC-11) [75-69-4]	CCl_3F	1000	5700	II (2)			C		889
Trichloromethane	see Chloroform								
1-Trichloromethyl-benzene	see Benzyl trichloride								
Trichloronaphthalenes	see Chlorinated naphthalenes								
Trichloronitromethane	see Chloropicrin								
2,4,5-Trichlorophenol [95-95-4]	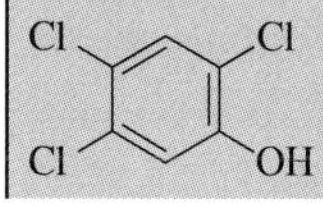	see Section II b							

Substance [CAS number]	Formula	MAK ml/m³ (ppm)	MAK mg/m³	Peak limitation	H;S	Carcinogen category	Pregnancy risk group	Germ cell mutagen categ.	Vapour pressure in hPa at 20°C
2,4,5-Trichlorophenoxy-acetic acid° [93-76-5]	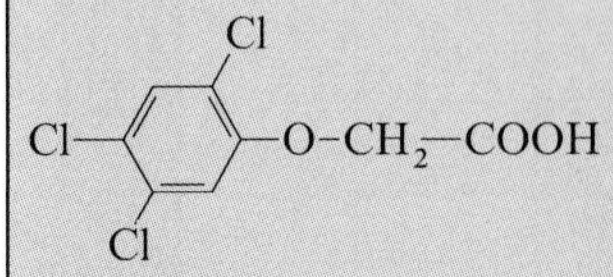		10 **I**	II(2)	H		C		
1,2,3-Trichloropropane [96-18-4]	$ClCH_2-CHCl-CH_2Cl$	–	–	–	H	2	–		4.5
1,1,2-Trichloro-1,2,2-trifluoroethane (FC-113) [76-13-1]	ClF_2C-CCl_2F	500	3900	II(2)			D		360
Tridymite	see Silica, crystalline								
Triethanolamine [102-71-6]	$N(CH_2-CH_2OH)_3$	see Section IV			–				
Triethylamine [29] [121-44-8]	$(H_3C-CH_2)_3N$	1	4.2	I(2)			D		72
Triethylene glycol [68] [112-27-6]	$HOCH_2-(CH_2-O-CH_2)_2-CH_2OH$		1000 **I**	II(2)			C		
Triethylene glycol *n*-butyl ether [143-22-6]	$HO-((CH_2)_2O)_3-(CH_2)_3-CH_3$	see Section IIb							
Triethylene glycol diacrylate [1680-21-3]	$H_2C{=}CH-C(=O)-(O-(CH_2)_2)_3-O-C(=O)-HC{=}CH_2$	see Section IV			Sh				
Triethylene glycol dimethacrylate [109-16-0]	$O-(CH_2-CH_2-O)_3-OC-C(CH_3){=}CH_2$ / $CO-C(CH_3){=}CH_2$	see Section IV			Sh				
Triethylenetetramine [112-24-3]	$H_2N-[(CH_2)_2-NH]_2-(CH_2)_2-NH_2$	see Section IV			Sh				
1,3,5-Triethylhexa-hydro-1,3,5-triazine [17] [7779-27-3]	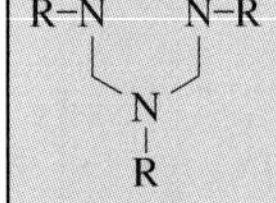 $R = CH_2CH_3$	see Section Xc				3B			
1,1,1-Trifluoro-2,2-dichloroethane	see 2,2-Dichloro-1,1,1-trifluoroethane								

29 Reaction with nitrosating agents can result in the formation of carcinogenic *N*-nitrosodiethylamine, see Section III "Amines which form carcinogenic nitrosamines on nitrosation", p. 147.
68 Because formation of a mist is possible, exposure should be minimized for reasons of occupational safety and hygiene.
17 releases formaldehyde

Substance [CAS number]	Formula	MAK ml/m³ (ppm)	MAK mg/m³	Peak limitation	H;S	Carcinogen category	Pregnancy risk group	Germ cell mutagen categ.	Vapour pressure in hPa at 20°C
Trifluoromonobromomethane	see Bromotrifluoromethane								
Trifluoromonochloromethane	see Chlorotrifluoromethane								
Triisobutyl phosphate [126-71-6]	$O{=}P(O{-}CH_2{-}CH(CH_3)_2)_3$	see Section II b			Sh				
Trimanganese tetroxide	see Manganese								
Trimellitic anhydride [552-30-7] (fume)	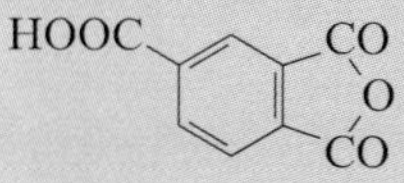		0.04	I(1)	Sa				
Trimethylamine [32] [75-50-3]	$N(CH_3)_3$	2	4.9	I(2)			C		
2,4,5-Trimethylaniline [137-17-7]	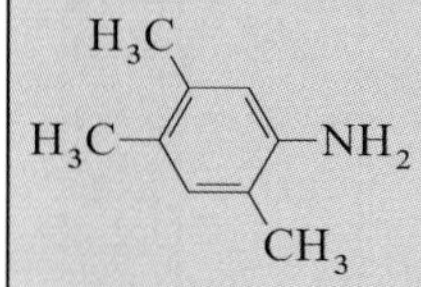	–	–	–	H	2	–		
Trimethylbenzene (all isomers): 1,2,3-Trimethylbenzene [526-73-8], 1,2,4-Trimethylbenzene [95-63-6], 1,3,5-Trimethylbenzene [108-67-8]	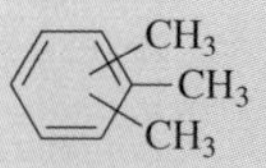	20 see Section XII	100	II(2)			C		2–6
3,5,5-Trimethyl-2-cyclo-1-hexenone	see Isophorone								
3,7,11-Trimethyl-2,6,10-dodecatrien-1-ol	see Farnesol								
3,5,5-Trimethylhexanoic acid	see Isononanoic acid								
Trimethylolpropane triacrylate [15625-89-5]	$H_3C{-}CH_2{-}C(CH_2{-}O{-}OC{-}CH{=}CH_2)_3$	see Section IV			Sh				
Trimethylpentane (all isomers)	$H_3C{-}C_6H_{12}{-}CH_3$	–	–	–		3A	–		

[32] Reaction with nitrosating agents can result in the formation of carcinogenic *N*-nitrosodimethylamine, see Section III "Amines which form carcinogenic nitrosamines on nitrosation", p. 147.

Substance [CAS number]	Formula	MAK ml/m³ (ppm)	MAK mg/m³	Peak limitation	H;S	Carcinogen category	Pregnancy risk group	Germ cell mutagen categ.	Vapour pressure in hPa at 20°C
Trimethyl phosphate [512-56-1]	$(H_3CO)_3PO$	–	–	–	H	3B	–	2	
Trimethylphosphite [121-45-9]	$(H_3CO)_3P$	see Section IIb			H				
2,4,7-Trinitrofluorenone [129-79-3]	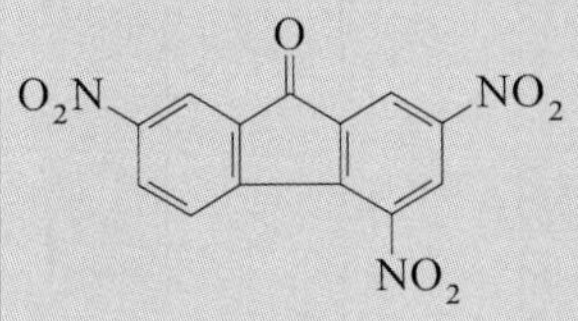	–	–	–		3B	–		
2,4,6-Trinitrophenol	see Picric acid								
2,4,6-Trinitrophenyl-methylnitramine	see *N*-Methyl-*N*,2,4,6-tetranitro-aniline								
2,4,6-Trinitrotoluene [118-96-7]	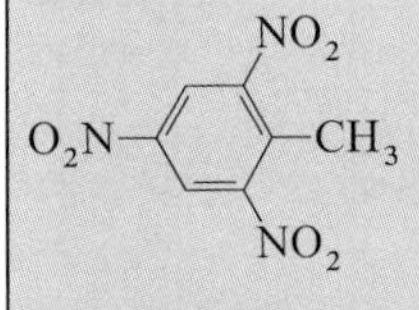	– see Section XII	–	–	HSh	2	–	3B	
Triphenylphosphate [115-86-6]	$(C_6H_5O)_3PO$	see Section IIb							
Triphenyl phosphine [603-35-0]	$P(C_6H_5)_3$		5 **I**	II(2)	Sh		C		$1.4 \cdot 10^5$
Triplochiton scleroxylon	see Woods								
Tripropylene glycol diacrylate [42978-66-5]	$H_2C{=}CH{-}\overset{O}{\overset{\Vert}{C}}(O\overset{CH_3}{\overset{\vert}{C}}HCH_2)_3O\overset{O}{\overset{\Vert}{C}}{-}CH{=}CH_2$	see Section IV			Sh				
***N,N',N''*-Tris(β-hydroxy-ethyl)-hexahydro-1,3,5-triazine** [17] [4719-04-4]	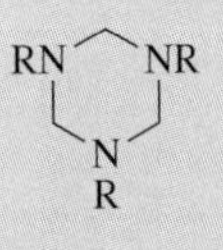 R = $CH_2{-}CH_2OH$	see Section IIb			Sh				
Tungsten [7440-33-7] and its compounds (as W)	W	see Section IIb							
Tungsten carbide	see Hard metal containing tungsten carbide and cobalt								
Turpentine [8006-64-2]				–	Sh	3A	–		6.6

[17] releases formaldehyde

Substance [CAS number]	Formula	MAK ml/m³ (ppm)	MAK mg/m³	Peak limitation	H;S	Carcinogen category	Pregnancy risk group	Germ cell mutagen categ.	Vapour pressure in hPa at 20°C
Urethane	see Carbamic acid ethyl ester								
Utile	see Woods, *Entandrophragma utile*								
Vanadium [7440-62-2] and its inorganic compounds (inhalable fraction)	V	see Section XIII		–		2	–	2	
Vinyl acetate [108-05-4]	$H_2C{=}CHOOC{-}CH_3$	–	–	–		3A	–		120
Vinylbutyrolactam	see *N*-Vinyl-2-pyrrolidone								
Vinylcarbazole [1484-13-5]	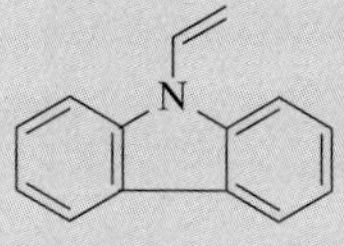	see Section IV			Sh				
Vinyl chloride [75-01-4]	$H_2C{=}CHCl$	see Section XIII		–		1	–		
4-Vinylcyclohexene [100-40-3]	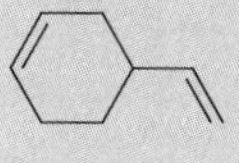	–	–	–	H	2	–		20
4-Vinyl-1,2-cyclohexene diepoxide	see 4-Vinyl-1-cyclohexene dioxide								
4-Vinyl-1-cyclohexene dioxide [106-87-6]	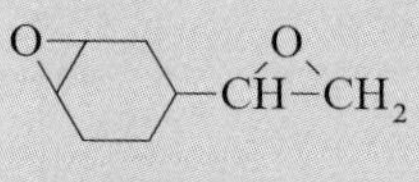	–	–	–	H	2	–		1.3
Vinylidene chloride [75-35-4]	$H_2C{=}CCl_2$	2	8.0	II(2)		3B	C		667
Vinylidene fluoride	see 1,1-Difluoroethylene								
***N*-Vinyl-2-pyrrolidone** [88-12-0]	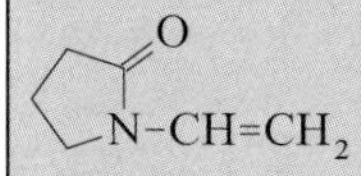	–	–	–	H	2	–		
Vinyl toluene	see Methyl styrene								
Warfarin [81-81-2]	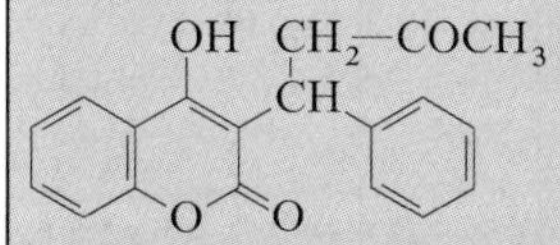		0.5 **I**	II(2)					
Western red cedar	see Woods, *Thuja plicata*								
Wheat	see Cereal flour dusts								

Substance [CAS number]	Formula	MAK ml/m³ (ppm)	MAK mg/m³	Peak limitation	H;S	Carcinogen category	Pregnancy risk group	Germ cell mutagen categ.	Vapour pressure in hPa at 20°C
Wollastonite [13983-17-0] (fibrous dust)	$CaSiO_3$	see Section II b and page 156							
Wood dust (beech and oak)	see Beech wood dust and Oak wood dust								
Wood dust (except beech and oak wood dust)		–	–	–		3B	–		
Wood ether	see Dimethyl ether								
Woods:		see Section IV							
Acacia melanoxylon R.Br.	Australian blackwood				Sh				
Bowdichia nitida Bentham	sapupira, (black) sucupira				–				
Brya ebenus DC.	cocus wood				Sh				
Calocedrus decurrens (Torr.) Florin	incense cedar, pencil cedar				–				
Chlorophora excelsa (Welw.) Benth. & Hook	iroko, kambala				Sh				
Dalbergia latifolia Roxb.	East Indian rosewood, Bombay blackwood				Sh				
Dalbergia melanoxylon Guill. et Perr.	African blackwood				Sh				
Dalbergia nigra Allem.	Brazilian rosewood				Sh				
Dalbergia retusa Hemsl.	cocobolo, rosewood				Sh				
Dalbergia stevensonii Standley	Honduras rosewood				Sh				
Diospyros celebica Bakh.	Macassar ebony, coromandel				–				
Diospyros crassiflora Hiern.	African ebony				–				
Diospyros ebenum Koenig	Ceylon ebony, Indian ebony				–				
Diospyros melanoxylon Roxb.	ebony				–				
Distemonanthus benthamianus Baill.	ayan				Sh				
Entandrophragma angolense C.DC.	gedu nohor, edinam, tiama				–				
Entandrophragma candollei Harms	heavy sapele, omu				–				
Entandrophragma cylindricum Sprague	sapele				–				
Entandrophragma utile Sprague	utile				–				
Gonystylus bancanus (Miq.) Baill.	ramin				–				
Grevillea robusta A. Cunn.	Australian silky oak				Sh				

Substance [CAS number]	Formula	MAK ml/m³ (ppm)	MAK mg/m³	Peak limitation	H;S	Carcinogen category	Pregnancy risk group	Germ cell mutagen categ.	Vapour pressure in hPa at 20°C
Khaya anthotheca C.DC.	African mahogany				Sh				
Khaya grandifoliola C.DC.	African mahogany, big leaf mahogany				–				
Khaya ivorensis A.Chev.	African mahogany, Grand Bassam mahogany				–				
Khaya senegalensis A.Juss.	African mahogany, Senegal mahogany				–				
Machaerium scleroxylon Tul.	pao ferro, Santos rosewood				Sh				
Mansonia altissima A.Chev.	mansonia, pruno, bété				Sh				
Paratecoma peroba (Record) Kuhlm.	ipe peroba				Sh				
Quercus petraea (Matuschka) Liebl.	durmast oak, sessile oak				–				
Quercus robur L.	European oak, common oak, pedunculate oak				–				
Quercus rubra L.	American red oak				–				
Swietenia macrophylla King	American mahogany, mahogany, broadleaf mahogany				–				
Swietenia mahagoni (L.) Jacq.	Caribbean mahogany, Cuban mahogany				–				
Tabebuia avellanedae (Griseb.) Lor.	lapacho, ipe				–				
Tabebuia serratifolia Nichols	bethabara, ipe				–				
Tectona grandis L.f.	teak				Sh				
Terminalia ivorensis A.Chev.	framiré, idigbo				–				
Terminalia superba Engl. & Diels	fraké, limba, afara, white afara				Sa				
Thuja occidentalis L.	arborvitae, eastern white cedar, northern white cedar				–				
Thuja plicata (D.Don.) Donn.	western red cedar, giant arborvitae, shinglewood				Sah				
Tieghemella africana A.Chev.	douka				–				
Tieghemella heckelii Pierre	makoré, "cherry mahogany", African "cherry"				–				
Triplochiton scleroxylon K.Schum.	obeche, wawa, African whitewood				Sah				
Xylanases [37278-89-0]		see Section IV			Sa				
Xylene (all isomers)[80] [1330-20-7]	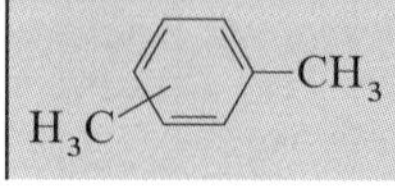	100 see Section XII	440	II(2)	H		D		7–9

[80] At high levels of physical activity the observance of the BAT value should be checked regularly by biological monitoring

Substance [CAS number]	Formula	MAK ml/m³ (ppm)	MAK mg/m³	Peak limitation	H;S	Carcinogen category	Pregnancy risk group	Germ cell mutagen categ.	Vapour pressure in hPa at 20°C
Xylidine (isomers): 2,3-Xylidine [87-59-2], 2,5-Xylidine [95-78-3], 3,4-Xylidine [95-64-7], 3,5-Xylidine [108-69-0]	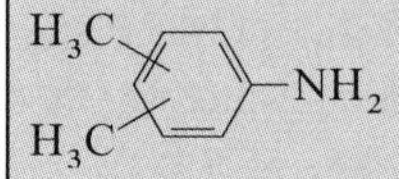	–	–	–	H	3A	–		
2,4-Xylidine [95-68-1] and **2,6-Xylidine** [87-62-7]		–	–	–	H	2	–		
***m*-Xylylenediamine** [1477-55-0]	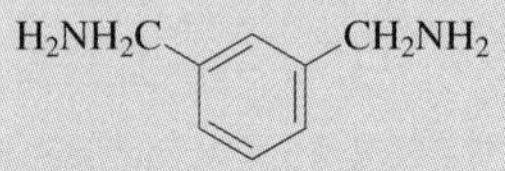	see Section IV			Sh				
Yttrium [7440-65-5] and its compounds	Y	see Section II b							
Zeolites (fibrous dust)	see Erionite								
Zinc, *O,O'*-di-2-ethylhexyl dithiophosphate [4259-15-8]	$[(H_3C{-}(CH_2)_3{-}CH(CH_2{-}CH_3){-}CH_2{-}O)_2P(S)S]_2Zn$	see Section II b, Xc and Xd							
Zinc chloride fume [7646-85-7]	$ZnCl_2$	see Section II b							
Zinc chromate [13530-65-9]	$ZnCrO_4$	–	–	–	Sh	1	–		
Zinc dichloride	see Zinc chloride fume								
Zinc molybdate	see Molybdenum and its compounds								
Zinc oxide fume [1314-13-2]	ZnO		1 **R**	I(1)					
Zirconium [7440-67-7] and its insoluble compounds	Zr		1 **I**	I(1)	Sah		D		
Zirconium, soluble compounds		see Section II b			Sah				

b. Substances for which no MAK value can be established at present

For a number of the substances examined by the Commission, studies of the effects in man or in experimental animals have yielded insufficient information for the establishment of MAK values. These substances are listed below. The toxicological documentation has been published by the Commission in the monograph collection *Toxikologisch-arbeitsmedizinische Begründung von MAK-Werten*. Some of these reviews are available in English in the series *Occupational Toxicants* (WILEY-VCH-Verlagsgesellschaft mbH, D-69451 Weinheim 1972–2008):

Acetoacetic acid ethyl ester [141-97-9]
Acrylic acid hydroxypropyl ester (all isomers) [25584-83-2]
3-Aminomethyl-3,5,5-trimethyl-cyclohexylamine (Isophorone diamine) [2855-13-2]
2-Aminopyridine [504-29-0]
Ammonium sulfamate [7773-06-0]
Arsine [7784-42-1]
Benzaldehyde [100-52-7]
★ Benzalkonium chloride [8001-54-5]
Benzoic acid [65-85-0]
Benzyl alcohol [100-51-6]
Boron oxide [1303-86-2]
Boron trifluoride [7637-07-2]
Bromine [7726-95-6]
sec-Butyl acetate [105-46-4]
sec-Butyl alcohol [78-92-2]
tert-Butylamine [75-64-9]
2-*tert*-Butyl-*p*-cresol [2409-55-4]
tert-Butyl-4-hydroxyanisole (BHA) [25013-16-5]
p-*tert*-Butyl toluene [98-51-1]
Calcium oxide [1305-78-8]
Chlorinated biphenyl oxides, several CAS Nos, e.g. [55720-99-5]
Chlorinated naphthalenes
Chlorine trifluoride [7790-91-2]
Chloroacetic acid [79-11-8]
Chloroacetyl chloride [79-04-9]
o-Chloroaniline [95-51-2]
m-Chloroaniline [108-42-9]
Chlorobenzoic acid (all isomers):
  o-Chlorobenzoic acid [118-91-2]
  m-Chlorobenzoic acid [535-80-8]
  p-Chlorobenzoic acid [74-11-3]
4-Chloromethyl-biphenyl [1667-11-4]
m-Chloronitrobenzene [121-73-3]
1-Chloro-1-nitropropane [600-25-9]
3-Chloro-1,2-propanediol (α-Chlorohydrin) [96-24-2]
★ Chromium(III) compounds
Cyanogen chloride [506-77-4]
Cyclohexene [110-83-8]

Cyclopentadiene [542-92-7]
Demeton°[25] [8065-48-3]
Diallyl phthalate [131-17-9]
Diborane [19287-45-7]
Dibromodifluoromethane [75-61-6]
3,4-Dichloroaniline [95-76-1]
1,1-Dichloro-1-nitroethane [594-72-9]
2,2-Dichloropropionic acid [75-99-0] and its sodium salt [127-20-8]
Dicyanodiamide [461-58-5]
Dicyclohexylamine [101-83-7]
Dicyclohexylamine nitrite [3129-91-7]
Diethylene glycol dinitrate [693-21-0]
Diisobutyl ketone [108-83-8]
Diketene [674-82-8]
Dimethyl adipate [627-93-0]
Dimethylaminopropionitrile [1738-25-6]
Dimethyl glutarate [1119-40-0]
Dimethyl succinate [106-65-0]
Dimethyl sulfide [75-18-3]
4,6-Dinitro-*o*-cresol [534-52-1]
Diphenyl cresyl phosphate [26444-49-5]
Divinylbenzene (all isomers) [1321-74-0]
Ethyl 2-cyanoacrylate [7085-85-0]
Ethylenediamine [107-15-3]
★ Ethylenediaminetetraacetic acid (EDTA)[38] [60-00-4]
2-Ethylhexanoic acid [149-57-5]
N-Ethylmorpholine [100-74-3]
Ferbam [14484-64-1]
Ferrovanadium [12604-58-9]
Fluorine [7782-41-4]
Formamide [75-12-7]
Germanium tetrahydride [7782-65-2]
Gold [7440-57-5] and its inorgqanic compounds
Hafnium [7440-58-6]
Hexachlorocyclopentadiene [77-47-4]
sec-Hexyl acetate [108-84-9]
Hydroxyacetic acid butyl ester [7397-62-8]
2-Hydroxyethyl methacrylate [868-77-9]
3-Hydroxy-2-naphthalenecarboxylic acid [92-70-6]
Imidazole [288-32-4]
Iodine [7553-56-2]
Isoflurane [26675-46-7]
4-Isopropylphenyl isocyanate [31027-31-3]
Ketene [463-51-4]
D,L-Limonene [138-86-3]

[25] see Section XII, List of BAT Values, Acetylcholinesterase inhibitors
[38] Avoid exposure to mixtures with iron compounds (formation of FeEDTA).

L-Limonene [5989-54-8]
Lithium hydride [7580-67-8]
Magnesium oxide fume [1309-48-4]
3-Methoxy-n-butyl acetate [4435-53-4]
Methyl acetylene [74-99-7]
Methylcyclohexanol (all isomers) [25639-42-3]
1-Methylcyclohexan-2-one [583-60-8]
Methyl vinyl ketone [78-94-4]
Molybdenum [7439-98-7] and its compounds apart from molybdenum trioxide
Monomethylhydrazine [60-34-4]
Nickel titanic yellow pigment [8007-18-9]
Nicotine [54-11-5]
Nitric acid [7697-37-2]
Osmium tetroxide [20816-12-0]
Palladium [7440-05-3] and its compounds
2-Pentanone [107-87-9]
Perchloromethyl mercaptan [594-42-3]
1*H*,1*H*,2*H*-Perfluorohexene [19430-93-4]
Phosphorus, red [7723-14-0]
Phosphorus pentasulfide [1314-80-3]
o-Phthalic acid [88-99-3]
Phthalic anhydride [85-44-9]
Platinum compounds (Chloroplatinates)[67]
Propionic acid [79-09-4]
Pyrethrum [8003-34-7]
Pyrrolidine[72] [123-75-1]
Resorcinol [108-46-3]
Rotenone [83-79-4]
Sodium hydroxide [1310-73-2]
Stibine [7803-52-3]
Strontium [7440-24-6] and its inorganic compounds
Strychnine° [57-24-9]
Sulfur monochloride [10025-67-9]
Sulfur pentafluoride [5714-22-7]
Tellurium [13494-80-9] and its inorganic compounds
1,1,2,2-Tetrabromoethane [79-27-6]
Tetramethyl succinonitrile [3333-52-6]
Tetramethyl urea (TMU) [632-22-4]
Thallium, soluble compounds
Tin [7440-31-5] and its inorganic compounds
Tri-*n*-butylamine[79] [102-82-9]
Trichloroacetic acid [76-03-9]

---

[67] A peak concentration of 2 µg/m³ should not be exceeded.

[72] Reaction with nitrosating agents can result in the formation of carcinogenic *N*-nitrosopyrrolidine, see Section III "Amines which form carcinogenic nitrosamines on nitrosation", p. 147.

[79] Reaction with nitrosating agents can result in the formation of carcinogenic *N*-Nitrosodi-*n*-butylamine, see Section III "Amines which form carcinogenic nitrosamines on nitrosation", p. 147.

2,4,5-Trichlorophenol [95-95-4]
Triisobutyl phosphate [126-71-6]
Trimethylphosphite [121-45-9]
Tungsten [7440-33-7]
Wollastonite [13983-17-0] (fibrous dust)
Yttrium [7440-65-5] and its compounds
Zinc chloride fume [7646-85-7]
Zirconium, soluble compounds

Metal-working fluids, components (see Section Xc)

Abietic acid [14] [514-10-3]
Alkyl benzenesulfonates C10–C14, linear [69669-44-9; 85117-50-6]
Alkyl ether carboxylic acids
2-(2-Aminoethoxy)ethanol [929-06-6]
2-Amino-2-ethyl-1,3-propanediol [115-70-8]
2-Amino-2-methyl-1-propanol [124-68-5]
1-Amino-2-propanol [78-96-6]
★ Aminotris(methylenephosphonic acid) [6419-19-8]
Behenic acid [112-85-6]
1,2-Benzisothiazol-3(2*H*)-one [2634-33-5]
1*H*-Benzotriazole [95-14-7]
Benzyl alcohol mono(poly)hemiformal [17] [14548-60-8]
1,3-Bis(hydroxymethyl)urea [17] [140-95-4]
Bithionol [97-18-7]
Boric acid [10043-35-3]
2-Bromo-2-nitro-1,3-propanediol [18] [52-51-7]
p-Chloro-*m*-cresol [59-50-7]
Citric acid [77-92-9] and its alkali metal salts
Decyl oleate [3687-46-5]
Dibenzyl disulfide [150-60-7]
1,2-Dibromo-2,4-dicyanobutane [35691-65-7]
2,6-Di-*tert*-butylphenol [128-39-2]
Diethylenetriaminepenta(methylene-phosphonic acid) [15827-60-8]
4-(Diiodomethylsulfonyl)-toluene [20018-09-1]
1,3-Dimethylol-5,5-dimethyl hydantoin [6440-58-0]
4,4'-Dioctyldiphenylamine [101-67-7]
2,2'-Dithiobis(N-methylbenzamide) [2527-58-4]
Dodecanedioic acid [693-23-2]
1-Dodecanol [35] [112-53-8]
5-Ethyl-3,7-dioxa-1-azabicyclo[3.3.0]octane (EDAO) [17] [7747-35-5]
2-Ethyl-1,3-hexanediol [94-96-2]

---

[14] An immunological genesis of the asthma often seen in persons working with materials containing abietic acid has not been proved.
[17] releases formaldehyde
[18] Use in metal-working fluids is not permitted: see TRGS 611.
[35] Provided the technical exposure limit of 10 mg/m³ I for metal-working fluids is observed, adverse effects on health are not to be expected.

1-Hexadecanol [35] [36653-82-4]
Hexamethylenetetramine [17] [100-97-0]
1-Hexanol [111-27-3]
2-Hexyl-1-decanol [2425-77-6]
1-Hydroxyethyl-2-heptadecenyl-imidazoline [21652-27-7]
2-Hydroxymethyl-2-nitro-1,3-propanediol [18] [126-11-4]
3-Iodo-2-propynyl butylcarbamate [55406-53-6]
Isodecyl oleate [59231-34-4]
★ Isononanoic acid [3302-10-1]
Isotridecanol [27458-92-0]
Methyl-1*H*-benzotriazole [29385-43-1]
Methyldiethanolamine [105-59-9]
N,N'-Methylene-bis(5-methyloxazolidine) [66204-44-2]
4,4'-Methylenedimorpholine [17] [5625-90-1]
Myristic acid [544-63-8]
1-Octadecanol [35] [112-92-5]
1-Octanol [111-87-5]
2-Octyl-1-dodecanol [35] [5333-42-6]
Oleoyl sarcosine [110-25-8]
Oleyl alcohol [143-28-2]
Palmitic acid [57-10-3]
★ Phenothiazine [63] [92-84-2]
1-Phenoxy-2-propanol [770-35-4]
★ N-Phenyl-1-naphthylamine [90-30-2]
o-Phenylphenol [90-43-7] and
Sodium *o*-phenylphenol [132-27-4]
Piperazine [65,66] [110-85-0]
Polydimethyl siloxanes, linear [63148-62-9; 9006-65-9; 9016-00-6]
Polyethylene glycol (average molecular weight > 600)
Polypropylene glycol (PPG) [25322-69-4]
Propylene glycol [57-55-6]
Stearic acid [57-11-4]
1-Tetradecanol [112-72-1]
Tetrahydrobenzotriazole [6789-99-7]
Triazinetriyltriiminotrishexanoic acid [35] [80584-91-4]
Triethylene glycol *n*-butyl ether [143-22-6]
Triphenylphosphate [115-86-6]
N,N',N''-Tris(β-hydroxyethyl)-hexahydro-1,3,5-triazine [17] [4719-04-4]
Zinc, *O,O'*-di-2-ethylhexyl dithiophosphate [4259-15-8]

---

[35] Provided the technical exposure limit of 10 mg/m^3 I for metal-working fluids is observed, adverse effects on health are not to be expected.
[17] releases formaldehyde
[18] Use in metal-working fluids is not permitted: see TRGS 611.
[63] phototoxic effect
[65] Reaction with nitrosating agents can result in the formation of carcinogenic *N,N'*-dinitrosopiperazine, see Section III "Amines which form carcinogenic nitrosamines on nitrosation", p. 147.
[66] Use in metal-working fluids is restricted: see TRGS 611.

III Carcinogenic Substances

Advances in our understanding of the modes of action and potency of carcinogens have made possible the improved differentiation of carcinogenic substances. Therefore, in 1998 an extended classification scheme was introduced.[81] The sections of the *List of MAK and BAT Values* previously called IIIA1, IIIA2 and IIIB were renamed as Categories 1, 2 and 3 of Section III and two new categories, 4 and 5, were added.

Substances which have been shown to be carcinogenic in man or in experimental animals are classified in the Categories 1 or 2 and are not assigned MAK or BAT values. Suspected carcinogens are classified in Category 3 and are assigned a MAK or BAT value only if neither the substance nor any of its metabolites is genotoxic.

In the Categories 4 and 5 are classified substances with carcinogenic properties for which the available data are sufficient for assessment of the carcinogenic potency. For these substances an occupational exposure level (MAK or BAT value) is defined at which no significant contribution to the cancer risk of the exposed persons is to be expected. The substances classified in Category 4 are known to act typically by non-genotoxic mechanisms. Category 5 contains genotoxic carcinogens of weak potency. For the monitoring of exposure to these substances, the establishment of BAT values is of particular importance.

1. Substances that cause cancer in man and can be assumed to make a significant contribution to cancer risk. Epidemiological studies provide adequate evidence of a positive correlation between the exposure of humans and the occurrence of cancer. Limited epidemiological data can be substantiated by evidence that the substance causes cancer by a mode of action that is relevant to man.

Aflatoxins [1402-68-2]
4-Aminobiphenyl [92-67-1]
Arsenic and inorganic arsenic compounds:
  Metallic arsenic [7440-38-2]
  Arsenic trioxide [1327-53-3]
  Arsenous acid [13464-58-9] and its salts, e.g.
  Sodium arsenite [7784-46-5]
  Arsenic pentoxide [1303-28-2]
  Arsenic acid [7778-39-4] and its salts, e.g.
  Lead arsenate [3687-31-8]
  Calcium arsenate [7778-44-1]
Asbestos [82] [1332-21-4] (chrysotile, crocidolite, amosite, anthophyllite, actinolite, tremolite) (fibrous dust)
Beech wood dust [83]
Benzene [71-43-2]
Benzidine [92-87-5] and its salts

[81] For detailed documentation see *Toxikologisch-arbeitsmedizinische Begründung von MAK-Werten* (26th issue 1998) and the English translation in *Occupational Toxicants* Volume 12, available from the publisher: WILEY-VCH, D-69451 Weinheim

[82] Cigarette smokers bear an increased risk of bronchial cancer.

[83] Dusts have been shown epidemiologically to be unequivocally carcinogenic. The active carcinogenic principle has not been identified to date.

List of MAK and BAT Values 2008. DFG, Deutsche Forschungsgemeinschaft

ISBN: 978-3-527-32305-0

Beryllium [7440-41-7] and its inorganic compounds
Bis(β-chloroethyl)sulfide (mustard gas) [505-60-2]
Bischloromethyl ether (Dichlorodimethylether) [84] [542-88-1]
1,3-Butadiene [106-99-0]
Cadmium [7440-43-9] and its inorganic compounds (inhalable fraction)
α-Chlorinated toluenes: mixture of benzoyl chloride [98-88-4],
  benzyl chloride [100-44-7], benzyl dichloride [98-87-3],
  benzyl trichloride [98-07-7]
4-Chloro-*o*-toluidine [95-69-2]
Erionite (fibrous dust) [12510-42-8]
Fibrous dusts, see p. 152
Hard metal containing tungsten carbide and cobalt (inhalable fraction)
N-Methyl-bis(2-chloroethyl)amine (nitrogen mustard) [51-75-2]
Monochlorodimethyl ether [55] [107-30-2]
2-Naphthylamine [91-59-8]
Nickel and nickel compounds (inhalable fraction):[57]
  Metallic nickel [7440-02-0]
  Nickel acetate [373-02-4] and similar soluble salts,
  Nickel carbonate [3333-67-3]
  Nickel chloride [7718-54-9]
  Nickel dioxide [12035-36-8]
  Nickel hydroxide [12054-48-7]
  Nickel monoxide [1313-99-1]
  Nickel sesquioxide [1314-06-3]
  Nickel subsulfide [12035-72-2]
  Nickel sulfate [7786-81-4]
  Nickel sulfide [16812-54-7]
Oak wood dust [83]
Pyrolysis products of organic materials, see p. 150
Sidestream smoke (passive smoking at the workplace)
Silica, crystalline (respirable fraction):
  Quartz [14808-60-7]
  Cristobalite [14464-46-1]
  Tridymite [15468-32-3]
o-Toluidine [95-53-4]
Trichloroethylene [79-01-6]
Vinyl chloride [75-01-4]
Zinc chromate [13530-65-9]

---

[84] not to be confused with the asymmetric (Dichloromethyl) methyl ether

[55] The classification in Category 1 applies to technical monochlorodimethyl ether which can be contaminated with up to 7% bischloromethyl ether.

[57] Regarding compounds which have been found to be unequivocally carcinogenic in man, see *Toxikologisch-arbeitsmedizinische Begründung von MAK-Werten*, available from the publisher: WILEY-VCH, D-69451 Weinheim.

[83] Dusts have been shown epidemiologically to be unequivocally carcinogenic. The active carcinogenic principle has not been identified to date.

2. Substances that are considered to be carcinogenic for man because sufficient data from long-term animal studies or limited evidence from animal studies substantiated by evidence from epidemiological studies indicate that they can make a significant contribution to cancer risk. Limited data from animal studies can be supported by evidence that the substance causes cancer by a mode of action that is relevant to man and by results of *in vitro* tests and short-term animal studies.

Acrylamide [79-06-1]
Acrylonitrile [107-13-1]
Allyl glycidyl ether [106-92-3]
Aluminium oxide [1344-28-1] (fibrous dust)
o-Aminoazotoluene [97-56-3]
6-Amino-2-ethoxynaphthalene [293733-21-8]
o-Anisidine [90-04-0]
Anthanthrene [191-26-4]
Antimony [7440-36-0] and its inorganic compounds (except stibine)
Attapulgite [12174-11-7] (fibrous dust)
Auramine [492-80-8] and Auramine hydrochloride [2465-27-2]
Benzo[*a*]anthracene [56-55-3]
Benzo[*b*]fluoranthene [205-99-2]
Benzo[*j*]fluoranthene [205-82-3]
Benzo[*k*]fluoranthene [207-08-9]
Benzo[*b*]naphtho[2,1-*d*]thiophene [239-35-0]
Benzo[*a*]pyrene [50-32-8]
Benzyl chloride [100-44-7], see also α-Chlorinated toluenes
Benzyl dichloride [98-87-3], see also α-Chlorinated toluenes
Benzyl trichloride [98-07-7], see also α-Chlorinated toluenes
Bitumen (vapour and aerosol) [8052-42-4]
Bromodichloromethane [75-27-4]
Bromoethane [74-96-4]
2,4-Butane sultone [1121-03-5]
Butanone oxime [96-29-7]
1,2-Butylene oxide [106-88-7]
Carbamic acid ethyl ester [51-79-6]
Ceramic fibers (fibrous dust)
Chlorinated camphene [8001-35-2]
p-Chloroaniline [106-47-8]
p-Chlorobenzotrichloride [5216-25-1]
Chlorofluoromethane (FC-31) [593-70-4]
N-Chloroformylmorpholine [15159-40-7]
2-Chloroprene [126-99-8]
Chromium(VI) compounds (inhalable fraction), with the exception of
  those practically insoluble in water such as lead chromate,
  barium chromate (but zinc chromate Section III Category 1)
Chrysene [218-01-9]
Cobalt and cobalt compounds (inhalable fraction):
  Metallic cobalt [7440-48-4]
  Cobalt(II) carbonate [513-79-1]

Cobalt(II) oxide [1307-96-6]
Cobalt(II,III) oxide [1308-06-1]
Cobalt(II) sulfate [10026-24-1] and similar salts,
Cobalt(II) sulfide [1317-42-6]
Cyclopenta[*cd*]pyrene [27208-37-3]
Dawsonite [12011-76-6] (fibrous dust)
2,4-Diaminoanisole [615-05-4]
4,4'-Diaminodiphenylmethane [101-77-9]
1,5-Diaminonaphthalene [2243-62-1]
Diazomethane [334-88-3]
Dibenz[*a,h*]anthracene [53-70-3]
Dibenzo[*a,e*]pyrene [192-65-4]
Dibenzo[*a,h*]pyrene [189-64-0]
Dibenzo[*a,i*]pyrene [189-55-9]
Dibenzo[*a,l*]pyrene [191-30-0]
1,2-Dibromo-3-chloropropane [96-12-8]
1,2-Dibromoethane [106-93-4]
Dichloroacetylene [7572-29-4]
1,4-Dichlorobenzene [106-46-7]
3,3'-Dichlorobenzidine [91-94-1]
1,4-Dichloro-2-butene [764-41-0]
1,2-Dichloroethane [107-06-2]
1,3-Dichloro-2-propanol [96-23-1]
1,3-Dichloropropene (*cis*- and *trans*-) [542-75-6]
Diesel engine emissions [27]
Diethyl sulfate [64-67-5]
Diglycidyl resorcinol ether [101-90-6]
3,3'-Dimethoxybenzidine [119-90-4]
3,3'-Dimethylbenzidine [119-93-7]
Dimethylcarbamoyl chloride [79-44-7]
1,1-Dimethylhydrazine [34] [57-14-7]
1,2-Dimethylhydrazine [34] [540-73-8]
Dimethylsulfamoyl chloride [13360-57-1]
Dimethyl sulfate [77-78-1]
Dinitrotoluene (mixtures of isomers) [25321-14-6]
Epichlorohydrin [106-89-8]
Ethylene oxide [75-21-8]
Ethylenimine [151-56-4]
Fibrous dusts, see p. 152
Furan [110-00-9]
Glass fibres (fibrous dust)
Glycidol (Glycide) [556-52-5]

[27] Because of the new diesel engine technology the emissions have changed significantly in quality and quantity. Since it must be assumed that these new diesel engines were introduced at the end of the 1990s, all the available epidemiological studies which were evaluated in 2007 are based on exposures to emissions from older diesel engines. The emissions from the new diesel engines can not be evaluated until appropriate studies become available.

[34] no longer produced in Germany

Glycidyl trimethylammonium chloride [3033-77-0]
Hexamethylphosphoric acid triamide [680-31-9]
Hydrazine [302-01-2]
Hydrazobenzene [122-66-7]
Hydroquinone [123-31-9]
Indeno[1,2,3-*cd*]pyrene [193-39-5]
Indium phosphide [22398-80-7]
Lead [7439-92-1] and its inorganic compounds (inhalable fraction) except lead arsenate and lead chromate
5-Methyl-*o*-anisidine [120-71-8]
4,4'-Methylene-bis(2-chloroaniline) [101-14-4]
4,4'-Methylene-bis(*N*,*N*-dimethylaniline) [101-61-1]
4,4'-Methylene-bis(2-methylaniline) [838-88-0]
Methyl iodide [74-88-4]
1-Methylpyrene [2381-21-7]
Michler's ketone [90-94-8]
Naphthalene [91-20-3]
5-Nitroacenaphthene [602-87-9]
2-Nitroanisole [91-23-6]
4-Nitrobiphenyl [92-93-3]
2-Nitronaphthalene [581-89-5]
2-Nitropropane [79-46-9]
N-Nitrosodi-*n*-butylamine [924-16-3]
N-Nitrosodiethanolamine [1116-54-7]
N-Nitrosodiethylamine [55-18-5]
N-Nitrosodiisopropylamine [601-77-4]
N-Nitrosodimethylamine [62-75-9]
N-Nitrosodi-*n*-propylamine [621-64-7]
N-Nitrosoethylphenylamine [612-64-6]
N-Nitrosomethylethylamine [10595-95-6]
N-Nitrosomethylphenylamine [614-00-6]
N-Nitrosomorpholine [59-89-2]
N-Nitrosopiperidine [100-75-4]
N-Nitrosopyrrolidine [930-55-2]
2-Nitrotoluene [88-72-2]
5-Nitro-*o*-toluidine [99-55-8]
Ochratoxin A [303-47-9]
4,4'-Oxydianiline [101-80-4]
Pentachlorophenol [87-86-5]
Phenyl glycidyl ether (PGE) [122-60-1]
Potassium titanates (fibrous dust), several CAS Nos and formulas
1,3-Propane sultone [1120-71-4]
β-Propiolactone [57-57-8]
Propylene imine [75-55-8]
Propylene oxide [75-56-9]
Pyrolysis products of organic materials, see p. 150
Rock wool (fibrous dust)
Silicon carbide [409-21-2] (fibrous dust)

Tetrafluoroethene [116-14-3]
Tetranitromethane [509-14-8]
4,4'-Thiodianiline [139-65-1]
Toluene-2,4-diamine [95-80-7]
2,3,4-Trichloro-1-butene [2431-50-7]
1,2,3-Trichloropropane [96-18-4]
2,4,5-Trimethylaniline [137-17-7]
2,4,6-Trinitrotoluene [118-96-7]
Vanadium [7440-62-2] and its inorganic compounds (inhalable fraction)
4-Vinylcyclohexene [100-40-3]
4-Vinyl-1-cyclohexene dioxide [106-87-6]
N-Vinyl-2-pyrrolidone [88-12-0]
2,4-Xylidine [95-68-1] and 2,6-Xylidine [87-62-7]

For substances in Categories 1 and 2, exposure to which is considered to involve a distinct cancer risk for man, no MAK value is listed in Section IIa since a safe concentration range cannot be given. For some of these substances, even uptake through the intact skin is very dangerous.

Where it is necessary to employ such substances for industrial purposes, special measures are required for protection and monitoring. These include: 1. routine analysis of the workplace air with analytical methods which are appropriate and sufficiently sensitive for the purpose; 2. special medical supervision of exposed individuals whereby, e.g., regular tests must be performed to determine whether the substance or its metabolites are detectable in the human body or whether appropriate effect parameters have been altered. Continual technical improvements should make it possible to prevent these substances from occurring in the workplace air or from directly affecting the individual at work. Where this goal cannot presently be attained, additional protective measures are required (e.g., individual respirators and protective clothing, shorter periods in the area of danger, etc.) so that exposure is minimal. The kind of protective measures which are necessary also depends on the particular physical characteristics of the substance and on the nature and intensity of its carcinogenic effect.

3. Substances that cause concern that they could be carcinogenic for man but cannot be assessed conclusively because of lack of data. The classification in Category 3 is provisional.

3 A. Substances for which the criteria for classification in Category 4 or 5 are fulfilled but for which the database is insufficient for the establishment of a MAK or BAT value.

Bisphenol A diglycidyl ether [1675-54-3]
Cresol (all isomers) [1319-77-3]
★ Di-n-butyl phosphate [107-66-4] and its technical mixtures
Dichloromethane [75-09-2]
Ethylbenzene [100-41-4]
Lauric acid [143-07-7]

Nitrilotriacetic acid [139-13-9] and its sodium salts[59]
4-Nitroaniline [100-01-6]
Oleic acid [112-80-1]
★ Tall oil, distilled [8002-26-4]
★ Titanium dioxide [13463-67-7] (inhalable fraction)[78]
Toluenediisocyanate:
  Toluene-2,4-diisocyanate [584-84-9]
  Toluene-2,6-diisocyanate [91-08-7]
Trimethylpentane (all isomers)
Turpentine [8006-64-2]
Vinyl acetate [108-05-4]
Xylidine (all isomers except 2,4-xylidine and 2,6-xylidine)

3B. Substances for which *in vitro* or animal studies have yielded evidence of carcinogenic effects that is not sufficient for classification of the substance in one of the other categories. Further studies are required before a final decision can be made. A MAK or BAT value can be established provided no genotoxic effects have been detected.[85]

Acetamide [60-35-5]
Acrolein [107-02-8]
Allyl alcohol [107-18-6]
Allyl chloride [107-05-1]
3-Amino-9-ethylcarbazole [132-32-1]
Amitrole [61-82-5]
p-Anisidine [104-94-9]
p-Aramid [26125-61-1] (fibrous dust)
Benzoyl chloride [98-88-4]
Biphenyl [92-52-4]
Bromochloromethane [74-97-5]
1,4-Butane sultone [1633-83-6]
tert-Butyl glycidyl ether [7665-72-7]
n-Butyl glycidyl ether (BGE) [2426-08-6]
tert-Butyl methyl ether [1634-04-4]
Calcium sodium metaphosphate [23209-59-8] (fibrous dust)
Carbon black (inhalable fraction)
Chlordane [57-74-9]
Chlordecone (Kepone) [143-50-0]
Chlorinated biphenyls [53469-21-9], [11097-69-1] (technical products)
Chlorinated paraffins (certain technical products) various CAS Nos, e.g. [63449-39-8]
Chloroacetaldehyde [107-20-0]

---

[59] Avoid simultaneous exposure to iron compounds (formation of FeNTA)
[78] except for ultrafine particles
[85] In the past, when a substance was classified in Category 3 it was given a MAK value provided that it had no detectable genotoxic effects. When all such substances have been examined for whether or not they may be classified in Category 4, this sentence may be omitted.

Chloroacetamide-*N*-methylol (CAM) [17] [2832-19-1]
2-Chloroacrylonitrile [920-37-6]
Chloroethane [75-00-3]
Chloroformic acid ethyl ester [541-41-3]
3-Chloro-2-methylpropene [563-47-3]
o-Chloronitrobenzene [88-73-3]
p-Chloronitrobenzene [100-00-5]
4-Chlorophenyl isocyanate [104-12-1]
Chlorothalonil [1897-45-6]
5-Chloro-*o*-toluidine [95-79-4]
Chromium carbonyl [13007-92-6]
Coal mine dust (respirable fraction)
Crotonaldehyde [123-73-9; 4170-30-3]
Cyclohexanone [108-94-1]
3,3'-Diaminobenzidine [91-95-2] and its tetrahydrochloride [7411-49-6]
1,2-Dichloromethoxyethane [41683-62-9]
3,4-Dichloronitrobenzene [99-54-7]
4-(2,4-Dichlorophenoxy)benzenamine [14861-17-7]
1,2-Dichloropropane [78-87-5]
2,2-Dichloro-1,1,1-trifluoroethane (FC-123) [306-83-2]
Diethanolamine [28] [111-42-2]
Diethylcarbamoyl chloride [88-10-8]
1,1-Difluoroethylene [75-38-7]
Diglycidyl ether (DGE) [2238-07-5]
2,5-Dimethoxy-4-chloroaniline [6358-64-1]
N,N-Dimethylaniline [121-69-7]
Dimethyl hydrogen phosphite [868-85-9]
Dinitrobenzene (all isomers) [25154-54-5]
Dinitronaphthalene (all isomers) [27478-34-8]
Ethidium bromide [1239-45-8]
Ethylene [74-85-1]
Ethylene thiourea [96-45-7]
Fibrous dusts, see p. 152
Furfural [98-01-1]
Furfuryl alcohol [98-00-0]
Glyoxal [107-22-2]
Halloysite [12298-43-0] (fibrous dust)
Hexachloro-1,3-butadiene [87-68-3]
Hydrogen selenide [7783-07-5]
Isophorone [78-59-1]
Isopropyl glycidyl ether (IGE) [4016-14-2]
Isopropyl oil (residue of isopropyl alcohol production)
Lead chromate [7758-97-6] and lead chromate oxide [18454-12-1]
Magnesium oxide sulfate [12286-12-3] (fibrous dust)

---

[17] releases formaldehyde

[28] Reaction with nitrosating agents can result in the formation of carcinogenic *N*-nitrosodiethanolamine, see Section III "Amines which form carcinogenic nitrosamines on nitrosation", p. 147.

2-Mercaptobenzothiazole [149-30-4]
Mercury (metallic mercury [7439-97-6] and inorganic mercury compounds)
Mercury, organic compounds
Metal-working fluids which contain nitrite or nitrite-forming compounds and substances which react with nitrite to yield nitrosamines
Methyl bromide [74-83-9]
Methyl chloride [74-87-3]
N-Methyl-*N*,2,4,6-tetranitroaniline [479-45-8]
Molybdenum trioxide [1313-27-5]
1,5-Naphthylene diisocyanate [3173-72-6]
Nemalite [1317-43-7] (fibrous dust)
2-Nitro-4-aminophenol [119-34-6]
Nitrobenzene [98-95-3]
Nitrogen dioxide [10102-44-0]
Nitroglycerin [55-63-0]
Nitromethane [75-52-5]
1-Nitronaphthalene [86-57-7]
2-Nitro-*p*-phenylenediamine [5307-14-2]
Nitropyrenes (Mono-, Di-, Tri-, Tetra-) (isomers)
N-Nitrosodiphenylamine [86-30-6]
3-Nitrotoluene [99-08-1]
4-Nitrotoluene [99-99-0]
Olaquindox (*N*-(2-Hydroxyethyl)-3-methyl-2-quinoxalinecarboxamide 1,4-dioxide) [23696-28-8]
Ozone [10028-15-6]
Peracetic acid [79-21-0]
Phenol [108-95-2]
o-Phenylenediamine [95-54-5]
m-Phenylenediamine [108-45-2]
p-Phenylenediamine [106-50-3]
Phenylhydrazine [100-63-0]
N-Phenyl-2-naphthylamine [135-88-6]
Picric acid [88-89-1]
★ Pyridine [110-86-1]
Pyrolysis products of organic materials, see p. 150
Quinone [106-51-4]
Rhodium [7440-16-6] and its inorganic compounds
Selenium [7782-49-2] and its inorganic compounds
Sepiolite, several CAS Nos and formulas (fibrous dust)
Slag wool (fibrous dust)
Talc [14807-96-6] (without asbestos fibres) (respirable fraction)
1,1,2,2-Tetrachloroethane [79-34-5]
Tetrachloroethylene [127-18-4]
Thiourea [62-56-6]
p-Toluidine [106-49-0]
Tribromomethane [75-25-2]
1,2,4-Trichlorobenzene [120-82-1]
1,1,2-Trichloroethane [79-00-5]

1,3,5-Triethylhexahydro-1,3,5-triazine[17] [7779-27-3]
Trimethyl phosphate [512-56-1]
2,4,7-Trinitrofluorenone [129-79-3]
Vinylidene chloride [75-35-4]
Wood dust (except beech and oak wood dust)

The monitoring of the health of employees using substances classified in Category 3 must be intensified. In addition, the branches of industry which produce and process such substances are requested – as are all relevantly involved research laboratories – to participate in the effort to shed light on the cancer-correlation question and, where necessary, to search for harmless alternative substances.Category 3 will be re-evaluated annually to determine whether substances must be reassigned to Categories 1 or 2, whether the database permits their transfer to one of the Categories 4 or 5 or whether they require no classification and can be dismissed completely from Section III of this list.

4. Substances with carcinogenic potential for which a non-genotoxic mode of action is of prime importance and genotoxic effects play no or at most a minor part provided the MAK and BAT values are observed. Under these conditions no significant contribution to human cancer risk is expected. The classification is supported especially by evidence that, for example, increases in cellular proliferation, inhibition of apoptosis or disturbances in cellular differentiation are important in the mode of action. To characterize the cancer risk, the manifold mechanisms contributing to carcinogenesis and their characteristic dose-time-response relationships are taken into consideration.

Acrylic acid polymer (neutralized, cross-linked)
Aniline [62-53-3]
n-Butyltin compounds
Carbon tetrachloride [56-23-5]
Chloroform [67-66-3]
2,6-Di-*tert*-butyl-*p*-cresol (3,5-Di-*tert*-butyl-4-hydroxytoluene) (BHT) [128-37-0]
Di(2-ethylhexyl) phthalate (DEHP) [117-81-7]
1,4-Dioxane [123-91-1]
Ethylene glycol monobutyl ether [111-76-2]
Ethylene glycol monobutyl ether acetate [112-07-2]
Formaldehyde [50-00-0]
Glutaraldehyde [111-30-8]
★ Heptachlor [76-44-8]
Hexachlorobenzene [118-74-1]
Hydrogen peroxide [7722-84-1]
Lindane [58-89-9]
4,4'-Methylene diphenyl isocyanate (MDI) [101-68-8] (inhalable fraction) [101-68-8]
★ n-Octyltin compounds
Perfluorooctanoic acid [335-67-1] and its inorganic salts

[17] releases formaldehyde

"polymeric MDI"[69] [9016-87-9] (inhalable fraction)
Sulfuric acid [7664-93-9]
2,3,7,8-Tetrachlorodibenzo-*p*-dioxin [1746-01-6]
Tetrahydrofuran [109-99-9]
Tributyl phosphate [126-73-8]

5. Substances with carcinogenic and genotoxic effects, the potency of which is considered to be so low that, provided the MAK and BAT values are observed, no significant contribution to human cancer risk is to be expected. The classification is supported by information on the mode of action, dose-dependence and toxicokinetic data pertinent to species comparison.

Acetaldehyde [75-07-0]
Ethanol [64-17-5]
★ Isoprene (2-Methyl-1,3-butadiene) [78-79-5]
Styrene [100-42-5]

The monitoring of the health of employees using substances classified in Categories 4 and 5 must be intensified since after exposures at levels exceeding the MAK or BAT value an increase in the cancer risk is possible or conceivable.

Groups of substances requiring special consideration

Carcinogenic medicines[86]

Results from animal studies or experience of effects in man suggest that a number of medicines have carcinogenic effects. Exposure of employees to such substances can occur during the manufacturing process, therapeutic use and in research laboratories.

Substances with a genotoxic therapeutic mechanism are assumed to be carcinogenic. This assumption is supported by the development of novel tumours in patients undergoing treatment with alkylating cytostatics such as cyclophosphamide, ethylenimine or chlornaphazine as well as with ointments containing arsenic or tar after use for long periods.

Consequently, it must be assumed that a hazard exists when these substances are handled occupationally. Suitable precautions must guarantee that exposure to such substances is prevented.

Amines which form carcinogenic nitrosamines on nitrosation

Nitrosatable amines require particular attention because in the presence of nitrosating agents they may be transformed into potentially strongly carcinogenic nitroso

[69] "polymeric MDI" (pMDI) is a technical grade MDI, containing 30% – 80% w/w 4,4'-methylene diphenyl isocyanate (MDI); the remainder consists of MDI oligomers and MDI homologues.

[86] see *Toxikologisch-arbeitsmedizinische Begründung von MAK-Werten* (11th issue, 1985) and *Occupational Toxicants* Vol. 1; available from the publisher: WILEY-VCH, D-69451 Weinheim

compounds. A detailed account of "Nitrosation of volatile amines at the workplace" may be found in *Occupational Toxicants*, Volume 1.

The formation of nitrosamines from such amines has not only been observed in model experiments but – at least for some of the compounds – has also been demonstrated at the workplace. The amine-containing substances and end products handled at work can themselves be contaminated to a considerable extent with the corresponding nitrosamines. Under conditions encountered in practice nitrosation is to be expected particularly with secondary amines, although in principle, primary and tertiary amines may also undergo nitrosation reactions. Nitrogen oxides are the most probable nitrosating agents. In addition, nitrosation of amines may be brought about by nitrosyl chloride, nitrite esters, metal nitrites and nitroso compounds.

The potential danger associated with any particular amine arises on the one hand from the readiness with which it undergoes nitrosation reactions, and on the other from the degree of carcinogenicity of the corresponding nitrosamine. For both parameters considerable differences are to be found between the various amines. In model studies several factors such as pH, temperature, catalysts and inhibitors are known to determine the extent of nitrosation. Nitrosation of amines can take place not only in acid milieu but also in alkaline. Because nitrogen oxides are effective nitrosating agents also in alkaline milieu, when nitrosatable amines are present nitrogen oxides should be excluded. The reaction of nitrite with nitrosatable amines is accelerated by the presence of formaldehyde, which also causes extension towards the alkaline of the pH range in which significant levels of nitrosation are possible (see documentation of MAK values[87] "Kühlschmierstoffe" (Metal-working fluids)). At present, however, it is not possible to make quantitative predictions as to the formation of nitrosamines under the complex conditions found at the workplace and in mixtures of substances found there.

Two precautionary measures are therefore necessary when handling amines at the workplace:

1. Simultaneous exposure to nitrosating agents should be reduced to a minimum. This can be put into practice by eliminating nitrosating agents, or – if they play a role in the actual process – by replacing them with substances which do not lead to the formation of carcinogenic nitrosamines. In particular, the level of nitrogen oxides at the workplace should be monitored and reduced when necessary.
2. The level of nitrosamines in the workplace air and in substances containing amines should be monitored. This applies particularly when amines are used from which highly carcinogenic nitroso compounds, e. g., nitrosodimethylamine or nitrosodiethylamine, can be formed.

Monocyclic aromatic amino and nitro compounds

The *List of MAK and BAT Values* includes 38 monocyclic aromatic amino and nitro compounds, most of which are classified in Categories 1 to 3 for carcinogenic substances, but there are also some with MAK values and others for which no MAK value could be established and which are therefore listed in Section IIb of the *List of MAK and BAT*

[87] *Toxikologisch-arbeitsmedizinische Begründung von MAK-Werten* and in English Translation in *Occupational Toxicants* Volumes 2, 5, 9, 10, 16, 20 available from the publisher: WILEY-VCH, D-69451 Weinheim

Values. Comparison of these compounds (see *"Toxikologisch-arbeitsmedizinische Begründungen von MAK-Werten"*) reveals that their acute and chronic toxic effects are very similar. When they are tested with appropriate methods, they may be shown to have carcinogenic potential (Categories 1 or 2) or at least to be suspected carcinogens (Category 3). And the substances all cause very similar kinds of tumours. The substances are generally only weakly genotoxic. Therefore it is considered that the acute toxic effects play an important role, a role in tumour promotion. The creation of the Categories 4 and 5 for carcinogenic substances made it necessary to review the contribution of genotoxic and non-genotoxic properties to the carcinogenicity of (especially) suspected carcinogens (substances in Category 3) and to decide whether they could be reclassified in one of the new categories. In addition, inconsistencies in the classification of these substances had become apparent. Because there is frequently insufficient information available for the classification of individual substances, it seems sensible to draw conclusions on the basis of analogy with structurally related compounds. The comparison reveals that this is possible within certain limits but that, in the absence of appropriate data, it is not possible to decide with any certainty where a substance belongs in the spectrum between weak and powerful carcinogens.

Practically all the monocyclic aromatic amino and nitro compounds reviewed here are methaemoglobin producers and most cause haemosiderosis. This suggests that the N-hydroxylamines formed from the compounds are responsible for the toxic effects in experimental animals and in man. It has, however, not yet been demonstrated whether the observed differences between sexes and species and in target organs may all be explained in terms of toxicokinetically induced differences in the bioavailability of the effective metabolites. It is also not clear whether the genotoxic or acute toxic effects are influenced by the release of iron during methaemoglobin formation or erythrocyte turnover and by the "oxidative stress" associated with these processes. In any case, toxic tissue changes and fibrosis precede tumour development in the spleen, liver and kidneys.

Genotoxic effects have been demonstrated for many monocyclic aromatic amino and nitro compounds and are likely for others. Because of this (albeit weak) genotoxicity, a classification in Category 5 for carcinogenic substances could seem appropriate. However, there is considerable evidence that tissue damage is decisive for the tumour development and that the substances should be classified in Category 4. But such a classification requires that the causes and dose-dependence of the tissue damage are understood.

The comparison of these substances also indicates that the haematotoxic members of the group must generally be seen to be risk factors for cancer and should be re-examined to decide whether they should be classified in one of the categories for carcinogenic substances.

Azo colourants

Azo colourants are characterised by the azo group —N=N—. They are made by the coupling of singly and multiply diazotized aryl amines. Of particular toxicological importance are colourants from doubly diazotized benzidine and benzidine derivatives (3,3'-dimethylbenzidine, 3,3'-dimethoxybenzidine, 3,3'-dichlorobenzidine). In addition, aminoazobenzene, aminonaphthalene and monocyclic aromatic amines are encountered. Reductive fission of the azo group, either by intestinal bacteria or by azo reductases of

the liver and of extrahepatic tissues, can cause these compounds to be released. Such breakdown products have been detected in animal experiments as well as in man (urine). Mutagenicity, which has been observed with numerous azo colourants in *in vitro* test systems, and the carcinogenicity in animal experiments are attributed to the release of amines and their subsequent metabolic activation. There are now epidemiological indications that occupational exposure to benzidine-based azo colourants can increase the incidence of bladder carcinoma.

Thus all azo colourants whose metabolism can liberate a carcinogenic aryl amine are suspected of having carcinogenic potential. Due to the large number of such dyes (several hundred) it seems neither possible nor justifiable to substantiate this suspicion in each individual case by means of animal experimentation according to customary classification criteria. Instead, scientific models have to be relied on. Therefore, as a preventive measure to avoid putting exposed persons at risk, it is recommended that the substances be dealt with as if they were classified in the same categories as the corresponding carcinogenic or suspected carcinogenic amines (Categories 1, 2, 3).

If there are indications that the colourant itself (e.g. a pigment) or any carcinogenic breakdown product is not biologically available, the absence of risk should be proved experimentally or substantiated by biomonitoring. Suitable animal experiments can also rule out a suspected carcinogenic potential.

Pyrolysis products of organic materials

If organic material is heated or combusted with a limited supply of oxygen, mixtures are produced whose compositions are dependent on the starting material and the reaction conditions. These mixtures contain, among numerous other substances, polycyclic aromatic hydrocarbons (PAH).

The extremely complex mixtures which have been examined to date contain, simultaneously and in widely differing proportions, carcinogenic components and substances which promote cancer development, as well as fractions which inhibit the carcinogenic effects of concurrently present components.

Many of the PAH which occur regularly in pyrolysis products are carcinogenic in animal studies. They are present at particularly high levels in

brown coal tars (soft coal tars),
coal tars (black coal tars),
coal tar pitches,
coal tar oils,
coke oven emissions.

The carcinogenic effect after occupational exposures to these mixtures of aromatic compounds has been demonstrated in epidemiological studies. Therefore they are classified in

Category 1.

Particularly the local carcinogenic effects of these mixtures are accounted for largely in terms of their content of PAH. Such effects are therefore also to be expected with other PAH-containing mixtures. The levels and significance of other carcinogenic components of these mixtures has not yet been studied in detail. Thus, although

diesel engine emissions[27]
also contain PAH, in this case it is probably the soot particles which determine the carcinogenic effect. This has been demonstrated only in animal studies and therefore diesel engine emissions are classified in
Category 2.

The carcinogenic effects of other mixtures such as, e.g., petrol engine emissions, used motor oils, curing smoke, used cutting oils have not yet been studied in as much detail. The composition of these mixtures also makes them difficult to define. If, however, exposure to PAH which have been shown in animal studies to be carcinogenic, e.g.,

anthanthrene,
benzo[*a*]anthracene,
benzo[*b*]fluoranthene,
benzo[*j*]fluoranthene,
benzo[*k*]fluoranthene,
Benzo[*b*]naphtho[2,1-*d*]thiophene,
benzo[*a*]pyrene,
chrysene,
cyclopenta[*cd*]pyren,
dibenz[*a,h*]anthracene,
dibenzo[*a,e*]pyrene,
dibenzo[*a,h*]pyrene,
dibenzo[*a,i*]pyrene,
dibenzo[*a,l*]pyrene,
indeno[1,2,3-*cd*]pyrene,
1-methylpyrene,
naphthalene,

can be demonstrated during work with such pyrolysis products, the mixtures should be handled
like the substances in **Category 2**, except for phenanthrene and pyrene, which are not classified in a Carcinogen category on the basis of the data (see documentation "PAH 2008").

It will be possible to establish a clearer, more quantitative relationship between exposure and an increase in cancer risk when more precise data for the compositions of specific mixtures and of their cancer-producing effects are available (see also documentation "PAH 2008"). The Commission emphasizes the urgency of such investigations.

Polycyclic aromatic hydrocarbons (PAH) may be readily absorbed through the skin. Therefore, pyrolysis products and other mixtures containing PAH should be handled like substances designated with an "H" (see Section VII Percutaneous absorption, p. 183; see also documentation "PAH 2008").

[27] Because of the new diesel engine technology the emissions have changed significantly in quality and quantity. Since it must be assumed that these new diesel engines were introduced at the end of the 1990s, all the available epidemiological studies which were evaluated in 2007 are based on exposures to emissions from older diesel engines. The emissions from the new diesel engines can not be evaluated until appropriate studies become available.

Fibrous dusts

Not only certain kinds of asbestos but also the fibrous zeolite, erionite, is considered to produce tumours in man. In addition, a number of fibrous dusts have been shown to produce tumours in experimental animals after inhalation or after intratracheal instillation or direct local administration into the chest (intrapleural) or abdominal (intraperitoneal) cavity.

When all the information as to the effects of dust on man and the effects seen in studies with animals and cultured cells is taken into account, it must be concluded that, unlike the non-fibrous insoluble dusts of corresponding composition,

- the fibrous asbestos dust particles which are durable in the organism must be seen as the cause of the tumorigenic effects of asbestos
- and that, in principle, all kinds of elongated dust particles have the potential, like asbestos fibres, to cause tumours if they are sufficiently long, thin and durable *in vivo*.

Factors also suggested to play a role include other properties of fibres such as their surface characteristics.

The animal studies have also demonstrated that longer or more durable fibres have higher carcinogenic potency than shorter or less durable fibres.

Classification criteria

a. Properties of carcinogenic fibres

According to the internationally accepted convention established in the 1960s for measuring levels of asbestos dust at workplaces by counting the fibres under the light microscope, only *particles with a ratio of length to diameter greater than 3:1 and which are longer than 5 μm and have a diameter less than 3 μm* are counted. The term *fibrous dust* is used here for fibres of these dimensions. With such fibrous dusts in animal studies, the number of fibres has been shown to correlate positively with the tumour incidence.

The above definition, however, does not distinguish clearly between carcinogenic and non-carcinogenic fibres. The presently available data do not make it possible to state precisely from which fibre length or diameter or from which length to diameter ratio and from which durability fibres possess the biological activity resulting in tumour induction. Nevertheless, at present there is no other definition which has a better scientific basis.[88]

The situation is made more difficult by the fact that, with the exception of a few inorganic and organic textile fibres, fibrous materials produce dusts in which the fibre lengths and diameters are spread over a wide range.

In addition, the diameter of fibres, e.g., asbestos fibres, can be reduced after incorporation by longitudinal splitting. Then fibres with diameters less than 3 μm can be found in the lungs although, before splitting, the fibres in the inhaled air did not fit the definition of fibrous dust.

---

[88] For reasons of technical analytical practicability, it would be of advantage if the length to diameter ratio defining a fibrous dust could be changed, e.g., from L:D > 3:1 to L:D > 5:1. Such decisions, however, are the responsibility of the AGS (The Committee on Hazardous Chemicals). The available experimental data would be compatible with such a change.

b. Effects in man

Epidemiological studies of the inhabitants of three villages in central Anatolia together with mineralogical studies and analyses of the fibres in lung dust produced convincing evidence that erionite fibres cause mesothelioma and lung cancer.

In epidemiological studies carried out in factories producing glass fibre and glass wool, no convincing evidence of an increased risk of developing mesothelioma or lung cancer was found. An increased risk of developing lung cancer was found for persons exposed to rock and slag wool but could not be associated unequivocally with the exposure to these fibrous dusts.

The studies available to date neither confirm nor refute the proposal that man-made mineral fibres have carcinogenic effects but this was not to be expected since, even if the individual fibres were as carcinogenic as asbestos fibres, the tumorigenicity would not be detectable at the low exposure concentrations measured in these studies. At present there are no appropriate studies of workplaces where persons processing or using fibres are exposed to the much higher fibre concentrations necessary to examine with sufficient sensitivity the question of the carcinogenic effects in man.

c. Animal inhalation studies

The results of inhalation studies with fibrous dusts are not always consistent so that positive results obtained in some studies could not be confirmed in others. The main reason for this inconsistency is that it is difficult to ensure that a sufficient dose of the carcinogenic fibre fraction reaches the target tissue. The fibres which are relevant for the effects in man, for example, penetrate the nasal filter of rodents either only poorly or not at all. For crocidolite, which has been shown to be carcinogenic in man, positive results have been obtained in only one adequately documented inhalation study with rats but negative results in several adequately documented studies.

Thus a negative result in an inhalation study does not exclude the possibility that the substance has carcinogenic effects. Positive results can also result from local overloading of the target tissue or from the effects of non-fibrous dust fractions. When carcinogenic effects of a fibre have been identified in inhalation studies, the fibre is classified in Category 2.

d. Animal studies with intratracheal instillation, intrapleural or intraperitoneal injection

Many kinds of fibre have proved to be carcinogenic after administration by intratracheal instillation or by intrapleural or intraperitoneal injection. These administration routes are unphysiological but they guarantee a high dose of fibres immediately after application at the sites which are relevant for man (bronchial tract, pleura and peritoneum). Thus, in the studies with intratracheal, intraperitoneal or intrapleural administration, a longer time and higher dose is available for tumour production than in inhalation studies where the fibre concentration in the target organs builds up only slowly.

With these methods, dose-response relationships can be established; they have demonstrated that the carcinogenic effect is determined by the form of the fibre. Recent inhalation studies with ceramic fibres have confirmed positive results obtained in injection studies. Although the possibility of overloading the target tissue cannot be

excluded with these administration routes, a positive result from such a study is considered to be good evidence that the fibre would be carcinogenic in man.

e. Genotoxicity and cell transformation studies

Genotoxicity and cell transformation studies with various fibres also demonstrate that fibre form largely determines the effects of fibres. Whereas numerical and structural chromosome changes were detected in a number of test systems, there was no conclusive evidence that fibres can induce point mutations.

f. Durability

From the results of animal studies with durable and non-durable fibres it is concluded that durability in the biological system has a considerable effect on the carcinogenicity of fibres. At present, however, it is not possible to define the degree of durability necessary for carcinogenic activity or to state to what extent the durability determines the carcinogenic potency of the fibres. Gypsum and wollastonite, e.g., dissolve in the organism within a period of some days to a few weeks and show no signs of carcinogenic effects even after intraperitoneal administration.

Conclusions

Thus it must be concluded that it is not possible at present to formulate a precise scientific definition of the factors which determine the carcinogenicity of fibres. However, it is expected that this will be possible within the next few years.

The carcinogenic properties of inorganic fibres must therefore be assessed on the basis of the experimental data available from animal and *in vitro* studies.

Organic fibrous dusts

Although it is suspected that organic fibres in the critical dimension range can produce tumours, the presently available data is insufficient to confirm this. Attention is drawn to the urgent requirement for appropriate studies, e.g., of carcinogenicity, surface properties, bioavailability and *in vivo* durability, so that the carcinogenic potential of organic fibres can be assessed.

Classification

The various materials from which fibrous dust can be produced are categorized in groups, e.g., glass fibres, and the groups are then classified.

After intraperitoneal or intrapleural administration, carcinogenic effects have been demonstrated for almost all inorganic fibres (see Table "Classification of fibrous dusts"). Therefore, in the interests of health protection, all inorganic fibres are currently suspected of having carcinogenic potential and, unless other evidence of carcinogenic effects is available, are classified in Category 3 B.

The negative results of the carcinogenicity studies with fibres are probably determined by the specific size distribution and chemical composition of the fibrous dust being studied. When these parameters are not or are insufficiently defined, negative study results cannot lead to classification of the fibres or group of fibres as non-carcinogenic. When, however, the necessary information is available and the methods used were appropriate, a negative result would lead to classification of the fibre type as non-carcinogenic.

Classification in the various categories in Section III is made according to the following criteria:

Category 1
positive results from epidemiological studies

Category 2
positive results from inhalation studies (often supported by the results of further studies with intraperitoneal, intrapleural or intratracheal administration)
or
unequivocally positive results (significant increase in tumour incidence) from studies with intraperitoneal, intrapleural or intratracheal administration

Category 3 B
questionable results from inhalation studies or from studies with intraperitoneal, intrapleural or intratracheal administration
or
no data

MAK value
negative results from studies with intraperitoneal administration, supported by other findings such as low durability.

The data base for the organic fibres is inadequate. The studies which are available require confirmation, and more extensive studies are necessary. Therefore, the Commission has decided not to classify organic fibres yet, with the exception of *p*-aramid.

Fibrous dust	Epi-demi-ology	Carcinogenicity				Cell-trans-form-ation	Geno-tox-icity	Classifi-cation	Reasons for classification
		in-hal.	i.tr.	i.p.	i.pl.				
inorganic fibrous dusts									
aluminium oxide					+			Section III Category 2	unequivocally positive results in i.pl. studies
attapulgite/ palygorskite	?	+		+	+		?	Section III Category 2	positive results in an inhalation study

Fibrous dust	Epi-demi-ology	Carcinogenicity				Cell-trans-form-ation	Geno-tox-icity	Classifi-cation	Reasons for classification
		in-hal.	i.tr.	i.p.	i.pl.				
calcium sodium metaphosphate			?	?				Section III Categ. 3B	data inadequate
calcium sulfate (gypsum)			?	–				Section II a MAK value	negative results in i. p. test, very low durability in the organism
ceramics		+	?	+	?			Section III Category 2	positive results in inhalation studies
dawsonite					+			Section III Category 2	unequivocally positive results in i.pl. studies
erionite	+	+	+	+	+	+	+	Section III Category 1	carcinogenicity demonstrated in epidemiological studies
glass	?	?	+	+	+	+	+	Section III Category 2	all the study results
halloysite					?			Section III Categ. 3B	data inadequate
magnesium oxide sulfate			?	?				Section III Categ. 3B	data inadequate
nemalite/ brucite		?		?	?			Section III Categ. 3B	data inadequate
potassium titanates		+	?	+	+	+	?	Section III Category 2	positive results in an inhalation study together with positive results in other studies
rock wool	?	?	?	+	?		?	Section III Category 2	positive results in i. p. studies
sepiolite	?	?		?	?			Section III Categ. 3B	data inadequate
silicon carbide			+	+	+	+		Section III Category 2	positive results in i. p., i.pl. and i.tr. studies, very durable *in vivo*
slag wool	?	?		?	?			Section III Categ. 3B	data inadequate
wollastonite	?	?		–	?		?	Section II b	negative results in i. p. test, low durability in the organism

Fibrous dust	Epi-demi-ology	Carcinogenicity				Cell-trans-form-ation	Geno-tox-icity	Classifi-cation	Reasons for classification
		in-hal.	i.tr.	i.p.	i.pl.				
all other inorganic dusts								Section III Categ. 3B	data inadequate
organic fibrous dusts									
p-aramid		–		?			?	Section III Categ. 3B	data inadequate

+ positive results; – negative results; ? results cannot be assessed

inhal. inhalation
i.tr. intratracheal instillation
i.p. intraperitoneal injection
i.pl. intrapleural injection

IV Sensitizing substances

The allergies caused by substances at the workplace affect mostly the skin (contact eczema, contact urticaria), the respiratory passages (rhinitis, asthma, alveolitis) and the conjunctiva (blepharoconjunctivitis). The kind of allergy is determined by the route of uptake, the chemical properties of the substance and its aggregation state.

Contact allergies are generally manifested as contact eczema, the pathogenesis of which involves a T lymphocyte-mediated immune reaction of delayed type. Contact eczema is almost always caused by reactive substances of low molecular weight. Immunologically, these low molecular weight substances must be seen as haptens or prohaptens. They become complete allergens in the organism either by binding to peptides or proteins as such (haptens) or after metabolism (prohaptens).

The development of a contact allergy of delayed type is determined by several factors, by the sensitization potential resulting from the chemical properties of the substance or the metabolites produced from it in the organism, by the exposure concentration and the duration and manner of exposure, by the genetic disposition of the person and, not least, by the state of the tissue with which the substance makes contact. ★ The release of (pro-)inflammatory cytokines (e.g. TNF-α or interleukin-1β), which is triggered by existing inflammation of the skin or by irritation from a foreign substance, is necessary for the induction of sensitization. Thus, the irritating properties of a substance can increase its sensitization potential. Cytokine induction, which stimulates the immune response, can also be triggered by the additional contact with other irritating substances, e.g. detergents such as sodium dodecyl sulfate, which then provide the necessary (pro-)inflammatory stimulus. Furthermore, the irritating effect of these kinds of substances leads to increased penetration of the sensitizing substance. An effect which enhances (or decreases) penetration is also possible from non-irritating substances with suitable/adequate polarity (such as dimethyl sulfoxide). These types of cofactors and combinatorial effects, as well as particular factors relevant under conditions at the workplace and expressly pointed out in the documentation, are taken into account in the evaluation, as described in Chapter IV.c. The s e n s i t i z a t i o n p o t e n t i a l of a substance is not the same as the i n c i d e n c e o f s e n s i t i z a t i o n s which it causes because the clinical significance of a contact allergen is not only determined by its sensitization potential but also by the distribution of the substance and the possibilities of exposure to it. At present, the sensitization potential of a substance can best be estimated in animal studies.

Other allergic skin reactions, e.g., urticaria, involve immune reactions mediated by specific antibodies. Similar symptoms can also be produced, however, by mechanisms not involving immune reactions (see below).

Most respiratory allergens are macromolecules, mainly peptides or proteins. But low molecular weight substances can also produce specific immunological reactions in the airways (see List of allergens). Some of the low molecular weight respiratory allergens are also contact allergens.

The allergic reactions of the airways and conjunctiva which take the form of bronchial asthma or rhinoconjunctivitis mostly involve reaction of the allergen with specific IgE antibodies and belong to the manifestations of immediate type. However, in the deeper airways they can also first appear after a delay of several hours. Exogenous allergic alveolitis is induced generally by allergen-specific immune complexes of IgG

List of MAK and BAT Values 2008. DFG, Deutsche Forschungsgemeinschaft

ISBN: 978-3-527-32305-0

type and by cell-mediated reactions. Allergic reactions of immediate type can also cause systemic reactions and even anaphylactic shock.

The development of allergies of the respiratory passages, like that of contact allergies, is dependent on a number of factors. In addition to the substance-specific potential for causing sensitization, the amount of the allergen, the exposure period and the genetically determined disposition of the exposed person play a decisive role. Factors which increase the sensitivity of the mucosa may play a role in predisposing a person to allergy; they may be genetically determined or acquired, for example, during infections or exposure to irritant substances. Particular attention should be drawn to atopic diathesis which is characterized by an increased susceptibility to atopic eczema (neurodermatitis) or to allergic rhinitis and allergic bronchial asthma and is often associated with increased IgE synthesis.

In addition, there are also a number of relatively rare disorders of quite different kinds which are immunologically induced and so belong with the allergic phenomena such as, for example, manifestations involving granuloma formation (e.g. berylliosis) and certain exanthematous skin disorders.

A number of substances only induce the formation of antigens and then contact sensitization when they have previously been put into an energetically excited state by the absorption of light (photocontact sensitization, "photoallergization"). Likewise, many other substances can cause a skin reaction after exposure to light but without proof of an immunological mechanism (phototoxicity). Differentiation between phototoxicity and immunological photocontact sensitization can be difficult, as the classical factors that distinguish between (photo)allergic and (photo)toxic effects are not always found. In Anglo-American usage the expression "photosensitization" is used for both mechanisms. Although photocontact sensitization and phototoxicity involve primarily the physical activation (photosensitization) of a chromophore, both types of reactions are in principle clinically and diagnostically distinguishable.

It is still not possible to determine (and document scientifically) generally applicable threshold concentrations either for the induction of an allergy (sensitization) or for triggering the allergic reaction in an already sensitized person. The likelihood of induction increases with the concentration of the allergen to which persons are exposed. The concentrations required for the triggering of acute symptoms are generally lower than those required for sensitization. Even when MAK values are observed, the induction or triggering of an allergic reaction cannot be excluded with any certainty.

Sensitizing substances are indicated in the List of MAK and BAT Values in the column "H;S" by "Sa" or "Sh". This designation refers only to the organ or organ system in which the allergic reaction is manifested. The pathological mechanism producing the symptoms is not taken into account. "Sh" designates substances which can cause allergic reactions of the skin and the mucosa close to the skin (skin-sensitizing substances). The designation "Sa" (substances causing airway sensitization) indicates that a sensitization can involve symptoms of the airways and also of the conjunctiva, and that other effects associated with reactions of immediate type are also possible. These include systemic effects (anaphylaxis) and local effects on the skin (urticaria). The latter reactions only result in the additional designation with "Sh" when the skin symptoms are relevant under workplace conditions. Substances which increase photosensitivity in exposed persons by mechanisms not involving immune reactions (e.g. furocoumarins) are not separately designated. On the other hand, substances which cause photocontact sensitization are designated with "SP" (e.g. bithionol). Separate

criteria for their evaluation are not necessary because, in essence, the criteria for the evaluation of substances causing contact sensitization may be applied.

Some substances can cause local or systemic reactions the symptoms of which are entirely or largely identical to those of allergic reactions but which do not involve specific immunological mechanisms; they involve, e.g., the release of various mediators by mechanisms which are not immunological. These reactions are not a result of antigen-antibody interactions and can therefore also appear on the very first contact with the substance. Such reactions are induced, e.g., by sulfites, by benzoic acid and acetylsalicylic acid and their derivatives and by a variety of dyes such as tartrazine. Such substances are not designated with an "S". However, attention is drawn to their potential for producing such non-immunological reactions in the documentation and in some cases in the List of MAK and BAT Values as well.

The criteria which are used in the evaluation of substances causing contact and airway sensitization are described below.

a. Criteria for the assessment of contact allergens

The allergological evaluation is based on a variety of information which must be seen as providing different qualities of evidence.

1) **Sufficient evidence** of an allergenic effect is provided by valid results from **either** i) **or** ii):

i) effects in man
- studies in which numerous clinically relevant cases of sensitization (i.e. association of symptoms and exposure) were observed in tests with large collectives of patients in at least two independent centres, or
- epidemiological studies which reveal a relationship between sensitization and exposure, or
- case reports of clinically relevant sensitization (association of symptoms and exposure) for more than one patient from at least two independent centres

or

ii) results of animal studies
- at least one positive result in an animal study without adjuvant carried out according to accepted guidelines, or
- positive results from at least two less well-documented animal studies carried out according to accepted guidelines, one of which did not use adjuvant.

2) An allergenic effect can be considered **probable** on the basis described in i) **and** ii) below:

i) effects in man
- studies in which numerous clinically relevant cases of sensitization (association of symptoms and exposure) were observed in tests in just one centre, or

  - studies in which numerous cases of sensitization without details of clinical relevance were observed in tests with large collectives of patients in at least two independent centres

and

ii) results of animal studies
  - a positive result in an animal study with adjuvant carried out according to accepted guidelines, or
  - positive results from in vitro studies, or
  - evidence from structural considerations based on sufficiently valid results for structurally closely related compounds.

3) An allergenic effect is **not sufficiently documented**, but also not excluded, when only the data listed below are available:

- insufficiently documented case reports, or
- only one positive result in an animal study with adjuvant carried out according to accepted guidelines, or
- positive results in animal studies which were not carried out according to accepted guidelines, or
- evidence from studies of structure-effect-relationships or from *in vitro* studies.

Commentary:
Effects in man
The data obtained in numerous clinics and allergy centres from serial patch tests give us a useful picture of the frequency of skin sensitization and of the practical importance of the individual contact allergens. In contrast, useful results of reliable epidemiological studies are available for only few allergens.

The allergens which are observed most frequently, e.g., nickel, are not always the most potent sensitizers. On the other hand, very strongly sensitizing substances such as 2,4-dinitrochlorobenzene play quantitatively only a small role because only a small number of persons have sufficiently intensive contact with them. A number of highly potent contact allergens have been identified from clinical observations obtained in only a few patients, often after the first and only exposure (sometimes even after the first patch test). Examples of such substances are chloromethylimidazoline, diphenylcyclopropenone, quadratic acid diethyl ester, *p*-nitrobenzoyl bromide. For such exceptional substances, given proper scientific data, the evidence could be considered as 'probable' (category a2) even when the data come from just one centre.

The results of use tests in man with substances found at the workplace – often internal studies of the producing company – are of considerable value when they are carried out properly. Nowadays, the use of experimental sensitization tests must be rejected for ethical reasons, but historical results can be of importance in the evaluation of a substance.

Results of animal studies
Animal studies to determine the potential of a substance to cause allergic sensitization are carried out mainly with guinea pigs. These tests can be carried out with or without the use of Freund's complete adjuvant (FCA). The most frequently used methods are

the maximization test of Magnusson and Kligman (with FCA), the Buehler test (without FCA) and the open epicutaneous test (without FCA). The methods with FCA are generally more sensitive and their use can therefore occasionally result in overrating of the risk of sensitization. For this reason, a positive result in a test without adjuvant is considered to be better evidence than a positive result in one with adjuvant.

The tests with experimental animals generally yield useful data; that is, for most substances they have yielded results in agreement with the data obtained in man. One advantage of the experimental animal methods is that dose-response relationships can be studied. Sensitization tests can also be carried out with mice. These methods, especially the local lymph node assay (LLNA), are being used increasingly and are included in the evaluation of sensitizing effects in the category of tests without adjuvant.

Substances to which people have not yet been exposed or known to be exposed (e. g. because they have been newly synthesized or are newly available products) and for which, therefore, clinical data cannot be available (neither negative nor positive results of clinical observations can be applied as a criterion) can also be classified as probably sensitizing (category a2) simply on the basis of positive results from animal studies with adjuvant carried out according to accepted guidelines. Even positive results from animal studies not carried out according to accepted guidelines can be accepted, provided the methods used were plausible and theoretical chemical structural considerations indicate that the substance is so closely related to known allergens that it may be expected to have analogous properties.

Theoretical considerations require practical confirmation; therefore they are generally of less importance in the final evaluation and cannot be the only criterion for a potential sensitizing effect in the absence of other clinical or experimental data.

b. Criteria for the evaluation of respiratory allergens

The kinds of data which may be used in the evaluation of respiratory allergens are listed below; here too the different kinds of data provide different qualities of evidence.

1) Sufficient evidence of allergenic effects of a substance in the airways or the lungs is provided by valid data from:

   - studies or case reports of a specific hyperreactivity of the airways or the lungs which are indicative of an immunological mechanism from more than one patient and at least two independent testing centres. In addition, the (clinical) symptoms or adverse effects on the function of the upper or lower airways or the lungs must be shown to be associated with the exposure to the substance.

2) An allergenic effect can be considered probable on the basis of the results listed below:

   - one single case report of a specific hyperreactivity of the airways or the lungs

   and

   - other indications of sensitizing effects, e.g., a close structure-effect relationship with known airway allergens.

3) An allergenic effect is not sufficiently documented, but also not excluded, when only the data listed below are available:
   - epidemiological studies which demonstrate an increased incidence of symptoms or impaired function in exposed persons, or
   - studies or case reports of a specific hyperreactivity of the airways or the lungs in only one patient, or
   - studies or case reports of sensitization (e.g. detection of IgE) without accompanying symptoms or impairment of function causally associated with the exposure, or
   - positive results of animal studies, or
   - structure-effect relationships with known respiratory allergens.

Commentary:
Generally the classification is based on the results of epidemiological studies. Case reports do not always withstand critical examination, not least because of the difficulty or impossibility of carrying out adequate control studies. This is particularly true of inhalation-provocation tests. In addition, it is not always possible to produce adequate exposure data.

Symptoms are usually not a sufficient criterion for the designation of a substance as a respiratory allergen; generally it is necessary to demonstrate sensitization and record objective changes such as exposure-related impairment of lung function or bronchial hyperreactivity to specific stimuli. An immunological mechanism can generally be recognized on the basis of *in vivo* (e.g. prick test) or in *vitro* test results, ideally by detection of a specific antibody after proved exposure.

For many substances, an immunological mechanism has not yet been demonstrated directly. Therefore indirect evidence of immunological mechanisms can also be taken into account in classification. These include:
- the existence of a latency period between the start of the exposure and the appearance of the first symptoms (sensitization period),
- the triggering of symptoms with low concentrations of the substance which do not cause symptoms in appropriate controls,
- occasional delayed reactions or sequential immediate and delayed reactions (dual reactions) in the inhalation-provocation test,
- associated cutaneous symptoms such as urticaria or Quincke's oedema.

An allergenic effect is not sufficiently documented, but also not excluded, when evidence of airway sensitization is available but the conditions described in the criteria are not fulfilled. In particular, epidemiological studies which demonstrate an increased incidence of symptoms or of impaired function in exposed persons (even with demonstrated dose-response relationships) do not provide sufficient evidence of sensitizing properties if no indications of a specific immunological mechanism are available. Likewise, studies or case reports which merely document workplace-related variations in lung function or bronchial hyperreactivity are not sufficient.

To date there is no thoroughly validated method to induce and detect respiratory allergies in an animal model.

In guinea pig models, sensitizing substances cause reactions like those seen in man. Antibody-mediated sensitization can be induced by inhalation or by intradermal, subcutaneous injection but, unlike in man, IgG antibodies play the main role. In these tests the respiratory hyperreactivity (respiration rate, tidal volume, respiratory minute volume, inhalation and exhalation times, exhalation rate) and the antibody levels are measured. In the mouse IgE test, the potential of a substance to cause sensitization in BALB/c mice is determined as a function of the increase in the level of total IgE but not, to date, as a function of substance-specific IgE.

With these models no observed effect levels (NOEL) can be established but it is questionable whether they apply for man. Systematic comparative tests have not yet been carried out.

To date, with few exceptions, validated sensitive and specific standard *in vitro* methods for detecting low molecular weight allergens of immediate type are not available.

c. Designation of a substance as an allergen

Whether or not it is necessary to designate a substance as an allergen in the List of MAK and BAT Values is determined on the basis of the available evidence of allergenic effects and, when possible, also on the basis of the expected levels of exposure.

- The substances characterized according to the criteria in Section IVa) or IVb) as belonging in Categories 1) or 2) are generally designated as allergens with "Sa", "Sh", "Sah" or "SP".
- Substances for which these criteria are fulfilled are also designated with an "S" when the observed sensitization is associated mainly with cofactors which are (only) relevant under workplace conditions (e.g. (previous) damage to the skin caused by chemical or physical agents).

- On the other hand, substances are not designated with an "S" when
- in spite of extensive handling of the substance, very few (well-documented) cases of sensitization are observed, or
- the observed cases of sensitization are mainly associated with cofactors which are not relevant under workplace conditions (e.g. the presence of eczema on the lower leg), or
- the criteria of Section IVa) or IVb) resulted in classification of the substance in ★ category 3). This also includes substances for which a positive result was obtained in a study with experimental animals using adjuvant (maximization test); at the same time, however, no case of contact sensitization in humans was observed despite relevant exposure. A substance is not designated with "Sa" if the reactions which occurred are caused by irritating or pharmacological effects, since these effects were taken into account in establishing a MAK value.

- Thus, in individual cases a designation which differs from the designation according to the EU regulations for hazardous substances is possible.

The criteria are to be seen as guidelines for an intelligible evaluation of the data but in certain special cases their strict application may not be obligatory.

d. List of allergens

The list below shows the substances in Section II a which are designated with Sa, Sh, Sah or SP. It does not claim to be a complete list of sensitizing substances and is subject to continual revision and extension.

Abietic acid [14] [514-10-3] (Sh)
Acrylamide [79-06-1] (Sh)
Acrylic acid *n*-butyl ester [141-32-2] (Sh)
Acrylic acid ethyl ester [140-88-5] (Sh)
Acrylic acid 2-ethylhexyl ester [103-11-7] (Sh)
Acrylic acid 2-hydroxyethyl ester [818-61-1] (Sh)
Acrylic acid hydroxypropyl ester (all isomers) [25584-83-2] (Sh)
Acrylic acid methyl ester [96-33-3] (Sh)
Acrylonitrile [107-13-1] (Sh)
Alkali persulfates (Sah)
Allyl glycidyl ether [106-92-3] (Sh)
o-Aminoazotoluene [97-56-3] (Sh)
2-Aminoethanol [141-43-5] (Sh)
3-Aminomethyl-3,5,5-trimethyl-cyclohexylamine
(Isophorone diamine) [2855-13-2] (Sh)
p-Aminophenol [123-30-8] (Sh)
Ammonium persulfate [7727-54-0] (Sah)
α-Amylase (Sa)
α-Amylcinnamaldehyde [122-40-7] (Sh)
Aniline [62-53-3] (Sh)
Animal hair, epithelia and other materials derived from animals (Sah)
Antibiotics
Benomyl [17804-35-2] (Sh)
1,2-Benzisothiazol-3(2*H*)-one [2634-33-5] (Sh)
Benzyl alcohol mono(poly)hemiformal [17] [14548-60-8] (Sh)
Beryllium [7440-41-7] and its compounds (Sah)
Bisphenol A [80-05-7] (SP)
Bisphenol A diglycidyl ether [1675-54-3] (Sh)
Bisphenol A diglycidyl methacrylate [1565-94-2] (Sh)
Bithionol [97-18-7] (SP)
Bromelain [9001-00-7] (Sa)
2-Bromo-2-nitro-1,3-propanediol [18] [52-51-7] (Sh)
1,4-Butanediol diacrylate [1070-70-8] (Sh)
1,4-Butanediol diglycidyl ether [2425-79-8] (Sh)
1,4-Butanediol dimethacrylate [2082-81-7] (Sh)
Butanone oxime [96-29-7] (Sh)
tert-Butyl acrylate [1663-39-4] (Sh)
p-*tert*-Butylcatechol [98-29-3; 27213-78-1] (Sh)

[14] An immunological genesis of the asthma often seen in persons working with materials containing abietic acid has not been proved.
[17] releases formaldehyde
[18] Use in metal-working fluids is not permitted: see TRGS 611.

n-Butyl glycidyl ether (BGE) [2426-08-6] (Sh)
tert-Butyl glycidyl ether [7665-72-7] (Sh)
n-Butyl methacrylate [97-88-1] (Sh)
p-tert-Butyl phenol [98-54-4] (Sh)
Butynediol [110-65-6] (Sh)
N-Carboxyanthranilic anhydride [118-48-9] (Sh)
Cellulases (Sa)
Cereal flour dusts (Sa)
 Rye
 Wheat
Chloroacetamide-*N*-methylol [2832-19-1] (Sh)
Chloroacetic acid methyl ester [96-34-4] (Sh)
m-Chloroaniline [108-42-9] (Sh)
★ p-Chloroaniline [106-47-8] (Sh)
p-Chloro-*m*-cresol [59-50-7] (Sh)
1-Chloro-2,4-dinitrobenzene [97-00-7] (Sh)
5-Chloro-2-methyl-2,3-dihydroisothiazol-3-one [26172-55-4] and
 2-Methyl-2,3-dihydroisothiazol-3-one [2682-20-4] mixture in ratio 3:1 (Sh)
Chlorothalonil [1897-45-6] (Sh)
Chlorpromazine (2-Chloro-10-(3-dimethylaminopropyl)phenothiazine)
 [50-53-3] (SP)
★ Chromium(III) compounds (Sh[22])
Chromium(VI) compounds (Sh)
Cinnamaldehyde [104-55-2] (Sh)
Cinnamyl alcohol [104-54-1] (Sh)
Cobalt and cobalt compounds: (Sah)
 Metallic cobalt [7440-48-4]
 Cobalt(II) carbonate [513-79-1]
 Cobalt(II) oxide [1307-96-6]
 Cobalt(II,III) oxide [1308-06-1]
 Cobalt(II) sulfate [10026-24-1] and similar salts,
 Cobalt(II) sulfide [1317-42-6]
Cyanamide [420-04-2] (Sh)
4,4'-Diaminodiphenylmethane [101-77-9] (Sh)
1,5-Diaminonaphthalene [2243-62-1] (Sh)
1,2-Dibromo-2,4-dicyanobutane [35691-65-7] (Sh)
3,4-Dichloroaniline [95-76-1] (Sh)
1,3-Dichloropropene (*cis* and *trans*) [542-75-6] (Sh)
Dicyclohexylcarbodiimide [538-75-0] (Sh)
Diethanolamine [28] [111-42-2] (Sh)
Diethylene glycol diacrylate [4074-88-8] (Sh)
Diethylene glycol dimethacrylate [2358-84-1] (Sh)

---

22 does not apply for chromium(III) oxide and similar poorly soluble chromium(III) compounds
28 Reaction with nitrosating agents can result in the formation of carcinogenic *N*-nitrosodiethanolamine, see Section III "Amines which form carcinogenic nitrosamines on nitrosation", p. 147.

Diethylenetriamine [111-40-0] (Sh)
Diglycidyl hexanediol [16096-31-4] (Sh)
Diglycidyl resorcinol ether [101-90-6] (Sh)
1,1-Dimethylhydrazine [34] [57-14-7] (Sh)
1,2-Dimethylhydrazine [34] [540-73-8] (Sh)
Dimethylol dihydroxyethyleneurea [1854-26-8] (Sh)
1,3-Dimethylol-5,5-dimethyl hydantoin [6440-58-0] (Sh)
Dispers blue 106/124 [68516-81-4; 15141-18-1] (Sh)
★ Disperse Orange 3 [730-40-5] (Sh)
★ Disperse Red 1 [2872-52-8] (Sh)
★ Disperse Red 17 [3179-89-3] (Sh)
★ Disperse Yellow 3 [2832-40-8] (Sh)
Disulfiram [29] [97-77-8] (Sh)
2,2'-dithiobis(*N*-methylbenzamide) [2527-58-4] (Sh)
Epichlorohydrin [106-89-8] (Sh)
5-Ethyl-3,7-dioxa-1-azabicyclo[3.3.0]octane (EDAO) [17] [7747-35-5] (Sh)
Ethylenediamine [107-15-3] (Sah)
Ethylene glycol dimethacrylate [97-90-5] (Sh)
Eugenol [97-53-0] (Sh)
Farnesol [4602-84-0] (Sh)
Formaldehyde [50-00-0] (Sh)
Formaldehyde condensation products with *p*-*tert*-butylphenol (low-molecular) (Sh)
Formaldehyde condensation products with phenol (low-molecular) (Sh)
Fragrance components
Geraniol [106-24-1] (Sh)
Glutaraldehyde [111-30-8] (Sah)
Glyceryl monothioglycolate [30618-84-9] (Sh)
Glycidyl trimethylammonium chloride [3033-77-0] (Sh)
Glyoxal [107-22-2] (Sh)
Gold [7440-57-5] and its inorganic compounds (Sh [45])
Hard metal containing tungsten carbide and cobalt (inhalable fraction) (Sah)
Hexahydrophthalic anhydride [85-42-7] (Sa)
1,6-Hexamethylene diisocyanate [822-06-0] (Sah)
Hexamethylenetetramine [100-97-0] (Sh)
1,6-Hexanediol diacrylate [13048-33-4] (Sh)
Hydrazine [302-01-2] (Sh)
Hydrazine hydrate [7803-57-8] and Hydrazine salts (Sh)
Hydroquinone [123-31-9] (Sh)
Hydroxycitronellal [107-75-5] (Sh)
2-Hydroxyethyl methacrylate [868-77-9] (Sh)
Hydroxylamine [7803-49-8] and its salts (Sh)
4-(4-Hydroxy-4-methyl pentyl)-3-cyclohexene-1-carboxaldehyde [31906-04-4] (Sh)
3-Iodo-2-propynyl butylcarbamate [55406-53-6] (Sh)

---

[34] no longer produced in Germany

[29] Reaction with nitrosating agents can result in the formation of carcinogenic *N*-nitrosodiethylamine, see Section III "Amines which form carcinogenic nitrosamines on nitrosation", p. 147.

[17] releases formaldehyde

[45] only soluble gold compounds

Isoeugenol [97-54-1] (Sh)
cis-Isoeugenol [5912-86-7]
trans-Isoeugenol [5932-68-3]
Isophorone diisocyanate [4098-71-9] (Sah)
4-Isopropylphenyl isocyanate [31027-31-3] (Sh)
D,L-Limonene [138-86-3] and similar mixtures (Sh)
D-Limonene [5989-27-5] (Sh)
L-Limonene [5989-54-8] (Sh)
Maleic anhydride [108-31-6] (Sah)
Manganous ethylenebis(dithiocarbamate) (Maneb) [12427-38-2] (Sh)
Merbromin [129-16-8] (Sh)
2-Mercaptobenzothiazole [149-30-4] (Sh)
Mercury (metallic mercury [7439-97-6] and inorganic mercury compounds) (Sh)
Mercury compounds, organic (Sh)
Methacrylic acid ethyl ester [97-63-2] (Sh)
Methacrylic acid 2-hydroxypropyl ester [923-26-2] (Sh)
Methacrylic acid methyl ester [80-62-6] (Sh)
N-Methyl-bis(2-chloroethyl)amine [51-75-2] (Sh)
N,N'-Methylene-bis(5-methyloxazolidine) [66204-44-2] (Sh)
4,4'-Methylene diphenyl diisocyanate (MDI) [101-68-8] (Sah)
Methyltetrahydrophthalic anhydride [11070-44-3] (Sa)
N-Methyl-2,4,6-*N*-tetranitroaniline (Tetryl) [479-45-8] (Sh)
Methyl vinyl ketone [78-94-4] (Sh)
Monomethylhydrazine [60-34-4] (Sh)
Naled [300-76-5] (Sh)
1,8-Naphthalic anhydride [81-84-5] (Sh)
1,5-Naphthylene diisocyanate [3173-72-6] (Sa)
Natural rubber latex [9006-04-6] (Sah)
Nickel and nickel compounds:[57] (Sah)
Metallic nickel [7440-02-0]
Nickel acetate [373-02-4] and similar soluble salts,
Nickel carbonate [3333-67-3]
Nickel chloride [7718-54-9]
Nickel dioxide [12035-36-8]
Nickel hydroxide [12054-48-7]
Nickel monoxide [1313-99-1]
Nickel sesquioxide [1314-06-3]
Nickel subsulfide [12035-72-2]
Nickel sulfate [7786-81-4]
Nickel sulfide [16812-54-7]
Nickel alloys (Sah)
4-Nitro-4'-aminodiphenylamine-2-sulfonic acid [91-29-2] (Sh)

[57] Regarding compounds which have been found to be unequivocally carcinogenic in man, see *Toxikologisch-arbeitsmedizinische Begründung von MAK-Werten*, available from the publisher: WILEY-VCH, D-69451 Weinheim.

4-(2-Nitrobutyl)morpholine [2224-44-4] (70% w/w) and
4,4'-(2-Ethyl-2-nitro-1,3-propanediyl)bismorpholine [1854-23-5]
(20% w/w) (mixture)[60, 18] (Sh)
p-Nitrocumene [1817-47-6] (Sh)
2-Nitro-*p*-phenylenediamine [5307-14-2] (Sh)
Oakmoss extracts (Sh)
2-Octyl-4-isothiazolin-3-one [26530-20-1] (Sh)
Olaquindox (*N*-(2-Hydroxyethyl)-3-methyl-2-quinoxalinecarboxamide
1,4-dioxide) [23696-28-8] (SP)
Palladium chloride [7647-10-1] and other bioavailable palladium(II) compounds (Sh)
Papain [9001-73-4] (Sa)
Pentaerythritol triacrylate [3524-68-3] (Sh)
o-Phenylenediamine [95-54-5] (Sh)
★ m-Phenylenediamine [108-45-2] (Sh)
p-Phenylenediamine [64] [106-50-3] (Sh)
Phenyl glycidyl ether (PGE) [122-60-1] (Sh)
Phenylhydrazine [100-63-0] (Sh)
Phenyl isocyanate [103-71-9] (Sah)
N-Phenyl-1-naphthylamine [90-30-2] (Sh)
Phthalic anhydride [85-44-9] (Sa)
Phytases (Sa)
Picric acid [88-89-1] (Sh)
Picryl chloride [88-88-0] (Sh)
Piperazine [65,66] [110-85-0] (Sah)
Platinum compounds (Chloroplatinates) (Sah)
"Polymeric MDI" [9016-87-9] (Sah)
Pyrethrum [71] [8003-34-7] (Sh)
Quinone [106-51-4] (Sh)
Resorcinol [108-46-3] (Sh)
Ricinus protein (Sa)
Rosin (colophony)[73] [8050-09-7] (Sh)
Rubber [9006-04-6] components
Dithiocarbamates (Sh)
p-Phenylenediamine compounds (Sh)

---

60 In this mixture formaldehyde can be released and nitrosamines formed.

18 Use in metal-working fluids is not permitted: see TRGS 611.

64 The "Ursol-Asthma" which used to be observed frequently, especially in persons dyeing furs with *p*-phenylenediamine, has not been demonstrated unequivocally to involve respiratory allergy to *p*-phenylenediamine; see *Toxikologisch-arbeitsmedizinische Begründung von MAK-Werten* (18th issue, 1992) and in English translation in *Occupational Toxicants* Volume 6, VCH-Verlagsgesellschaft mbH, Weinheim 1994

65 Reaction with nitrosating agents can result in the formation of carcinogenic *N,N'*-dinitrosopiperazine, see Section III "Amines which form carcinogenic nitrosamines on nitrosation", p. 147.

66 Use in metal-working fluids is restricted: see TRGS 611.

71 does not apply for the constituents of insecticides (pyrethrins and cinerins) or for synthetic derivatives (pyrethroids) but only for the constituents of the plant drug and its crude extracts, including α-methylene sesquiterpene lactones (e.g. pyrethrosin)

73 An immunological genesis of the asthma often seen in persons working with materials containing rosin has not been proved.

Thiazoles (Sh)
Thiurams (Sh)
Sesquiterpene lactones (Sh)
Alantolactone [546-43-0]
Anthecotulide [23971-84-8]
Arteglasin A [33204-39-6]
Carabrone [1748-81-8]
Costunolide [553-21-9]
Dehydrocostus lactone [477-43-0]
(+)-Frullanolide and (−)-Frullanolide [40776-40-7; 27579-97-1]
Helenalin [6754-13-8]
Isoalantolactone [470-17-7]
Lactucin [1891-29-8]
Laurenobiolide [35001-25-3]
Parthenin [508-59-8]
Parthenolide [20554-84-1]
α-Peroxyachifolide [134954-21-5]
Pyrethrosin [28272-18-6]
Sodium diethyldithiocarbamate [29] [148-18-5] (Sh)
Soya bean constituents (Sa)
Subtilisins (Sa)
★ Tall oil, distilled [8002-26-4] (Sh [77])
Tetraethylene glycol diacrylate [17831-71-9] (Sh)
Tetraethylene glycol dimethacrylate [109-17-1] (Sh)
Tetrahydrofurfuryl methacrylate [2455-24-5] (Sh)
Thimerosal [54-64-8] (Sh)
Thiourea [62-56-6] (Sh SP)
Thiram [32] [137-26-8] (Sh)
Toluene-2,4-diamine [95-80-7] (Sh)
Toluene-2,5-diamine [95-70-5] (Sh)
Toluenediisocyanate: (Sa)
Toluene-2,4-diisocyanate [584-84-9]
Toluene-2,6-diisocyanate [91-08-7]
p-Toluidine [106-49-0] (Sh)
Triethylene glycol diacrylate [1680-21-3] (Sh)
Triethylene glycol dimethacrylate [109-16-0] (Sh)
Triethylenetetramine [112-24-3] (Sh)
Triisobutyl phosphate [126-71-6] (Sh)
Trimellitic anhydride [552-30-7] (Sa)
Trimethylolpropane triacrylate [15625-89-5] (Sh)
2,4,6-Trinitrotoluene [118-96-7] (Sh)
Triphenyl phosphine [603-35-0] (Sh)

---

[29] Reaction with nitrosating agents can result in the formation of carcinogenic *N*-nitrosodiethylamine, see Section III "Amines which form carcinogenic nitrosamines on nitrosation", p. 147.

[77] only applies to tall oil distillates containing abietic acid, see also *Toxikologisch-arbeitsmedizinische Begründung von MAK-Werten* (34th issue 2002)

[32] Reaction with nitrosating agents can result in the formation of carcinogenic *N*-nitrosodimethylamine, see Section III "Amines which form carcinogenic nitrosamines on nitrosation", p. 147.

Tripropylene glycol diacrylate [42978-66-5] (Sh)
N,N',N''-Tris(β-hydroxyethyl)-hexahydro-1,3,5-triazine [4719-04-4] (Sh)
Turpentine [8006-64-2] (Sh)
Vinylcarbazole [1484-13-5] (Sh)
Woods
Acacia melanoxylon R.Br., Australian blackwood (Sh)
Brya ebenus DC., cocus wood (Sh)
Chlorophora excelsa (Welw.) Benth. & Hook, iroko, kambala (Sh)
Dalbergia latifolia Roxb., East Indian rosewood, Bombay blackwood (Sh)
Dalbergia melanoxylon Guill. et Perr., African blackwood (Sh)
Dalbergia nigra Allem., Brazilian rosewood (Sh)
Dalbergia retusa Hemsl., cocobolo, rosewood (Sh)
Dalbergia stevensonii Standley, Honduras rosewood (Sh)
Distemonanthus benthamianus Baill., ayan (Sh)
Grevillea robusta A. Cunn., Australian silky oak (Sh)
Khaya anthotheca C.DC., African mahogany (Sh)
Machaerium scleroxylon Tul., pao ferro, Santos rosewood (Sh)
Mansonia altissima A.Chev., mansonia, pruno, bété (Sh)
Paratecoma peroba (Record) Kuhlm., ipe peroba (Sh)
Tectona grandis L.f., teak (Sh)
Terminalia superba Engl. & Diels, fraké, limba, afara, white afara (Sa)
Thuja plicata (D.Don.) Donn., western red cedar, giant arborvitae, shinglewood (Sah)
Triplochiton scleroxylon K.Schum., obeche, wawa, African whitewood (Sah)
Xylanases [37278-89-0] (Sa)
m-Xylylenediamine [1477-55-0] (Sh)
Zinc chromate [13530-65-9] (Sh)
Zirconium [7440-67-7] and its insoluble compounds (Sah)
Zirconium, soluble compounds (Sah)

e. Evaluation of members of specific groups of substances

For numerous substances, a reliable evaluation of the sensitizing effects according to the criteria described above is not possible. Often the substance of interest is one of the many members of a specific group of substances. Valid data for man are generally available only for individual members of such groups of substances, those considered to be typical of the group and commercially available as test substances because they are used for this purpose. With other less frequently used substances or substances for which no reliable data as to the extent of their use is available, patch tests are carried out relatively rarely, with some substances – because of the danger of sensitization – only in special cases. The effects in man are made even more difficult to assess because these substances are often used in mixtures with other members of the same group of substances and so can be involved in concomitant sensitizations and in cross-reactions. Mixtures containing members of other groups of allergenic substances are also often used and then too it is not readily possible to determine the causality of the observed disorder. In addition, it is not always possible to establish all the components of the mixture involved and so an allergologically relevant component can be missed.

Therefore, substances which are not listed in the List of MAK and BAT Values and which belong to groups of substances known to be able to cause sensitization should be handled with appropriate care.

It is emphasized that in general there is no danger of sensitization from fully polymerized plastics. A danger of sensitization, but only little, can result from release of residual monomer, e. g. during mechanical processing.

The groups of substances of which numerous members have sensitizing effects on the skin or airways include:

- acrylates and methacrylates
- dicarboxylic acid anhydrides
- diisocyanates
- glycidyl compounds (epoxides)
- dusts containing enzymes
- certain plant or animal proteins

In current usage, the general expression "**isocyanate**" is used for both monoisocyanates and di- or polyisocyanates. These classes of compounds must be strictly differentiated with regard to the areas of use as well as the toxicological and allergological properties: monoisocyanates such as methyl isocyanate or phenyl isocyanate are used practicallyalmost exclusively during syntheses as precursors or intermediate products, for example in the production of insecticides or pesticides. On the other hand, diisocyanates in particular are used in the production of polyurethanes, which are processed to adhesives, insulating foams, lacquers, and foams. Findings of a sensitizing effect on the respiratory tract in humans are available almost only for diisocyanates because of the widespread use. Also monoisocyanates can have a marked irritating effect on the airways and a sensitizing effect on the respiratory tract cannot be excluded. However, data for the diisocyanates, which are assessed as potent respiratory allergens, does not justify classifying monoisocyanates as substances causing airway sensitization solely in analogy; an evaluation of the individual case is necessary.

The **antibiotics** are a group of substances which are very heterogeneous in chemical structure and in sensitizing effects. Persons may be exposed to these substances at work during isolation or production of the active principles, during preparation and packing of the medicines, and during their medical use in man and animals. Sensitization of the skin can result in the development of haematogenic contact dermatitis after later parenteral use. Sensitization of the airways and allergic contact dermatitis have often been reported in persons exposed occupationally to β-lactam antibiotics (especially penicillins and cephalosporins). Allergic reactions after medicinal use of these antibiotics (enteral or parenteral), on the other hand, generally take the form of IgE-mediated reactions of immediate type. However, other immunological reactions such as medicinal skin eruptions and, in serious cases, also *erythema exsudativum multiforme*, Stevens-Johnson syndrome or Lyell's syndrome can also develop. Some of the aminoglycoside antibiotics are also conspicuous for the relatively high rates of sensitization which they produce, especially as a result of application of medicaments to (chronically) eroded skin. Sensitization of the skin resulting from occupational contact with aminoglycosides has been reported more rarely. Individual macrolide antibiotics, especially those used in veterinary medicine, can cause

immunological reactions in the airways and also (inhalation-mediated) contact dermatitis. Only rare individual cases of contact allergy or allergic airway reactions to most other macrolide antibiotics and to polyene or peptide antibiotics and tetracyclines have been reported.

Components of fragrance mixtures, another group of substances which differ widely in their structures, allergenic potencies and clinical significance, must also be evaluated individually. This becomes clear even on consideration of the components of the standard fragrance test mixture. For many other fragrance components the clinical findings are inadequate because the substances are never or only very rarely used in patch tests. Non-occupational exposure to these practically ubiquitous fragrance mixtures can rarely be excluded and this makes the demonstration that sensitization was occupational more difficult.

V Aerosols

a. General definitions

Aerosols are multiphase systems of particulate solids or liquids dispersed in gases, in particular in air. Aerosols which occur at the workplace include dusts, fumes and mists.

Dusts consist of particles of solid matter which have been produced in mechanical processes or have been stirred up and dispersed in gases, in particular in air.

Fibrous dusts consist of inorganic or organic fibres of certain dimensions dispersed in gases, in particular in air (see Section III Carcinogenic substances, Fibrous dust). Inorganic fibrous dusts arise during mechanical processing especially of fibrous minerals and of products made from or containing natural or artificial fibres. Fibre-shaped fragments of non-fibrous minerals and of non-fibrous products also count as fibrous dust. Fibres can also be released by erosion processes.

Fumes are dispersions of very finely divided solid matter in gases, in particular in air. They arise in thermal processes (e.g., welding fumes, metal (oxide) fumes, soot and flue ash) or chemical processes (e.g., the reaction of ammonia with hydrogen chloride).

Mists are dispersions of particulate liquids (droplets) in gases, in particular in air. They arise during nebulization of liquids, during condensation from the vapour phase and during chemical processes (e.g., oil mist, hydrogen chloride in damp air).

Ultrafine particles and their aggregates and agglomerates see Section Vh.

The **respirable dust fraction (R)** which can enter the alveoli and the **inhalable fraction (I)** of the dust are the fractions which are relevant for health and for these there are threshold values (see Section Vd).

b. Properties of aerosols which determine their effects

Particulate substances encountered at the workplace can cause disorders of the respiratory organs. These are mostly a result of overloading of the lung, or of carcinogenic, fibrotic (fibrogenic) or allergenic effects, or of chemical irritation or toxicity. The effects are determined in part by the site of deposition of inhaled particles or droplets in the respiratory tract. The deposition pattern of the particles or droplets and the intensity and rapidity of appearance of the effects are determined essentially by the size, shape, surface area, chemical composition, stability in the organism, and hygroscopic properties of the particles.

With all aerosols of ultrafine particles, an important role is played by the solubility, the large specific surface area and the uptake into the cells. These properties of ultrafine particles can result in other kinds of toxicologically relevant effects.

List of MAK and BAT Values 2008. DFG, Deutsche Forschungsgemeinschaft

ISBN: 978-3-527-32305-0

c. Inhalation, deposition and clearance of aerosols in the respiratory tract

Uptake

The uptake of dusts and fumes into the body takes place mostly via the airways. Mists can also be taken up in relevant amounts through the skin.

Transport and deposition of particulate solids and droplets in the airways are determined by the size, shape and density of the particles or droplets.

The distribution of the inhaled aerosol within the various parts of the airways is affected not only by the properties of the particles but also markedly by:

1. individual breathing habits, especially the different transition from nasal to oral breathing during physical activity and differences in respiration rate, respiratory flow and thus respiratory volumes,
2. morbid changes in the respiratory organs (e.g. obstructive airway disease caused by tobacco smoking, catarrhal infections, etc.),
3. individual differences in the anatomy of the airways.

The critical dimension for aerosol particles > 0.5 µm is the **aerodynamic diameter** (d_{ae}). The aerodynamic diameter of a particle whatever its shape and density is defined as the geometric diameter of a sphere with the density 1 g/cm^3 which sediments at the same rate as the particle in still or laminarly flowing air. This definition also applies for fibrous particles. The aerodynamic diameter of a fibre is determined essentially by the diameter of the fibre and less by its length. For long fibres ($l \gg d$) the aerodynamic diameter is about three times the fibre diameter.

For isometric particles with diameters less than 0.5 µm, the **diffusion-equivalent diameter** (d_D) determines the site of deposition in the airways. The diffusion-equivalent diameter of a particle is defined as the geometric diameter of a sphere which diffuses at the same rate as the particle in the same dispersion medium (at the workplace, in air).

On principle, it is necessary to distinguish between the aerosol fractions which e n t e r the various regions of the airways during inhalation and exhalation and the parts of these fractions which a r e d e p o s i t e d in these airway regions.

Deposition can take place during inhalation or during exhalation. Some of the inhaled particles are not deposited in the airways but are exhaled.

Of particular importance for occupational health are the aerosol fractions which penetrate into the respiratory organs and are deposited there; they are described below (Figure 1).

Only a fraction of the total particles present in the breathing zone (the part designated as the **inhaled fraction**) is inhaled. It is determined by the flow rates into the mouth and nose as well as the conditions of air flow around the head. Whereas almost all the smaller particles (d_{ae} < 5 µm) are inhaled, the fraction of particles which can be inhaled decreases with increasing particle size.

Of the particles in the inhaled fraction, larger solid particles and droplets (d_{ae} > 15 µm) are deposited almost exclusively in the extrathoracic region, i.e., in the region of the nose, pharynx and larynx.

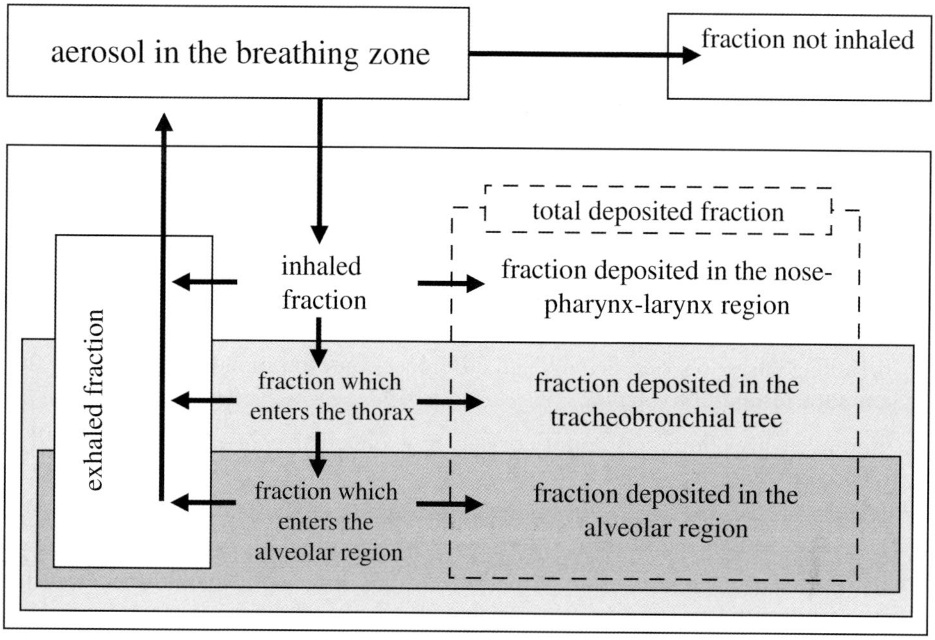

Figure 1. Subdivision of the aerosol in the breathing zone according to occupational medical criteria and deposition behaviour of the fractions.
The transfer of the inhaled fraction of the aerosol in the breathing zone into the thorax and the alveolar region, i.e., the alveoli, the non-ciliated bronchioles and the alveolar ducts, is represented by arrows. The arrows pointing to the right show the fractions deposited in the three regions of the respiratory tract, those pointing to the left show the contribution from these regions to the exhaled fraction.

Of the **fraction which enters the thorax (thoracic fraction)** some of the smaller solid particles and droplets are deposited in the tracheobronchial region or in the alveolar region.

The **fraction which enters the alveolar region (respirable fraction)** contains those particles which can penetrate into the airway regions which are not ciliated, i.e., the alveoli, the non-ciliated bronchioles and the alveolar ducts; some of this fraction is deposited there.

Deposition and Clearance

Fraction deposited in the nose-pharynx-larynx region (extrathoracic fraction)

This is the aerosol fraction which is deposited after inhalation in the region of the nose, the mouth, the throat and the larynx; part of this fraction can be swallowed and so enter the digestive tract. The clearance from this region of the respiratory tract is complete within a few hours at most.

Fraction deposited in the tracheobronchial region

This is that part of the fraction which enters the thorax which is deposited in the region of the tracheobronchial tree in which the mucociliary clearance mechanism operates.

Isometric particles with diameters > 7 µm are completely eliminated from the tracheobronchial region of a healthy person within one day. There is evidence that some of

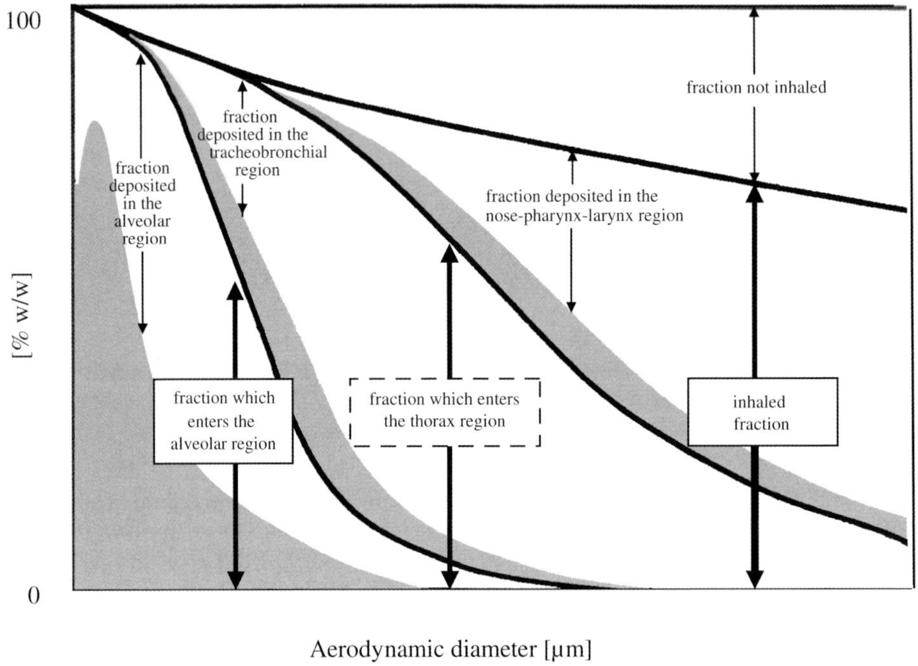

Figure 2. Diagram showing the fractions of the aerosol in the respiratory organs which are relevant for occupational health. Alongside the curves for the fractions deposited in the various regions, the fractions exhaled from those regions are shown as shaded areas. The two fractions in solid boxes are those corresponding to the conventions for measuring particle concentrations for checking the observance of MAK values (see Figure 3).

the smaller particles and especially ultrafine particles may persist for several weeks in the tracheobronchial region. The rate of transport out of this region decreases with decreasing particle size.

Fraction deposited in the alveolar region

This is the fraction of the aerosol which is deposited in the alveolar region including the non-ciliated bronchioles (*bronchioli respiratorii*) and the alveolar ducts (*ductuli alveolares*). In this region there is no mucociliary clearance. This aerosol fraction can be transferred via the pulmonary interstitial tissue (interstitium) into the lymphatic system and especially ultrafine particles can also enter the blood capillaries. Alveolar macrophages can take in particles by phagocytosis and transport these through the tracheobronchial tree; swallowing then transfers them into the digestive tract. The half-times for the elimination from the lung of insoluble particles deposited in the alveolar region are of the order of months or years.

Total deposited fraction

The total deposited fraction is that aerosol fraction which is inhaled and then not exhaled. This fraction includes the particles and droplets deposited in the nose, pharynx and larynx, the tracheobronchial tree and the non-ciliated deeper airways.

It should be remembered that deposited droplets and soluble particles spread on the surfaces of the respiratory organs and lose their droplet or particulate form. Soluble

components can be absorbed, which means that the constituents of the dissolved particles may be distributed and their cellular effects may no longer be only localized. They can enter the circulation and the lymphatic system and have systemic effects.

Insoluble components can be taken in by macrophages or bronchial epithelial cells by phagocytosis and transferred from the alveolar region into the interstitial tissue. Especially ultrafine particles can enter the bloodstream by this route.

Components which are neither dissolved nor absorbed can be removed from the tracheobronchial tree by mucociliary clearance and, like particles from the nose-pharynx-larynx region, are swallowed, enter the digestive system and perhaps have effects there.

d. Conventions for measuring concentrations of particles: definition of fractions

Measured particle concentrations should reflect the concentrations of those particles responsible for the pathogenic effects in the respiratory organs, as described in Section c. This requires that in sampling and assay devices the particles from the air are fractionated according to their aerodynamic diameters in a way which reflects the deposition pattern of the particles in the airways during breathing.

However, for measuring and sampling devices for the determination of various particle fractions in the workplace air, international conventions have been established for only three deposition curves (see DIN/EN 481, 1993).[89] They are based on average analytical values obtained under defined experimental conditions, values for the aerosol fractions which enter the various regions of the respiratory organs (Figure 3).

Thus the analytical methods yield data for the three fractions which may be deposited, in each case including the fraction which is exhaled. That means that the aerosol fractions determined are those which enter the regions of the lung which are relevant for occupational health (see Figures 1 and 2).

The use of this procedure for hygroscopic particles is justified by the fact that their aerodynamic diameters increase during transport into the respiratory organs as a result of uptake of water and that therefore the sites of deposition and proportion of particles deposited cannot be predicted.

The relationships between the fractions shown in Figure 3, defined for sampling purposes, and those shown in Figures 1 and 2, relevant for occupational health, are described below.

1. **Inhalable fraction (I):** the deposition curve expresses, as a function of aerodynamic diameter, the mean probability that particles and droplets will be inhaled (inhaled fraction).
2. **Thoracic fraction:** the curve for this part of the inhalable fraction expresses, as a function of aerodynamic diameter, the mean probability that particles and droplets will enter the tracheobronchial tree and the alveolar region (fraction which enters the thorax).

---

[89] European Committee for Standardization (CEN): *EN 481 Workplace atmospheres – Size fraction definitions for measurement of airborne particles*. Brussels 1993, Beuth Verlag, Berlin 1993

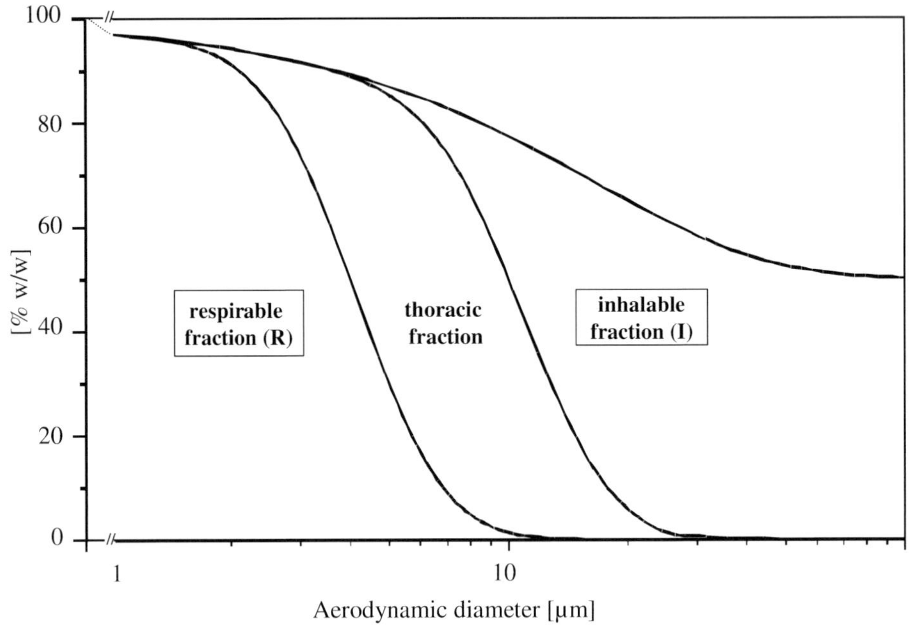

Figure 3. Deposition functions for the inhalable fraction, thoracic fraction and respirable fraction of the aerosol in the breathing zone, defined for the standardization of sampling devices. MAK values have been established to date only for the respirable and inhalable fractions (boxed in the figure).

3. **Respirable fraction (R):** the curve for this part of the thoracic fraction expresses, as a function of aerodynamic diameter, the mean probability that particles and droplets will enter the alveolar region (fraction which enters the alveolar region).
4. **Extrathoracic fraction:** this fraction is obtained by subtracting the thoracic fraction from the inhalable fraction.
5. **Tracheobronchial fraction:** this fraction is obtained by subtracting the alveolar fraction from the thoracic fraction.

The definitions of the "inhalable fraction" (I [90]) and "respirable fraction" (R [91]) correspond [92,93] to the definitions of **"total dust"** (G) and **"fine dust"** (F) used until 1996 in the establishment of MAK values.[94] Since 1996 the internationally accepted definitions have been used.

Notes:

[90] German: "E" for "Einatembare Fraktion"

[91] German: "A" for "Alveolengängige Fraktion"

[92] Health and Safety Executive, Health and Safety Laboratory, Project Report: *Pilot study of CEN Protocols for the Performance Testing of Workplace Aerosol Sampling Instruments* by L.C. Kenny. Sheffield, September 1995

[93] BIA-Arbeitsmappe *Messung von Gefahrstoffen. Expositionsermittlung bei chemischen und biologischen Einwirkungen*. Berufsgenossenschaftliches Institut für Arbeitssicherheit (BIA) (Ed.), Erich Schmidt Verlag

[94] DFG (1995): *List of MAK and BAT Values 1995*, Commission for the Investigation of Health Hazards of Chemical Compounds in the Work Area, Report No. 31, page 132, VCH Weinheim

Depending on the definition of the threshold value, for dusts and fumes either the inhalable fraction "I" or the respirable fraction "R" is determined. For mists, the inhalable fraction "I" is determined.

Sampling devices which sample fine dust according to the Johannesburg convention, which used to be used in Germany, fulfil the requirements of DIN/EN 481 for the sampling of respirable dust.

When sampling devices are used which collect fractions for assay according to deposition functions which differ from those described above, the results must be corrected using a correction factor which is dependent on the particle size distribution. The validity of the procedure must be documented.

It must be emphasized that the total dust fraction (G) which used to be determined in Germany and also the inhalable dust fraction (I) used today may not be automatically assumed to be equivalent to **"total dust"**, a term which is still widely found in the international literature. The term "total dust" does not describe a standardized dimension. Sampling devices which collect "total dust" must be validated.

The fractions PM_{10} and $PM_{2.5}$ collected during sampling of environmental air outdoors are defined by ISO 7708. PM_{10} corresponds to the thoracic fraction (function with 50% deposition at 10 μm) whereas $PM_{2.5}$ is described by a curve with 50% deposition at 2.5 μm.

For the determination of fibrous dusts, fractions are not defined according to aerodynamic criteria. Instead the fibre lengths and diameters must be determined microscopically (see Section III Carcinogenic substances, Fibrous dusts).

e. Fibrogenic aerosols

As **fibrogenic dusts** are designated aerosols, including droplet aerosols, which contain insoluble particles which can cause dust lung diseases (e.g. silicosis) involving formation of connective tissue. Prerequisite for the development of such disorders is the deposition of the aerosol in the alveolar region. Therefore the effective levels of fibrogenic aerosols are determined after sampling the respirable fraction (R) (previously "fine dust", (F)).

f. General threshold limit value for dust

The "general threshold value for dust" is established as a concentration of the respirable fraction (R) (previously "fine dust", (F)) of 1.5 mg/m^3 and a concentration of the inhalable fraction (I) (previously "total dust", (G)) of 4 mg/m^3.

Excursions above the threshold as described in Section Vg are permitted. The permitted excursions may not exceed the "general threshold value for dust" by a factor of more than two (see *Toxikologisch-arbeitsmedizinische Begründungen von MAK-Werten*, 25th issue, 1997, in English translation in *Occupational Toxicants* Volume 12).

Observance of the general threshold value for dust should prevent unspecific effects of dust (e.g. overloading effects) on the respiratory organs. The threshold applies for poorly soluble and insoluble dusts which are not subject to other regulations and for mixtures of dusts even when for individual components of a dust specific MAK values exist and are observed. The threshold value does not apply for soluble particles, especially not for salts from rock salt and potash deposits, or for ultrafine (see Section Vh) or dispersed coarse particle fractions.

Even when the general threshold value for dust is observed, a health hazard may be ruled out only if it has been demonstrated that genotoxic, carcinogenic, fibrogenic, allergenic or other toxic effects of the dust are not to be expected.

g. Exposures exceeding the MAK value

MAK values for aerosols which are designated with a reference to Section Vg ("Vg") have been derived from average long-term exposure levels without detectable effects (no observed adverse effect levels, NOAEL).

Impairment of respiratory organ function by these dusts is a result of long-term effects which are determined largely by the aerosol concentration to which the person is exposed over long periods of time. The MAK values correspond to the average long-term exposure levels without detectable effects (NOAEL) but apply to the concentration values averaged over a single shift. As the long-term exposure level is an average of variously high shift average levels, the occasional exceeding of the MAK value by single shift average levels can be tolerated. The permitted frequency and extent of the excursions above the MAK value are established on the basis of occupational medical and toxicological findings (see *Toxikologisch-arbeitsmedizinische Begründung von MAK-Werten*, 23rd issue, 1996 and in English in *Occupational Toxicants* Volume 11). In these cases the peak limitation categories do not apply.

For all other aerosols the peak limitation categories must be observed (see Section VI Limitation of exposure peaks).

h. Ultrafine particles, their aggregates and agglomerates

For the characterization of the potential danger associated with ultrafine particles (diffusion equivalent diameter < 100 nm) and their aggregates[95] and agglomerates,[96] the three facts listed below are of significance.

- The particles are formed mostly in combustion processes and gas phase reactions.
- The mechanisms of deposition in the respiratory tract involve the Brownian motion of the particles.
- The effects of the particles in the respiratory tract increase not so much in proportion to the weight as in proportion to the surface area or number of particles per air volume.

[95] aggregate: assemblage of primary particles or agglomerates which are loosely coherent (held together by adhesion)

[96] agglomerate: assemblage of primary particles rigidly joined together

VI Limitation of exposure peaks

MAK values are conceived and applied as 8-hour time-weighted average values. The actual concentrations of substances in the workplace air are, however, frequently subject to considerable variation. Excursions above the average value must be limited in order to prevent local irritation, unreasonable annoyance and adverse systemic effects.

The effects on health of exceeding the MAK value for brief periods depend decisively on the mode of action of the substance in question. Since the year 2000, substances have been assessed individually and substance-specific excursion factors (ratio of permitted short-term peak value to the MAK value) have been established. For substances in Category I, the MAK value may generally not be exceeded (excursion factor = 1 is the default value) unless the available data permit the establishment of a different excursion factor. For some substances excursion factors > 1 have been derived. For substances in Category II, the default value is 2. In this category too, in appropriate cases, other excursion factors have been established. For reasons of analytical practicability, peak values for the substances in these two categories have now been established for a sampling period of 15 minutes. For a discussion of the use of longer sampling periods see "Toxikologisch-arbeitsmedizinische Begründung von MAK-Werten".[1] The permitted frequency per shift of excursions above the MAK value, the minimum period between individual exposure peaks, and the total permitted duration of excursions above the MAK value are to be seen as a convention.

For all substances, however, the 8-hour time-weighted average value must be observed.[97]

This concept takes into account both the toxicological situation and the analytical practicability.

Thus the two categories shown in the table below have been established for the limitation of peak concentrations at the workplace.

Excursion factors, maximum duration of peaks, maximum number per shift and minimum interval between the peaks

	Category	Excursion factor	Duration	Number per shift	Interval ***
I	Substances for which local irritant effects determine the MAK value, also respiratory allergens	1*	15 min, average value**	4	1 h
II	Substances with systemic effects	2*	15 min, average value	4	1 h

* default value, or a substance-specific value (maximum 8)

** In certain cases, a momentary value (concentration which should not be exceeded at any time) can also be established.

*** only for excursion factors > 1

[1] obtainable from the publisher: WILEY-VCH, D-69451 Weinheim

[97] but see Section Vg

List of MAK and BAT Values 2008. DFG, Deutsche Forschungsgemeinschaft

ISBN: 978-3-527-32305-0

In Section IIa of the *List of MAK and BAT Values*, the Peak limitation category for each substance is listed and in brackets also the appropriate excursion factor. Carcinogenic substances without a MAK value have no entry (–) in this column.

A description of analytical methods for monitoring workplaces (*Analytische Methoden zur Prüfung gesundheitsschädlicher Arbeitsstoffe – Luftanalysen* and in English translation as *Analyses of Hazardous Substances in Air*)[1] has been published. Data for the individual substances may be found in the documentation of the MAK values.[1]

VII Percutaneous absorption

At the workplace the absorption of substances through the skin can make a significant contribution to the systemic exposure of the employee or can even be the main exposure route.

The only relevant barrier to absorption of substances at work is the horny layer (*stratum corneum*) of the skin. The ability of a substance to penetrate this barrier is determined by its physicochemical properties. The rate of dermal penetration is also affected by workplace conditions and by individual factors. Solid, liquid and gaseous substances can be taken up percutaneously. For many substances the skin acts as a depot from which absorption continues even after the end of exposure. Normal working clothes do not generally provide any protection against percutaneous absorption. Quantification of the amount of a substance absorbed through the skin can only be realized by biological monitoring (see Section XI Significance and Use of BAT Values – Surveillance).

Substances are designated with an “H” if through dermal exposure the observance of the MAK value on its own no longer guarantees the prevention of important adverse effects on health which were considered for establishment of the threshold value. In addition to systemic effects these can also include the sensitization of the respiratory tract if it has been demonstrated to be induced by skin contact. Substances are not designated with an “H” if toxic effects are not to be expected under workplace conditions, independent of the ability of the substance to penetrate the skin. It may not be assumed that the absence of a designation with “H” means that wearing inhalation protection is sufficient to adequately protect an employee from the substance if the MAK value can not be observed. Under these conditions, considerable absorption from the gas phase was detected, especially for amphiphilic substances. Substances in section IIb are dealt with in analogy to substances with MAK values and designated with “H” when a toxicologically relevant uptake can be assumed and one of the criteria for designation is fulfilled. Carcinogenic substances in Categories 1 and 2 and suspected carcinogens without a MAK value in Category 3 are designated with an “H” whenever it appears that dermal absorption can make a significant contribution to a person's body burden. For an assessment of the measures necessary for adequate occupational hygiene, the reader is referred to the documentation for the substance in question.

A substance is designated with an “H” when one of the criteria listed below is fulfilled.

[1] obtainable from the publisher: WILEY-VCH, D-69451 Weinheim

List of MAK and BAT Values 2008. DFG, Deutsche Forschungsgemeinschaft

ISBN: 978-3-527-32305-0

1. Designation with "H" on the basis of workplace studies
Field studies or scientifically documented casuistics demonstrate that percutaneous absorption is significant in practice in persons handling the substance:
The percutaneous absorption is certainly responsible for part of the systemic dose and can contribute to toxic effects.

2. Designation with "H" on the basis of animal studies
Percutaneous absorption can be demonstrated in animal studies and the exposure can contribute to toxic effects.

3. Designation with "H" on the basis of *in vitro* studies
A relevant level of percutaneous absorption which can contribute to toxic effects has been quantified with recognized methods. The flux through the skin has been determined and the permeability constant has been or may be calculated, or details of percentage absorption of the applied dose (percentage absorbed per unit of time and skin surface area) are available.

4. Designation with "H" on the basis of theoretical models
On the basis of data for analogous substances or calculations with mathematical models, a relevant level of percutaneous absorption may be expected.

The criteria 1 to 4 are arranged in order of decreasing significance; data obtained with exposed persons are most important.

The designation "H" is shown in the *List of MAK and BAT Values* in the column marked "H; S" and does not indicate that the substance can cause skin irritation.

VIII MAK values and pregnancy

Observance of the MAK values and BAT values does not guarantee, in every case, that the unborn child is reliably protected because numerous substances have not yet been investigated or have been only partially tested for prenatal toxicity.

Definition
The expression "prenatal toxicity" or developmental toxicity is taken in its broadest sense by the Commission; it includes any effect of the substance which elicits an alteration from the physiological norm in the development of the organism and leads to prenatal or postnatal death of the offspring or to permanent morphological or functional damage.

Effects in humans
Epidemiological studies that yield evidence of toxic effects of substances on the human embryo or foetus are of particular importance for the assessment. Because of the limitations of such studies, e.g. inadequate methods, low statistical power, exposures to mixtures of substances, personal factors and life styles, a clear statement as to substance-specific effects and effect thresholds is usually not possible.

List of MAK and BAT Values 2008. DFG, Deutsche Forschungsgemeinschaft

ISBN: 978-3-527-32305-0

Animal Studies

The evaluation of the developmental toxicity of substances is based mainly on animal studies. Studies which have been carried out according to internationally recognized testing guidelines such as OECD or similar test guidelines (e.g. EU, Japan) play a decisive role. The OECD Test Guideline 414 in particular is appropriate for the determination of prenatal toxicity. Testing for perinatal and postnatal toxicity, to a limited extent also for prenatal toxicity, is carried out in one-generation studies according to OECD Test Guideline 415, in two-generation studies according to OECD Test Guideline 416 or in screening tests according to OECD Test Guidelines 421 and 422. If studies are available that were not conducted according to these guidelines, their validity is to be determined individually. The most important criteria are a sufficiently large number of animals, the use of different dose groups with derivation of a NOAEL (no observed adverse effect level), in-depth studies (external, skeletal and visceral examinations of the foetuses in the developmental toxicity studies) and adequate documentation of the results.

Inhalation studies are of particular importance in assessment of the prenatal toxicity of substances present at the workplace. Also studies with oral administration or dermal application can be taken into consideration if the available data do not present evidence against extrapolation to inhalative administration (e.g. by a pronounced "first pass" effect). Studies carried out with routes of administration which are not relevant in humans (e.g. intraperitoneal) are not included in the evaluation as a rule.

Studies with an oral route of administration usually reach higher doses than those with inhalative or dermal application. For this reason effects are also reported which occur only in the high dose range. Therefore, the test guidelines mentioned consider 1000 mg/kg body weight to be the maximum dose to be tested (limit dose). Such high dose effects are mostly irrelevant for assessing prenatal toxicity at concentrations near the MAK value. Prenatal toxic effects which are observed in the presence of marked maternal toxicity are of low relevance for the situation at the workplace as they are prevented by observance of the MAK value. Findings at doses or concentrations at which no or only slight maternal toxicity is observed are of particular relevance.

The preferred animal species usually recommended in the test guidelines for prenatal developmental toxicity (OECD 414) are female rats and rabbits. The generation studies (e.g. OECD 415 and 416) including the screening tests (e.g. OECD 421 and 422) are usually carried out only with rats of both sexes.

To consider the factor of uncertainty in assessing animal studies, the margin between the NOAEL for developmental toxicity in animal studies and the resulting exposure level or body burden if the MAK or BAT value is observed must be adequate. The necessary margin depends on a number of very different factors:

- comparative toxicokinetic data for humans and animals
- toxicokinetic data for a substance in the dams and embryos or foetuses to evaluate differences in level of exposure between maternal and foetal organs/tissues
- If such data are not available, the evaluation of specific substance properties such as molecular size, lipid solubility and protein binding plays an important role; such data determine the transplacental transfer of the substance from the mother animal and the internal exposure of the embryos or foetuses.
- The kind and severity of the results observed are important factors. Serious effects such as the increased occurrence of specific malformations at doses not causing si-

multaneous maternal toxicity should receive more emphasis than rather unspecific or less severe foetotoxic effects such as slightly decreased foetal body weight or delayed skeletal maturation.

Thus, determination of an adequate margin is a substance-specific process which will result in documentations based on different justifications.

Pregnancy risk groups
Based on the criteria mentioned, the Commission is evaluating substances with MAK or BAT values as to whether prenatal toxic effects are unlikely when the MAK value or the BAT value is observed (Group C), whether, according to the currently available information, such effects must be expected (Group B) or whether they have been unequivocally demonstrated (Group A). For a number of substances, however, it is not yet possible to make a statement as to prenatal toxicity (Group D).

The following pregnancy risk groups are defined:

Group A: Damage to the embryo or foetus in humans has been unequivocally demonstrated and is to be expected even when MAK and BAT values are observed.

Group B: According to currently available information damage to the embryo or foetus must be expected even when MAK and BAT values are observed.

Group C: There is no reason to fear damage to the embryo or foetus when MAK and BAT values are observed.

Group D: Either there are no data for an assessment of damage to the embryo or foetus or the currently available data are not sufficient for classification in one of the groups A – C.

Substances without a MAK or BAT value (carcinogenic substances or substances included in Section IIb) have no entry (–) in this column.

IX Germ cell mutagens

Germ cell mutagens produce heritable gene mutations, and heritable structural and numerical chromosome aberrations in germ cells. The consequences of germ cell mutations in subsequent generations include genetically determined phenotypic alterations without signs of illness, reduction in fertility, embryonic or perinatal death, more or less severe congenital malformations, and genetic diseases with various degrees of health impairment. The term "germ cell mutagenicity" refers specifically to mutagenicity in male and female germ cells and is distinguished from mutagenicity in somatic cells which can initiate cancer.

Epidemiological studies, however, have been unable to provide any evidence as yet that exposure to chemicals or to radiation results in hereditary diseases in man. Although structural changes have been demonstrated in the chromosomes of the germ cells of men exposed to radiation, even this finding can only provide indirect evidence that such exposures could lead to hereditary disorders in the offspring. The proof that an increased

List of MAK and BAT Values 2008. DFG, Deutsche Forschungsgemeinschaft

ISBN: 978-3-527-32305-0

frequency of hereditary diseases is related to a particular exposure would be associated with great methodological difficulties. In the human population there are a large number of hereditary diseases of unknown origin with frequencies which differ widely in different subpopulations. Since mutational events occur largely randomly in the genome, it is not to be expected that one particular substance would induce one characteristic genetic disease. Therefore, it is most unlikely that proof of a causal relationship between exposure to a chemical and occurrence of heritable diseases will become available in the foreseeable future.

In this situation, for the identification of germ cell mutagens the results of animal experiments must be given particular attention. The mutagenic effect of chemicals on the germ cells of exposed parent animals can be demonstrated by observing an increased mutant frequency among the progeny. In addition, the demonstration of genotoxic effects of a substance in germ cells or somatic cells provides evidence of a potential hazard for subsequent generations.

The categories for classification of germ cell mutagens have been established in analogy to the categories for carcinogenic chemicals at the workplace.

1. Germ cell mutagens which have been shown to increase the mutant frequency in the progeny of exposed humans
2. Germ cell mutagens which have been shown to increase the mutant frequency in the progeny of exposed mammals

3A. Substances which have been shown to induce genetic damage in germ cells of humans or animals, or which produce mutagenic effects in somatic cells of mammals *in vivo* and have been shown to reach the germ cells in an active form

3B. Substances which are suspected of being germ cell mutagens because of their genotoxic effects in mammalian somatic cells *in vivo*; in exceptional cases, substances for which there are no *in vivo* data but which are clearly mutagenic *in vitro* and structurally related to known *in vivo* mutagens

4. not applicable (⁂)
5. Germ cell mutagens or suspected substances (according to the definition of Category 3A and 3B), the potency of which is considered to be so low that, provided the MAK value is observed, their contribution to genetic risk for man is expected not to be significant

(⁂) Category 4 carcinogenic substances are those with non-genotoxic mechanisms of action. By definition, germ cell mutagens are genotoxic. Therefore, a Category 4 for germ cell mutagens cannot apply. At some time in the future it is conceivable that a Category 4 could be established for genotoxic substances with primary targets other than the DNA (e.g. purely aneugenic substances) if research results make this seem sensible.

X Substances requiring special consideration

a. Organic peroxides

The inflammatory and caustic effects of organic peroxides on the skin and mucous membranes vary considerably. For some of these compounds, even very small amounts of very dilute solutions produce severe necrosis of the skin or the cornea, resulting in loss of eyesight. Inhalation of the vapours causes various degrees of irritation in the respiratory passages. In practice, the danger of systemic effects is low. Sensitizations of the immediate type have been observed after inhalation of these substances. With hydroperoxides and with certain peroxides contact sensitization may be expected as well.

A number of organic peroxides have produced mutagenic effects in *in vitro* tests. In addition, tumours have been produced in animal experiments with, e.g., diacetyl peroxide, *tert*-butyl peroxide, dilauroyl peroxide and α,α-dimethylbenzyl hydroperoxide.

Negligible or very weak effects on skin:	Di-*tert*-butyl peroxide	
	Dibenzoyl peroxide	(50 %)
	Dilauroyl peroxide	(50 %)
Moderate effects on skin:	*tert*-Butylhydroperoxide	
	tert-Butyl peracetate	(50 %)
Very severe effects on skin:	*α,α*-Dimethylbenzyl hydroperoxide (Cumene hydroperoxide)	
	Methyl ethyl ketone peroxide (2-Butanone peroxide)	(40 %)
	Cyclohexanone peroxide mixtures	(50 %)
	Dicyclohexyl peroxide	(50 %)
	Diacetyl peroxide	(30 %)
	Peracetic acid	(40 %)

b. Gasolines

The Commission could not agree to assign a MAK value to "gasolines" because this term describes a number of very different mixtures such as motor gasolines (petrol), special boiling point gasolines, white spirits and pyrolysis gasolines. The toxicity of gasolines depends primarily on their content of aromatic compounds (benzene, toluene, xylenes, ethyl benzene, cumene), which varies markedly with the production method.

Procedures suggested for establishing MAK values by the mathematical evaluation of the composition of such mixtures of liquid solvents must be rejected on principle because such calculations cannot provide information as to the actual concentrations in the workplace air. Only when results are available from studies with defined gasoline-vapour mixtures (see Section I) can the Commission make any concrete statements.

Levels of additives such as 1,2-dibromoethane and 1,2-dichloroethane must be evaluated independently (see these listings).

List of MAK and BAT Values 2008. DFG, Deutsche Forschungsgemeinschaft

ISBN: 978-3-527-32305-0

c. Metal-working fluids

Metal-working fluids are used to cool and/or lubricate metallic workpieces during cutting and shaping. They are subdivided into water-immiscible (ca. 60 %) and water-miscible (ca. 40 %) metal-working fluids. The water-immiscible fluids are used undiluted, whereas water-miscible fluids are used in concentrations of 1–20 % in water. Individual components may be present in both water-miscible and water-immiscible metal-working fluids.

Of importance in this context is the formation of nitrosamines in alkaline metal-working fluids which contain secondary amines and also formaldehyde (see Section III "Amines which form carcinogenic nitrosamines on nitrosation"). Such conditions are found, for example, in some metal-working fluids and so in these fluids the formation of significant levels of nitrosamines is possible. However, appropriate formaldehyde-releasers which do not contain or release nitrosatable compounds can, as a result of the bacteriostatic effects of the trace amounts of formaldehyde that they release, prevent the bacterial reduction of nitrate to nitrite and so inhibit nitrosamine formation. Because nitrogen oxides can also act as nitrosating agents and the nitrite concentration does not always correlate with the nitrosamine concentration, it is more reliable to determine the nitrosamines than the nitrites in metal-working fluids containing secondary amines (these do not comply with TRGS 611 unless Paragraph 3.4 applies). In particular, the absence of nitrite in a particular sample at a particular time does not exclude the possibility that nitrosamines are present. *N*-Nitroso-oxazolidines may be formed in small amounts from biocides which contain the necessary precursors (see documentation of MAK values[87] "Kühlschmierstoffe" (Metal-working fluids)).

In addition, a differentiation is made between petroleum-bearing and nonpetroleum-bearing metal-working fluids, and also between doped (additive type) and straight (no additive type) metal-working fluids.

The toxicological assessment of metal-working fluids is dependent on the composition and the type of components, which vary greatly in number and proportion according to the intended use. There are no fixed formulations. New components and compositions are to be expected with advancing technology.

When metal-working fluids are in use, it is possible for vapours and aerosols to pass into the air of the work area. To date, hardly any animal-experimental or epidemiological data are available for long-term effects following uptake in the lungs. It can, however, be assumed that the toxic effects on the whole organism after inhalation of mists and vapours, as well as the effects of liquids on the skin – in the sense of a toxic irritation or allergic sensitization – are mainly effects of the additives.

The mineral oil component alone is therefore not representative of the potential effect. The MAK value of 5 mg/m^3 previously established for pure mineral oil is, as a result, not applicable to present-day metal-working fluids since, as a rule, one is dealing with mixtures whose composition varies considerably according to the intended use. For this reason, it is not possible to establish a single MAK value for all types of metal-working fluids.

Since there is no regulation requiring declaration of components of metal-working fluids it is difficult to attain systematic registration. A list compiled according to the best

[87] *Toxikologisch-arbeitsmedizinische Begründung von MAK-Werten* and in English Translation in *Occupational Toxicants* Volumes 2, 5, 9, 10, 16, 20 available from the publisher: WILEY-VCH, D-69451 Weinheim

information available was published by the Commission in 1990 and brought up to date in 1994 and 2000.[98] This list includes substances having proved or suspected acute and/or chronic toxic effects or carcinogenic potential. There is also the possibility that carcinogenic or otherwise toxic substances be formed secondarily during technical use of metal-working fluids.

The list, which is subject to revision, should assist in the case to case assessment of the effects of metal-working fluids and in taking any necessary action for health protection.

The Commission prepares toxicological/occupational-medical reviews of individual components with the aim of making practicable recommendations, possibly in the form of MAK values.

Documentation has been published for the following substances:[98]

Abietic acid [514-10-3]
Alkyl benzenesulfonates C10–C14, linear [69669-44-9; 85117-50-6]
Alkyl ether carboxylic acids
2-(2-Aminoethoxy)ethanol [929-06-6]
2-Amino-2-ethyl-1,3-propanediol [115-70-8]
2-Amino-2-methyl-1-propanol [124-68-5]
1-Amino-2-propanol [78-96-6]
★ Aminotris(methylenephosphonic acid) [6419-19-8]
Behenic acid [112-85-6]
1,2-Benzisothiazol-3(2*H*)-one [2634-33-5]
1*H*-Benzotriazole [95-14-7]
Benzyl alcohol mono(poly)hemiformal [17] [14548-60-8]
1,3-Bis(hydroxymethyl)urea [17] [140-95-4]
Bithionol [97-18-7]
Boric acid [10043-35-3]
2-Bromo-2-nitro-1,3-propanediol [18] [52-51-7]
4-*tert*-Butylbenzoic acid [98-73-7]
Chloroacetamide-*N*-methylol [17] [2832-19-1]
p-Chloro-*m*-cresol [59-50-7]
5-Chloro-2-methyl-2,3-dihydroisothiazol-3-one [26172-55-4] and
 2-Methyl-2,3-dihydroisothiazol-3-one [2682-20-4] mixture in ratio 3:1
Citric acid [77-92-9] and its alkali metal salts
Decyl oleate [3687-46-5]
Dibenzyl disulfide [150-60-7]
1,2-Dibromo-2,4-dicyanobutane [35691-65-7]
2,6-Di-*tert*-butylphenol [128-39-2]
★ Di-n-butyl phosphate [107-66-4]
Diethylenetriaminepenta(methylene-phosphonic acid) [15827-60-8]
4-(Diiodomethylsulfonyl)-toluene [20018-09-1]
1,3-Dimethylol-5,5-dimethyl hydantoin [6440-58-0]
4,4'-Dioctyldiphenylamine [101-67-7]
Dipropylene glycol [25265-71-8]

[98] published in *Toxikologisch-arbeitsmedizinische Begründung von MAK-Werten* and in English in *Occupational Toxicants*, available from the publisher: WILEY-VCH, D-69451 Weinheim
[17] releases formaldehyde
[18] Use in metal-working fluids is not permitted: see TRGS 611.

2,2'-Dithiobis(*N*-methylbenzamide) [2527-58-4]
Dodecanedioic acid [693-23-2]
1-Dodecanol [112-53-8]
5-Ethyl-3,7-dioxa-1-azabicyclo[3.3.0]octane (EDAO) [17] [7747-35-5]
2-Ethyl-1,3-hexanediol [94-96-2]
2-Ethylhexanol [104-76-7]
Glycerin [56-81-5]
1-Hexadecanol [36653-82-4]
Hexamethylenetetramine [17] [100-97-0]
1-Hexanol [111-27-3]
2-Hexyl-1-decanol [2425-77-6]
Hexylene glycol [107-41-5]
1-Hydroxyethyl-2-heptadecenyl-imidazoline [21652-27-7]
2-Hydroxymethyl-2-nitro-1,3-propanediol [18] [126-11-4]
3-Iodo-2-propynyl butylcarbamate [55406-53-6]
Isodecyl oleate [59231-34-4]
★ Isononanoic acid [3302-10-1]
Isotridecanol [27458-92-0]
Lauric acid [143-07-7]
2-Mercaptobenzothiazole [149-30-4]
Methyl-1*H*-benzotriazole [29385-43-1]
Methyldiethanolamine [105-59-9]
N,*N*'-Methylene-bis(5-methyloxazolidine) [66204-44-2]
4,4'-Methylenedimorpholine [17] [5625-90-1]
Myristic acid [544-63-8]
4-(2-Nitrobutyl)morpholine [2224-44-4] (70% w/w) and 4,4'-(2-Ethyl-2-nitro-1,3-propanediyl)bismorpholine [1854-23-5] (20% w/w) (mixture) [60, 18]
1-Octadecanol [112-92-5]
1-Octanol [111-87-5]
2-Octyl-1-dodecanol [5333-42-6]
2-Octyl-4-isothiazolin-3-one [26530-20-1]
Oleic acid [112-80-1]
Oleoyl sarcosine [110-25-8]
Oleyl alcohol [143-28-2]
Palmitic acid [57-10-3]
★ Phenothiazine [63] [92-84-2]
2-Phenoxyethanol [122-99-6]
1-Phenoxy-2-propanol [770-35-4]
N-Phenyl-1-naphthylamine [90-30-2]
o-Phenylphenol [90-43-7] and Sodium *o*-phenylphenol [132-27-4]

---

18 Use in metal-working fluids is not permitted: see TRGS 611.
17 releases formaldehyde
60 In this mixture formaldehyde can be released and nitrosamines formed.
63 phototoxic effect

Piperazine [65,66] [110-85-0]
Polydimethyl siloxanes, linear [63148-62-9; 9006-65-9; 9016-00-6]
Polyethylene glycol (PEG)
Polypropylene glycol (PPG) [25322-69-4]
Propylene glycol [57-55-6]
Sodium diethyldithiocarbamate [29] [148-18-5]
Sodium pyrithione [3811-73-2; 15922-78-8]
Stearic acid [57-11-4]
★ Tall oil, distilled [8002-26-4]
1-Tetradecanol [112-72-1]
Tetrahydrobenzotriazole [6789-99-7]
★ Thiabendazole [148-79-8]
Triazinetriyltriiminotrishexanoic acid [80584-91-4]
Triethylene glycol *n*-butyl ether [143-22-6]
1,3,5-Triethylhexahydro-1,3,5-triazine [17] [7779-27-3]
Triphenylphosphate [115-86-6]
N,N',N''-Tris(β-hydroxyethyl)-hexahydro-1,3,5-triazine [17] [4719-04-4]
Zinc, *O,O'*-di-2-ethylhexyl dithiophosphate [4259-15-8]

d. Hydraulic fluids and lubricants

Hydraulic fluids and lubricants are groups of compounds of heterogeneous and often complex composition, whose use often results in skin contact. Skin contact with components of hydraulic fluids is mainly expected due to their entry into metal-working fluid solutions during the metalworking process.

Lubricants are differentiated as fats, oils and emulsions, hydraulic fluids only as oils and emulsions. Lubricating greases are oils with thickeners. In both groups the oils can be mineral oils, natural oils or synthetic liquids. Primarily metal soaps are used as thickeners, but minerals, polymers and other substances can be used as well.

Significant technical properties such as antiwear, corrosion protection, load-carrying ability, increased viscosity index and decreased pour point are only achieved by means of additives. Among other things, antioxidants prevent the decomposition of lubricating greases, while metal deactivators inhibit the catalytic activity and corrosion of non-ferrous metals.

In hydraulic oils, additives for improving load-carrying ability and fluidity, increasing the viscosity index, and decreasing corrosion, ageing and wear play an important role, as do additives with detergent, demulsifying and dispersant effects.

The Commission put forward a list of current components in 2003 (see "Hydraulikflüssigkeiten und Schmierstoffe" [99]), which is subject to revision in collaboration with the

---

[65] Reaction with nitrosating agents can result in the formation of carcinogenic *N,N'*-dinitrosopiperazine, see Section III "Amines which form carcinogenic nitrosamines on nitrosation", p. 147.

[66] Use in metal-working fluids is restricted: see TRGS 611.

[29] Reaction with nitrosating agents can result in the formation of carcinogenic *N*-nitrosodiethylamine, see Section III "Amines which form carcinogenic nitrosamines on nitrosation", p. 147.

[17] releases formaldehyde

[99] published in *Toxikologisch-arbeitsmedizinische Begründung von MAK-Werten*, available from the publisher: WILEY-VCH, D-69451 Weinheim (not yet available in English)

association of German lubricant producers ("Verband Schmierstoff-Industrie e.V."). There is some overlap with the list of metal-working fluid components.

Because of the intensive skin contact, effects on health are expected most frequently after absorption by the skin or as a result of a sensitizing, irritative reaction on the skin or also on the respiratory tract following exposure to metal-working fluid solutions after aerosolization.

Documentation has been published for the following substances:

Zinc, *O,O*'-di-2-ethylhexyl dithiophosphate [4259-15-8]

e. Metals and metal compounds

In the *List of MAK and BAT Values*, metals are listed as the element "and its inorganic compounds"; the threshold value is then expressed consistently in terms of the metal content. For the individual compounds of most metals, the data available from animal studies or from known effects on man are insufficient for evaluation. Whenever analogy of various compounds of a metal and the element itself seems plausible, these substances should be put in a single category. Therefore it is necessary that the individual metal compounds be specified as exactly as possible. Generally organic metal compounds should be evaluated separately from the inorganic compounds with respect to the establishment of a MAK value and of carcinogenic potential.

And since the type and extent of metal-related damage depends markedly on the nature of the chemical bond, differences in water solubility of metal compounds can influence their acute and chronic toxicity. On principle, therefore, every metal compound should be tested individually and then categorized according to its toxicity and any carcinogenic potential. At present, sufficient data for such a classification is available for only a few metal compounds.

f. Radioactive materials

For procedures in handling radionuclides, reference is made to the special regulations of the "Strahlenschutzverordnung" (radiation protection guidelines). The current version of the guideline may be found in the relevant issue of the *Bundesgesetzblatt*.

Biological Tolerance Values

XI Significance and use of BAT values and BLW

Definition

The Commission establishes BAT values ("**B**iologische **A**rbeitsstoff-**T**oleranzwerte": biological tolerance values) and BLW (**B**iologische **L**eit-**W**erte) to enable the evaluation of the risk to an individual's health which results from exposure to a substance at the workplace.

The BAT value describes the occupational-medical and toxicological derived concentration for a substance, its metabolites or an effect parameter in the corresponding biological material at which the health of an employee generally is not adversely affected even when the person is repeatedly exposed during long periods. BAT values are based on a relationship between external and systemic exposure or between the systemic exposure and the resulting effect of the substance. The derivation of the BAT value is based on the average of systemic exposures.

The BAT value is exceeded when, following several individual examinations, the average concentration of the parameter is greater than the BAT value; measured values greater than the BAT value must be evaluated in relation to occupational medical and toxicological data. Adverse effects on health can not necessarily be deduced from one single excursion above the BAT value.

The BLW is the amount of a chemical substance or its metabolites or the deviation from the norm of biological parameters induced by the substance in exposed humans which serves as an indicator for necessary protective measures. BLW are derived for carcinogenic substances and for substances without sufficient data: these are likewise established as averages.

Prerequisites

By definition, BAT values can be established only for such substances which can be taken up by the body in substantial quantities via the lungs and/or other body surfaces (skin, gastrointestinal tract) during occupational exposure. Another prerequisite for the establishment of a BAT value is that sufficient occupational medical and toxicological data are available for the substance and that these data are supported by observations in man. The data must have been obtained with reliable methods. For the establishment of new BAT values and the annual review of the list, the submission of suggestions and reports of experience with such substances in man is requested.

List of MAK and BAT Values 2008. DFG, Deutsche Forschungsgemeinschaft

ISBN: 978-3-527-32305-0

Derivation of BAT values

The derivation of a BAT value can be based on various constellations of scientific data which reveal a quantitative relationship between exposure concentration and body burden and therefore permit the linking of MAK and BAT values. These include

- studies which reveal a direct relationship between concentrations of a substance, metabolite or adduct in biological material (body burden) and adverse effects on health
- studies which reveal a relationship between a biological indicator (effect parameter) and adverse effects on health.

The following considerations of sex-specific factors apply for the establishment of BAT values:

1. The range of the variation in human anatomical and physiological differences which affect the toxicokinetics of a substance is very wide even for a single sex; the ranges for the two sexes overlap.
2. The resulting sex-specific differences in toxicokinetics vary in a range which is insignificant compared with the uncertainty involved in establishing threshold values.
3. Pregnancy can be associated with certain changes in the toxicokinetics of xenobiotics. In practice, however, the effects of these changes are limited so that for health protection at the workplace it is the effects on the embryo and foetus which are of particular importance (see Section VIII MAK values and pregnancy p. 184).

Documentation

The reasons why a BAT value was established at a particular level are documented by the Commission for the Investigation of Health Hazards of Chemical Compounds in the Work Area in a loose-leaf collection entitled *Arbeitsmedizinisch-toxikologische Begründungen von BAT-Werten*. Some of these documents are available in English in the series *Biological Exposure Values for Occupational Toxicants*. They combine a critical review of the available data with comments on the values for the parameters which have been shown in practice to make a useful contribution to occupational hygiene.[100]

As a rule, the Commission makes its decisions only on the basis of data which have been published in the scientific literature. When necessary, other sources such as unpublished internal company reports are cited and are then identified as such in the reference list at the end of the documentation.

The unabridged reports are made available to the Commission and are filed at the Commission's scientific central office. Information required by a third party about the company reports cited in the Commission's documentation is supplied in writing by the chairman of the Commission at his discretion. Access to company reports is not made available to third parties. Copies, even of parts of reports, are not provided.

---

[100] *Arbeitsmedizinisch-toxikologische Begründungen für BAT-Werte*, available from the publisher: WILEY-VCH, D-69451 Weinheim, also in English in the series *The MAK-Collection, Part II, BAT Value Documentations* and *Part IV, Biomonitoring Methods*

Purpose

In the context of specific occupational medical check-ups, BAT values are intended to protect employees from impairment of health at work. They provide a basis for deciding whether the amount of a chemical substance taken up by the organism may be harmful or not. For substances that can be absorbed through the skin, individual exposures can be determined only by biological monitoring. When using BAT values, the medical exclusion criteria defined by the "Berufsgenossenschaft" (Employers' Liability Insurance Association) in the guidelines for occupational medical check-ups must be observed. BAT values are not suitable for the derivation, by means of fixed conversion factors, of biological threshold values for long-term non-occupational exposures such as from air pollution or contaminants in food.

Correlations between BAT and MAK values

When a substance is inhaled under steady state conditions in controlled laboratory experiments, the relationship between the BAT and MAK values can be expressed in terms of pharmacokinetic functions. Under workplace conditions, however, it is not necessarily possible to deduce the level of a substance to which a particular person was exposed from its specific biological parameter in that person because a series of other factors in addition to the amount of substance in the air can determine the extent of exposure of the organism. These factors include the level of physical activity (respiratory minute volume), absorption through the skin and individual variations in metabolic or excretory patterns.

It is therefore, particularly difficult to evaluate field studies which describe the relationships between internal and external exposure to substances which can be absorbed percutaneously. Experience has shown that studies of such substances frequently yield discrepant results. These discrepancies are attributed to different levels of dermal exposure under the different study conditions. When evaluating such results to determine relationships between MAK and BAT values, priority should be given to studies in which the data suggest that skin absorption played a minor role.

In general for substances with low vapour pressure which are readily absorbed through the skin, there is no correlation between exposure concentration and body burden. For these substances (see also TRGS 150) a BAT value can often be established only on the basis of a relationship between body burden and effect.

In addition, the concentrations of substances in the workplace air may vary with time and the biological parameters may not vary to the same extent. Therefore observance of BAT values does not make it unnecessary to monitor the concentrations of substances in the workplace air. This applies especially for local irritants and caustic substances. When evaluating macromolecular adducts of foreign substances it should be borne in mind that the persistence of such adducts can lead to discrepancies between the pattern of external exposure and the behaviour of the biological parameters. Similar considerations apply for all highly cumulative substances such as heavy metals and polyhalogenated hydrocarbons.

In spite of all these interfering factors and the consequent differences in the definitions of MAK and BAT values, the two thresholds are generally based on equivalent effects of substances on the organism. However, for substances for which the MAK value is not

established on the basis of systemic effects but because of local irritation of skin and mucous membranes, a BAT value can still be based on "critical toxicity" resulting from systemic exposure. In such exceptional cases where the MAK and BAT values are based on different end points, the two values do not necessarily correspond.

Surveillance

The protection of the health of the individual, which is the reason for establishing BAT values, can be monitored by periodic quantitative determination of the chemical compounds or their metabolites or of biological parameters in biological material. The methods used must be diagnostically specific and sensitive enough for the purpose, acceptable to the employee and practicable for the physician. The sampling time, that is, the measurement strategy, must take into account both the exposure conditions at the workplace and the pharmacokinetics of the substance. As a rule, especially for substances which accumulate in the organism, this may be achieved by taking samples at the end of a working day after an extended period of work (working week).

During exposure to gaseous substances which are metabolized rapidly and for which the blood/air distribution coefficient is larger than 10, it must be taken into account that the concentrations of the substances in blood and tissues are positively correlated with the level of physical activity.

Likewise, the concentrations of inhaled gaseous substances in blood and tissues of persons working under hyperbaric pressure have been shown to correlate positively with the pressure. In such cases the observance of the BAT value must be monitored more frequently as the BAT value is attained in such workers at lower exposure concentrations than in persons working at normal pressures (see p. 13).

Whole blood, serum and urine samples are used as assay materials, occasionally and under certain conditions, also samples of alveolar air. Saliva and hair samples are not suitable assay materials for occupational medical biomonitoring.

The analytical methods must yield reliable results and meet the requirements of statistical quality control. In the collection *Analysen in biologischem Material* (available in English in the series *Analyses of Hazardous Substances in Biological Materials*), the Commission's "Analytical Chemistry" group has compiled a series of methods which may be considered reliable for this purpose.

For workers who come into direct skin contact with substances which are designated with an "H", it is necessary to check that the BAT value has not been exceeded or, in the case of carcinogenic substances, to assess the systemic dose in terms of the EKA (TRGS 150).

Evaluation of analytical data

Like any results of laboratory investigations, toxicological analytical data can only be evaluated given knowledge of the whole situation. As well as the other medical findings, especially

- the dynamics of pathophysiological processes

- the short-term effects of exposure-free periods
- the long-term effects of ageing
- the specific workplace conditions
- intensive physical activity and unusual conditions of atmospheric pressure

and any individual background exposures must be taken into account.

In occupational-medical health practice analyses of urine specimens for the purpose of biological monitoring are carried out using spontaneously voided urine samples (spot samples). These are not suitable for an analysis if they have been highly concentrated or highly diluted through diuresis. In occupational medical practice the creatinine content of the urine specimen is used as a criterion for the specimen's acceptance while the specific weight or the osmolality is of little importance as a basis for evaluation. Creatinine concentrations < 0.5 g/l or > 2.5 g/l are criteria which would exclude the usability of the spot sample (see "Creatinine as a reference parameter", Volume 3, p. 35–44, *Biological Exposure Values for Occupational Toxicants and Carcinogens*, Wiley-VCH, Weinheim, 1999).

Results from analyses of substances in biological material are subject to medical discretion. Only the physician who is responsible may interpret the results.

BAT values are established on the basis of the results of scientific studies and practical medical experience.

Allergenic substances

Depending on individual disposition, allergic reactions can be induced by various kinds of substance, more or less rapidly and in differing degrees of severity after sensitization of, for example, the skin or respiratory passages. The observance of BAT values cannot provide a guarantee that such reactions will not occur.

Carcinogenic substances

See Section XIII.

Mixtures of substances

BAT values apply as a rule for exposure to pure substances. They are not necessarily applicable for persons exposed to preparations containing more than one toxic substance (blends, mixtures, solutions). This is especially true for BAT values requiring determination of the substance itself or its metabolites. For mixtures of components with similar effects, a BAT value based on a biological parameter can be helpful in the assessment of health risks, as long as it provides a measure of critical clinical-functional effects of the components. The Commission makes every effort to define and publish such criteria for the biological effects of interfering components of mixtures.

XII List of substances

For interpretation of the occupational-medical and experimental toxicological data, reference should also be made to the *Arbeitsmedizinisch-toxikologische Begründungen von BAT-Werten, EKA, BLW und BAR.*[100]

Abbreviations

BV = biological value (BAT/EKA/BLW/BAR)
BAT = biological tolerance value
EKA = exposure equivalents for carcinogenic substances
BLW = BLW ("biologischer Leitwert")
★ BAR = BAR ("biologischer Arbeitsstoff-Referenzwert")

In the table under Substance:
H = danger from percutaneous absorption (see p. 198 and p. 183)

Assay material
B = blood
E = erythrocytes
U = urine
P/S = plasma/serum

Sampling time:
a not fixed
b end of exposure or end of shift
c for long-term exposures: after several shifts
d at the beginning of the next shift
e time after end of exposure: ... hours

1 Substances which have been examined for possible biological monitoring and for which there are documentations in *Arbeitsmedizinisch-toxikologische Begründungen für BAT-Werte, EKA, BLW und BAR*

Substance	H	Carcinogen category	Parameter	BV	Value or correlation	Assay material	Sampling time
Acetone [67-64-1]			Acetone	BAT	80 mg/l	U	b
Acetylcholine esterase inhibitors			Acetylcholine esterase	BAT	Reduction of activity to 70% of reference value	E	c, b
Acrylamide [79-06-1]	H	2	*N*-(2-Carbonamideethyl)-valine	BLW	15 µg/l see section XIV.1	B	a
				EKA	not established see section XIII.2	E	a
Acrylonitrile [107-13-1]	H	2	Cyanoethylvaline	EKA	see section XIII.1	E	a

[100] *Arbeitsmedizinisch-toxikologische Begründungen für BAT-Werte*, available from the publisher: WILEY-VCH, D-69451 Weinheim, also in English in the series *The MAK-Collection, Part II, BAT Value Documentations* and *Part IV, Biomonitoring Methods*

List of MAK and BAT Values 2008. DFG, Deutsche Forschungsgemeinschaft

ISBN: 978-3-527-32305-0

Substance	H	Carcinogen category	Parameter	BV	Value or correlation	Assay material	Sampling time
Alkali chromates (Cr(VI))		2	Chromium	EKA	see section XIII.1	E,U	c,b
★ Aluminium [7429-90-5]			Aluminium	BAT	60 µg/g creatinine	U	a
4-Aminobiphenyl [92-67-1]	H	1	4-Aminobiphenyl, released from the 4-aminobiphenyl-haemo-globin-adduct	BLW	10,0 ng/l [101] see section XIV.1	B	a
Aniline [62-53-3]	H	4	Aniline, free	BAT	1 mg/l	U	c, b
			Aniline, released from aniline-haemoglobin conjugate	BAT	100 µg/l	B	c, b
Antimony [7440-36-0] and its inorganic compounds		2	Antimony	EKA	not established see section XIII.2	U	c, b
Arsenic [7440-38-2] and inorganic arsenic compounds [102]		1	Inorganic arsenic and methylated metabolites in urin [103]	BLW	50 µg/l see section XIV.1	U	c, b
Arsenic trioxide [1327-53-3]		1	Arsenic	EKA	see section XIII.1	U	b
Benzene [71-43-2]	H	1	Benzene	EKA	see section XIII.1	B	b
			S-Phenylmercapturic acid	EKA	see section XIII.1	U	b
			trans, trans-Muconic acid	EKA	see section XIII.1	U	b
Benzidine [92-87-5] and its salts	H	1	Benzidine adducts	EKA	not established see section XIII.2	B	a
			Benzidine	EKA	not established see section XIII.2	U	c, b
Beryllium [7440-41-7] and its compounds		1	Beryllium	EKA	not established see section XIII.2	U	c, b
Bisphenol A (4,4'-Isopropylidene-diphenol) [80-05-7]			Bisphenol A, released after hydrolysis	BLW	80 mg/l see section XIV.1	U	b
1,3-Butadiene [106-99-0]		1	*N*-Acetyl-*S*-(3,4-di-hydroxybutyl)-L-cysteine	EKA	see section XIII.1	U	b
2-Butanone (Methyl ethyl ketone) [78-93-3]	H		2-Butanone	BAT	5 mg/l	U	b

101 Blood levels up to 35 ng/l of 4-aminodiphenyl, released from the 4-aminodiphenyl-haemoglobin adduct, have been detected in smokers.

102 apart from arsine

103 volatile arsenic compounds determined by direct hydrogenation

Substance	H	Carcinogen category	Parameter	BV	Value or correlation	Assay material	Sampling time
n-Butyl alcohol [71-36-3]			*n*-Butyl alcohol	BAT	2 mg/g creatinine	U	d
				BAT	10 mg/g creatinine	U	b
tert-Butyl methyl ether [1634-04-4]		3B	*tert*-Butyl methyl ether	BAT	not established see section XII.2	B, U	–
			tert-Butyl alcohol	BAT	not established see section XII.2	B, U	–
p-tert-Butylphenol (PTBP) [98-54-4]	H		PTBP	BAT	2 mg/l	U	b
Cadmium [7440-43-9] and its inorganic compounds	H	1	Cadmium	BLW	7 µg/l see section XIV.1	U	a
★ Carbon disulfide [75-15-0]	H		2-Thio-4-thiazolidine carboxylic acid (TTCA)	BAT	2 mg/g creatinine	U	b
Carbon monoxide [630-08-0]			CO-Hb	BAT	5%	B	b
Carbon tetrachloride [56-23-5]	H	4	Carbon tetrachloride	BAT	3,5 µg/l	B	c, b
★ Chlorobenzene [108-90-7]			Total 4-chlorocatechol	BAT	25 mg/g creatinine	U	d
				BAT	150 mg/g creatinine	U	b
★ Chromium [7440-47-3] and its inorganic compounds			Total chromium	BAR	0,6 µg/l see section XV	U	–
Cobalt [7440-48-4] and its compounds	H	2	Cobalt	EKA	see section XIII.1	U	a
Cresol (all isomers) [1319-77-3]	H	3A	Total cresol	BLW	200 mg/l see section XIV.1	U	b
Cumene [98-82-8]	H		2-Phenyl-2-propanol	BAT	50 mg/g creatinine	U	b
			Cumene	BAT	2 mg/l	B	b
Cyclohexane [110-82-7]			Total 1,2-cyclohexanediol	BAT	170 mg/g creatinine	U	c, b
Cyclohexanone [108-94-1]	H	3B	Total 1,2-cyclohexanediol	EKA	see section XIII.1	U	b, c
			Total cyclohexanol	EKA	see section XIII.1	U	b
4,4'-Diaminodiphenyl-methane [101-77-9]	H	2	4,4'-Diaminodiphenyl-methane	BLW	10,0 µg/l see section XIV.1	U	b

Substance	H	Carcinogen category	Parameter	BV	Value or correlation	Assay material	Sampling time
1,2-Dichlorobenzene [95-50-1]	H		1,2-Dichlorobenzene	BAT	140 µg/l	B	b
			3,4-Dichlorocatechol and 4,5-dichlorocatechol	BAT	150 mg/g creatinine	U	b
1,4-Dichlorobenzene [106-46-7]	H	2	2,5-Dichlorophenol	EKA	see section XIII.1	U	b
Dichloromethane [75-09-2]		3A	Dichlormethane	EKA	see section XIII.1	B	b
N,N-Dimethyl acetamide [127-19-5]	H		*N*-Methyl acetamide	BAT	30 mg/g creatinine	U	c, b
Dimethylformamide [68-12-2]	H		*N*-Methylformamide	BAT	35 mg/l	U	b
Dimethyl sulfate [77-78-1]	H	2	*N*-Methylvaline	EKA	see section XIII.1	E	a
1,4-Dioxane [123-91-1]	H	4	β-Hydroxyethoxy acetic acid	BAT	not established see section XII.2	U	b
★ 1-Ethoxy-2-propanol [1569-02-4]	H		1-Ethoxy-2-propanol	BAT	not established see section XII.2	U	b
★ 1-Ethoxy-2-propylacetate [54839-24-6]			1-Ethoxy-2-propanol	BAT	not established see section XII.2	U	b
Ethylbenzene [100-41-4]	H	3A	2- and 4-Ethylphenol	EKA	see section XIII.1	U	c, b
			Mandelic acid plus phenyl glyoxylic acid	EKA	see section XIII.1	U	c, b
Ethylene [74-85-1]		3B	Hydroxyethylvaline	EKA	see section XIII.1	E	a
Ethylene glycol dinitrate [628-96-6]	H		Ethylene glycol dinitrate	BAT	0,3 µg/l	B	b
★ Ethylene glycol mono-butyl ether [111-76-2]	H	4	Butoxyacetic acid	BAT	100 mg/l	U	c
			Total butoxyacetic acid	BAT	200 mg/l	U	c
★ Ethylene glycol mono-butyl ether acetate [112-07-2]	H	4	Butoxyacetic acid	BAT	100 mg/l	U	c
			Total butoxyacetic acid	BAT	200 mg/l	U	c
Ethylene glycol mono-ethyl ether [110-80-5]	H		Ethoxyacetic acid	BAT	50 mg/l	U	c, b
Ethylene glycol mono-ethyl ether acetate [111-15-9]	H		Ethoxyacetic acid	BAT	50 mg/l	U	c, b

Substance	H	Carcinogen category	Parameter	BV	Value or correlation	Assay material	Samplin time
★ Ethylene glycol monomethyl ether [109-86-4]	H		Methoxyacetic acid	BAT	15 mg/g creatinine	U	b
★ Ethylene glycol monomethyl ether acetate [110-49-6]	H		Methoxyacetic acid	BAT	15 mg/g creatinine	U	b
Ethylene oxide [75-21-8]	H	2	Hydroxyethylvaline	EKA	see section XIII.1	E	a
Formic acid methyl ester [107-31-3]	H		Methanol	BAT	not established see section XII.2	U	–
			Formic acid	BAT	not established see section XII.2	U	–
Halothane [151-67-7] (2-Bromo-2-chloro-1,1,1-trifluoroethane) [151-67-7]			Trifluoroacetic acid	BAT	2,5 mg/l	B	c, b
n-Heptane [142-82-5]			*n*-Heptane	BAT	not established see section XII.2	B	–
			2,5-Heptanedion	BAT	not established see section XII.2	U	–
Hexachlorobenzene [118-74-1]	H	4	Hexachlorobenzene	BAT	150 µg/l	P/S	a
n-Hexane [110-54-3]			2,5-Hexanedione plus 4,5-dihydroxy-2-hexanone	BAT	5 mg/l	U	b
2-Hexanone (Methyl butyl ketone) [591-78-6]	H		2,5-Hexanedione plus 4,5-dihydroxy-2-hexanone	BAT	5 mg/l	U	b
Hexone (Methyl isobutyl ketone) [108-10-1]	H		Hexone	BAT	3,5 mg/l	U	b
Hydrazine [302-01-2]	H	2	Hydrazine	EKA	see section XIII.1	U,P	b
Hydrogen fluoride [7664-39-3] and inorganic fluorine compounds (fluorides)	H		Fluoride	BAT	7 mg/g creatinine	U	b
			Fluoride	BAT	4 mg/g creatinine	U	d
Isopropyl alcohol [67-63-0]			Acetone	BAT	50 mg/l	B	b
				BAT	50 mg/l	U	b

Substance	H	Carcinogen category	Parameter	BV	Value or correlation	Assay material	Sampling time
Lead [7439-92-1]		2	Lead	BLW	400 μg/l 100 μg/l (women<45 yrs)[104] see section XIV.1	B	a
Lindane (γ-hexachloro-cyclohexane) [58-89-9]	H	4	Lindane	BAT	25 μg/l	P/S	b
Manganese [7439-96-5] and its inorganic compounds			Manganese	BAT	20 μg/l	B	c, b
Mercury [7439-97-6] and its inorganic compounds		3B	Mercury	BAT	25 μg/g creatinine[105]	U	a
Mercury, organic compounds	H	3B	Mercury	EKA	not established see section XIII.2	B	a
Methanol [67-56-1]	H		Methanol	BAT	30 mg/l	U	c, b
Methemoglobin-forming substances			MetHb	BAT	not established see section XII.2	B	b
Methyl bromide [74-83-9]	H	3B	Bromide	BLW	12 mg/l see section XIV.1	P/S	c
			S-Methylcysteine albumin adducts	EKA	not established see section XIII.2	S	a
4,4'-Methylene diphenyl isocyanate (MDI) [101-68-8]	H	3B	4,4'-Diaminodiphenyl-methane	BLW	10 μg/l see section XIV.1	U	b
N-Methyl-2-pyrrolidone (vapour) [872-50-4]	H		5-Hydroxy-*N*-methyl-2-pyrrolidone	BAT	150 mg/l	U	b
Molybdenum [7439-98-7] and its compounds except molybdenum trioxide			Molybdenum	BAT	not established see section XII.2	U, P	–
2-Naphthylamine [91-59-8]	H	1	2-Naphthylamine	EKA	not established see section XIII.2	U	b
			2-Naphthylamine adducts	EKA	not established see section XIII.2	E	a
1,5-Naphthylene diisocyanate [3173-72-6]		3B	1,5-Diaminonaphthalene	BLW	not established see section XIV.2	U	b

To minimize the potential risk, a BLW value of 100 μg/l blood has been established specifically for women under 45 years old. The value is based on the background level of exposure of the general population.

30 μg/l Urine

Substance	H	Carcinogen category	Parameter	BV	Value or correlation	Assay material	Samplin time
Nickel [7440-02-0] (nickel metal, nickel oxide, nickel carbonate, nickel sulfide, sulfidic ores)		1	Nickel	EKA	see section XIII.1	U	c
Nickel (easily soluble nickel compounds, e.g. nickel acetate and similar soluble salts, nickel chloride, nickel hydroxide, nickel sulfate)		1	Nickel	EKA	see section XIII.1	U	c
Nitrobenzene [98-95-3]	H	3B	Aniline, released from aniline-haemoglobin conjugate	BAT	100 µg/l	B	c
Nitroglycerin [55-63-0]	H	3B	1,2-Glyceryl dinitrate	BLW	not established see section XIV.2	P/S	b
			1,3-Glyceryl dinitrate	BLW	not established see section XIV.2	P/S	b
Parathion [56-38-2]	H		*p*-Nitrophenol	BAT	500 µg/l	U	c
			Acetylcholine esterase	BAT	Reduction of activity to 70% of reference value	E	c
Pentachlorophenol [87-86-5]	H	2	Pentachlorophenol	EKA	see section XIII.1	U,P/S	a
Perfluorooctanoic acid [335-67-1] and its inorganic salts	H	4	Perfluorooctanoic acid	BAT	5 mg/l	S	a
Phenol [108-95-2]	H	3B	Total phenol	BLW	200 mg/l see section XIV.1	U	b
Propylene glycol 1-methyl ether [107-98-2]			Propylene glycol 1-methyl ether	BAT	15 mg/l	U	b
Pyrethroids (e.g. cyfluthrin, cypermethrin, deltamethrin, permethrin, allethrin, resmethrin, phenothrin, tetramethrin)			*trans*-chrysanthemum-dicarboxylic acid, 4-fluoro-3-phenoxy-benzoic acid, *cis*- and *trans*-3-(2,2-dichloro-vinyl)-2,2-dimethyl-cyclopropanecarboxylic acid or *cis*-3-(2,2-di-bromovinyl)-2,2-dimethyl-cyclopropanecarboxylic acid	BAT	not established see section XII.2	U	b
Styrene [100-42-5]		5	Mandelic acid plus phenyl glyoxylic acid	BAT	600 mg/g creatinine	U	c, b

Substance	H	Carcinogen category	Parameter	BV	Value or correlation	Assay material	Sampling time
Tetrachloroethylene [127-18-4]	H	3B	Tetrachloroethylene	EKA	see section XIII.1	B	e
Tetraethyllead [78-00-2]	H		Diethyllead	BAT	25 µg/l, as Pb	U	b
			Total lead (also applies for mixtures of tetra-ethyllead with tetramethyllead)	BAT	50 µg/l	U	b
Tetrahydrofuran [109-99-9]	H	4	Tetrahydrofuran	BAT	2 mg/l	U	b
Tetramethyllead [75-74-1]	H		see Tetraethyllead	BAT			
Toluene [108-88-3]	H		Toluene	BAT	1,0 mg/l	B	b
			o-Cresol	BAT	3,0 mg/l	U	c, b
Toluene-2,4-diamine [95-80-7]	H	2	Total toluene-2,4-diamin	EKA	see section XIII.1	U	b
1,1,1-Trichloroethane (Methyl chloroform) [71-55-6]	H		1,1,1-Trichloroethane	BAT	550 µg/l	B	c, d
Trichloroethylene [79-01-6]	H	1	Trichloroacetic acid	EKA	see section XIII.1	U	b
★ Trimethylbenzene (all isomers) 1,2,3-Trimethylbenzene [526-73-8], 1,2,4-Trimethylbenzene [95-63-6], 1,3,5-Trimethylbenzene [108-67-8]			Total dimethyl benzoic acid (after hydrolysis)	BAT	400 mg/g creatinine	U	c, b
★ 2,4,6-Trinitrotoluene (and isomers in technical mixtures) [118-96-7]	H	2	4-Amino-2,6-dinitro-toluene	BAR	< 1 µg/l see section XV	U	
			2-Amino-4,6-dinitro-toluene	BAR	< 4 µg/l see section XV	U	
Vanadium [7440-62-2] and its inorganic compounds		2	Vanadium	EKA	see section XIII.1	U	b, c
Vinyl chloride [75-01-4]		1	Thiodiglycolic acid	EKA	see section XIII.1	U	c
Xylene (all isomers) [1330-20-7]	H		Xylene	BAT	1,5 mg/l	B	b
			Methylhippuric (toluric) acid	BAT	2000 mg/l	U	b

2 For the substances listed below, there is at present insufficient data for the derivation of a BAT valu however, documentation for this substances has been published in *Arbeitsmedizinisch-toxikologische Be gründungen für BAT-Werte, EKA, BLW und BAR*

tert-Butyl methyl ether [1634-04-4]
1,4-Dioxane [123-91-1]
★ 1-Ethoxy-2-propanol [1569-02-4]
★ 1-Ethoxy-2-propylacetate [54839-24-6]
Formic acid methyl ester [107-31-3]
n-Heptane [142-82-5]
Methemoglobin-forming substances
Molybdenum [7439-98-7] and its compounds except molybdenum trioxide
Pyrethroids (e.g. cyfluthrin, cypermethrin, deltamethrin, permethrin,
allethrin, resmethrin, phenothrin, tetramethrin)

XIII Carcinogenic substances

Chemical substances which, by their own action or by that of their reactive intermediates or metabolites, are known to cause cancer in man or for which there is good evidence of a human cancer risk (Carcinogen categories 1 and 2) or which cause concern because they are or could be carcinogenic (Carcinogen categories 3A and 3B) and for which no MAK value can be derived are not given BAT values because at present it is not possible to specify safe levels of such substances in biological materials. Therefore the handling of such substances must take place under the conditions described in Section III of the *List of MAK and BAT Values.* The analysis of carcinogenic substances in biological material is not carried out for the application of BAT values in the strict sense but rather for the occupational medical detection and quantification of the individual exposure to the substances. Concentrations of a substance or its metabolites in biological material which are higher than those known to correspond to the concentration of the substance in the workplace air are indicative of additional exposure by other routes, usually percutaneous.

For this reason for substances in Carcinogen categories 1 to 3, the Commission investigates the relationships between the concentration of the carcinogen in the workplace air and that of the substance or its metabolites in biological material ("Expositionsäquivalente für krebserzeugende Arbeitsstoffe", EKA: exposure equivalents for carcinogenic substances). From these relationships, the body burden which results from uptake of the substance exclusively by inhalation may be determined.

In addition, the considerations expressed in Section XI "Correlations between MAK and BAT Values" apply to substances which may be absorbed percutaneously ("H" after the name of the substance indicates danger from percutaneous absorption) (see p. 198 and p. 183).

1 Carcinogenic substances and suspected carcinogens for which correlations ("exposure equivalents for carcinogenic materials" EKA) can be evaluated:

Acrylonitrile [107-13-1] **H**

Air Acrylonitrile (ml/m³)	Air Acrylonitrile (mg/m³)	Sampling time: not fixed Erythrocytes Cyanoethylvaline (µg/l blood)
0.14	0.3	16
0.23	0.5	35
0.45	1	60
3	7	420

List of MAK and BAT Values 2008. DFG, Deutsche Forschungsgemeinschaft

ISBN: 978-3-527-32305-0

Alkali chromates (Cr(VI))

Air CrO_3 (mg/m³)	Sampling time: long-term exposure: after several shifts Erythrocytes * Chromium (µg/l whole blood)	Sampling time: end of exposure or end of shift Urine ** Chromium (µg/l)
0.03	9	12
0.05	17	20
0.08	25	30
0.10	35	40

* n o t applicable for exposure to welding fumes
** a l s o applicable for exposure to welding fumes

Arsenic trioxide [1327-53-3]

Air Arsenic (mg/m³)	Sampling time: end of exposure or end of shift Urine * Arsenic (µg/l)
0.01	50**
0.05	90
0.10	130

* volatile arsenic compounds by hydrogenation
** see Section XII

Benzene [71-43-2] **H**

Air Benzene (ml/m³)	(mg/m³)	Sampling time: end of exposure or end of shift Whole blood Benzene (µg/l)	Urine *S*-Phenyl-mercapturic acid (mg/g creatinine)	*trans, trans*-Muconic acid (mg/l)
0.3	1.0	0.9	0.010	–
0.6	2.0	2.4	0.025	1.6
0.9	3.0	4.4	0.040	–
1.0	3.3	5	0.045	2
2	6.5	14	0.090	3
4	13	38	0.180	5
6	19.5	–	0.270	7

1,3-Butadiene [106-99-0]

Air 1,3-Butadiene (ml/m³)	 (mg/m³)	Sampling time: end of exposure or end of shift Urine *N*-Acetyl-*S*-(3,4-dihydroxybutyl)-L-cysteine (mg/l)
0	0	0.4
0.5	1.1	1.3
1	2.2	2.2
2	4.5	4.1
3	6.7	5.9
4	9.0	7.8
5	11	9.6

Cobalt [7440-48-4] and its compounds **H**

Air Cobalt (mg/m³)	Sampling time: not fixed Urine Cobalt (µg/l)
0.010	6
0.025	15
0.050	30
0.100	60
0.500	300

Cyclohexanone [108-94-1] **H**

Air Cyclohexanone (ml/m³)	 (mg/m³)	Sampling time: end of exposure or end of shift; long-term exposure: after several shifts Urine Total 1,2-cyclohexanediol (mg/l)	Sampling time: end of exposure or end of shift Urine Total cyclohexanol (mg/l)
10	40	50	6
20	80	100	12
50	200	250	30

1,4-Dichlorobenzene [106-46-7] **H**

Air 1,4-Dichlorobenzene (ml/m³)	 (mg/m³)	Sampling time: end of exposure or end of shift; long-term exposure: after several shifts Urine 2,5-Dichlorophenol (mg/g creatinine)
10	61	20
20	122	40
50	305	100

Dichloromethane [75-09-2]

Air Dichloromethane (ml/m³)	Air Dichloromethane (mg/m³)	Sampling time: during exposure, at least 2 hours after beginning of exposure Whole blood Dichloromethane (mg/l)
10	35	0.1
20	70	0.2
50	175	0.5
100	350	1

Dimethyl sulfate [77-78-1] **H**

Air Dimethyl sulfate (ml/m³)	Air Dimethyl sulfate (mg/m³)	Sampling time: not fixed Erythrocytes *N*-Methylvaline (µg/l blood)
0.002	0.01	10
0.006	0.03	13
0.01	0.05	17
0.04	0.20	40

Ethylbenzene [100-41-4] **H**

Air Ethylbenzene (ml/m³)	Air Ethylbenzene (mg/m³)	Sampling time: end of exposure or end of shift; long-term exposure: after several shifts Urine 2- and 4-Ethylphenol (mg/l)	Urine Mandelic acid plus phenyl glyoxylic acid (mg/l)
10	44	1	160
25	110	3	400
50	220	6	800
100	440	12	1600

Ethylene [74-85-1]

Air Ethylene (ml/m³)	Air Ethylene (mg/m³)	Sampling time: not fixed Erythrocytes Hydroxyethylvaline (µg/l blood)
25	29	45
50	59	90
100	117	180

Ethylene oxide [75-21-8] **H**

Air Ethylene oxide (ml/m³)	Air Ethylene oxide (mg/m³)	Sampling time: not fixed Erythrocytes Hydroxyethylvaline (µg/l blood)
0.5	0.92	45
1	1.83	90
2	3.66	180

Hydrazine [302-01-2] **H**

Air Hydrazine (ml/m³)	Air Hydrazine (mg/m³)	Sampling time: end of exposure or end of shift Urine Hydrazine (µg/g creatinine)	Plasma Hydrazine (µg/l)
0.01	0.013	35	27
0.02	0.026	70	55
0.05	0.065	200	160
0.08	0.104	300	270
0.10	0.130	380	340

Nickel [7440-02-0] (nickel metal, nickel oxide, nickel carbonate, nickel sulfide, sulfidic ores)

Air Nickel (mg/m³)	Sampling time: after several shifts Urine Nickel (µg/l)
0.10	15
0.30	30
0.50	45

Nickel (easily soluble nickel compounds, e.g. nickel acetate and similar soluble salts, nickel chloride, nickel hydroxide, nickel sulfate)

Air Nickel (mg/m³)	Sampling time: after several shifts Urine Nickel (µg/l)
0.025	25
0.050	40
0.100	70

Pentachlorophenol [87-86-5] **H**

Air Pentachlorophenol (mg/m³)	Sampling time: not fixed Urine Pentachlorophenol (µg/l)	 Serum/plasma Pentachlorophenol (µg/l)
0.001	6*	17*
0.05	300	1000
0.10	600	1700

* value obtained by extrapolation

Tetrachloroethylene [127-18-4] **H**

Air Tetrachloroethylene (ml/m³)	 (mg/m³)	Sampling time: 16 hours after end of shift Whole blood Tetrachloroethylene (mg/l)
10	69	0.2
20	138	0.4
30	206	0.6
50	344	1.0

Toluene-2,4-diamine [95-80-7] **H**

Air Toluene-2,4-diamine (mg/m³)	Sampling time: end of exposure or end of shift Urine Total toluene-2,4-diamine (µg/g creatinine)
0.0025	6
0.01	13
0.017	20
0.035	37
0.100*	100*

* value obtained by extrapolation

Trichloroethylene [79-01-6] **H**

Air Trichloroethylene (ml/m³)	 (mg/m³)	Sampling time: end of shift Urine Trichloroacetic acid (mg/l)
10	55	20
20	109	40
30	164	60
50	273	100

Vanadium [7440-62-2] and its inorganic compounds

Air Vanadium (mg/m³)	Sampling time: end of exposure or end of working week Urine Vanadium (µg/g creatinine)
0.025	35
0.050	70
0.100	140

Vinyl chloride [75-01-4]

Air Vinyl chloride (ml/m³)	 (mg/m³)	Sampling time: after several shifts Urine Thiodiglycolic acid (mg/24 h)
1	2.6	1.8
2	5.2	2.4
4	10	4.5
8	21	8.2
16	41	10.6

2 Carcinogenic substances and suspected carcinogens for which correlations ("exposure equivalents for carcinogenic materials", EKA) cannot be evaluated, or only evaluated incompletely, but which are documented in *Arbeitsmedizinisch-toxikologische Begründungen für BAT-Werte, EKA, BLW und BAR*: [100]

Acrylamide [79-06-1]
Antimony [7440-36-0] and its inorganic compounds
Benzidine [92-87-5] and its salts
Beryllium [7440-41-7] and its compounds
Mercury, organic compounds
Methyl bromide [74-83-9]
2-Naphthylamine [91-59-8]

[100] *Arbeitsmedizinisch-toxikologische Begründungen für BAT-Werte*, available from the publisher: WILEY-VCH, D-69451 Weinheim, also in English in the series *The MAK-Collection, Part II, BAT Value Documentations* and *Part IV, Biomonitoring Methods*

XIV BLW

The BLW ("**B**iologischer **L**eit-**W**ert") is the amount of a chemical substance or its metabolites or the deviation from the norm of biological parameters induced by the substance in exposed humans which serves as an indicator for necessary protective measures. BLWs are assigned only for hazardous materials for which the available toxicological or occupational-medical data are insufficient for the establishment of BAT values (i. e. for carcinogenic substances and suspected carcinogens in the categories 1 to 3 and for non-carcinogens for which the toxicological data are inadequate).

BLW values are generally established on the assumption that persons are exposed at work for at most 8 hours daily and 40 hours weekly during their working lives.

The BLW is based on occupational-medical information as to the effects of handling the hazardous material together with toxicological data. Since observance of the BLW does not exclude a risk of adverse effects on health, it is necessary to extend our knowledge of the relationships between exposure to the substance, the systemic dose and the resulting risks for health so that BAT values may be derived. The BLW values are intended to advance this aim by providing a basis for biomonitoring of exposed persons by the physician. By continual improvement of the industrial situation, occupational hygiene and the protective aspects of work planning, concentrations as far as possible below the BLW should be attained.

1 Substances for which BLW can be derived:

Acrylamide [79-06-1]
4-Aminobiphenyl [92-67-1]
Arsenic [7440-38-2] and inorganic arsenic compounds [102]
Bisphenol A (4,4'-Isopropylidenediphenol) [80-05-7]
Cadmium [7440-43-9] and its inorganic compounds
Cresol (all isomers) [1319-77-3]
4,4'-Diaminodiphenylmethane [101-77-9]
Lead [7439-92-1]
Methyl bromide [74-83-9]
4,4'-Methylene diphenyl isocyanate (MDI) [101-68-8]
Phenol [108-95-2]

2 For the substances listed below, there is at present insufficient data for the derivation of a BLW; however, documentation for this substances has been published in *Arbeitsmedizinisch-toxikologische Begründungen für BAT-Werte, EKA und BLW*:

1,5-Naphthylene diisocyanate [3173-72-6]
Nitroglycerin [55-63-0]

[102] apart from arsine

List of MAK and BAT Values 2008. DFG, Deutsche Forschungsgemeinschaft

ISBN: 978-3-527-32305-0

★ XV BAR

BAR ("**B**iologische **A**rbeitsstoff-**R**eferenzwerte") describe the background levels of substances which are present concurrently in the environment at a particular time in a reference population of persons of working age who are not occupationally exposed to the substances. The BAR are based on the 95th percentile without regarding effects on health. It must be taken into account that the reference level of the background exposure can be influenced by such factors as age, sex, social status, residential environment and life style.
The reference level for a substance or its metabolite in biological material is derived with the help of the measured level in a random sample from a defined population group. Occupational exposure can be assessed by comparing biomonitoring values in occupationally exposed persons with the BAR.

BARs have been derived for the following substances with documentations in "*Arbeitsmedizinisch-toxikologische Begründungen für BAT-Werte, EKA, BLW und BAR*":

★ Chromium [7440-47-3] and its inorganic compounds
★ 2,4,6-Trinitrotoluene (and isomers in technical mixtures) [118-96-7]

List of MAK and BAT Values 2008. DFG, Deutsche Forschungsgemeinschaft

ISBN: 978-3-527-32305-0

CAS Number Index

CAS numbers of the substances listed in Sections II to XV and on the yellow pages

CAS number	Substance
50-00-0	Formaldehyde
50-29-3	DDT (Dichlorodiphenyltrichloroethane)
50-32-8	Benzo[*a*]pyrene (pyrolysis product)
50-53-3	Chlorpromazine (2-Chloro-10-(3-dimethylaminopropyl)phenothiazine)
51-75-2	*N*-Methyl-bis(2-chloroethyl)amine (nitrogen mustard)
51-79-6	Carbamic acid ethyl ester
52-51-7	2-Bromo-2-nitro-1,3-propanediol
53-70-3	Dibenz[*a,h*]anthracene (pyrolysis product)
54-11-5	Nicotine
54-64-8	Thimerosal
55-18-5	*N*-Nitrosodiethylamine
55-38-9	Fenthion
55-63-0	Nitroglycerin
56-23-5	Carbon tetrachloride
56-35-9	Bis(tributyltin) oxide (Tri-*n*-butyltin compounds)
56-38-2	Parathion
56-55-3	Benz[*a*]anthracene (pyrolysis product)
56-81-5	Glycerin
57-10-3	Palmitic acid
57-11-4	Stearic acid
57-14-7	1,1-Dimethylhydrazine
57-24-9	Strychnine
57-55-6	Propylene glycol
57-57-8	β-Propiolactone
57-74-9	Chlordane
58-89-9	Lindane (γ-Hexachlorocyclohexane)
59-50-7	*p*-Chloro-*m*-cresol
59-89-2	*N*-Nitrosomorpholine
60-00-4	Ethylenediaminetetraacetic acid (EDTA)
60-09-3	*p*-Aminoazobenzene
60-29-7	Ethyl ether
60-34-4	Monomethylhydrazine
60-35-5	Acetamide
60-57-1	Dieldrin
61-82-5	Amitrole
62-50-0	Methanesulfonic acid ethyl ester
62-53-3	Aniline
62-56-6	Thiourea
62-73-7	Dichlorvos (DDVP)
62-74-8	Sodium fluoroacetate
62-75-9	*N*-Nitrosodimethylamine
63-25-2	Carbaryl
64-02-8	Ethylenediaminetetraacetic acid tetrasodium salt (Na EDTA)
64-17-5	Ethanol
64-18-6	Formic acid
64-19-7	Acetic acid
64-67-5	Diethyl sulfate
65-85-0	Benzoic acid
66-27-3	Methanesulfonic acid methyl ester
67-56-1	Methanol

List of MAK and BAT Values 2008. DFG, Deutsche Forschungsgemeinschaft

ISBN: 978-3-527-32305-0

CAS number	Substance
67-63-0	Isopropyl alcohol
67-64-1	Acetone
67-66-3	Chloroform
67-68-5	Dimethyl sulfoxide
67-72-1	Hexachloroethane
68-11-1	Thioglycolic acid
68-12-2	Dimethylformamide
69-72-7	Salicylic acid
71-23-8	1-Propanol
71-36-3	*n*-Butyl alcohol
71-41-0	1-Pentanol
71-43-2	Benzene
71-55-6	1,1,1-Trichloroethane
72-20-8	Endrin
72-43-5	Methoxychlor (DMDT)
74-11-3	*p*-Chlorobenzoic acid
74-83-9	Methyl bromide
74-85-1	Ethylene
74-87-3	Methyl chloride
74-88-4	Methyl iodide
74-89-5	Methylamine
74-90-8	Hydrogen cyanide
74-93-1	Methyl mercaptan
74-96-4	Bromoethane
74-97-5	Bromochloromethane
74-98-6	Propane
74-99-7	Methyl acetylene
75-00-3	Chloroethane
75-01-4	Vinyl chloride
75-04-7	Ethylamine
75-05-8	Acetonitrile
75-07-0	Acetaldehyde
75-08-1	Ethanethiol
75-09-2	Dichloromethane
75-12-7	Formamide
75-15-0	Carbon disulfide
75-18-3	Dimethyl sulfide
75-21-8	Ethylene oxide
75-25-2	Tribromomethane
75-26-3	Isopropyl bromide
75-27-4	Bromodichloromethane
75-28-5	Isobutane
75-31-0	Isopropylamine
75-34-3	1,1-Dichloroethane
75-35-4	Vinylidene chloride
75-38-7	1,1-Difluoroethylene
75-43-4	Dichlorofluoromethane (FC-21)
75-44-5	Phosgene
75-45-6	Chlorodifluoromethane (FC-22)
75-50-3	Trimethylamine
75-52-5	Nitromethane
75-55-8	Propylene imine
75-56-9	Propylene oxide
75-61-6	Dibromodifluoromethane
75-63-8	Bromotrifluoromethane
75-64-9	*tert*-Butylamine

CAS number	Substance
75-65-0	*tert*-Butyl alcohol
75-68-3	1-Chloro-1,1-difluoroethane (FC-142b)
75-69-4	Trichlorofluoromethane (FC-11)
75-71-8	Dichlorodifluoromethane (FC-12)
75-72-9	Chlorotrifluoromethane (FC-13)
75-74-1	Tetramethyllead
75-83-2	2,2-Dimethylbutane (Hexane isomers)
75-84-3	2,2-Dimethyl-1-propanol (pentanol isomers)
75-85-4	2-Methyl-2-butanol (pentanol isomers)
75-91-2	*tert*-Butyl hydroperoxide
75-99-0	2,2-Dichloropropionic acid
76-01-7	Pentachloroethane
76-03-9	Trichloroacetic acid
76-06-2	Chloropicrin
76-11-9	1,1,1,2-Tetrachloro-2,2-difluoroethane (FC-112a)
76-12-0	1,1,2,2-Tetrachloro-1,2-difluoroethane (FC-112)
76-13-1	1,1,2-Trichloro-1,2,2-trifluoroethane (FC-113)
76-14-2	1,2-Dichloro-1,1,2,2-tetrafluoroethane (FC-114)
76-22-2	Camphor
76-44-8	Heptachlor
77-09-8	Phenolphthalein
77-47-4	Hexachlorocyclopentadiene
77-73-6	Dicyclopentadiene
77-78-1	Dimethyl sulfate
77-92-9	Citric acid
78-00-2	Tetraethyllead
78-10-4	Silicic acid tetraethyl ester
78-18-2	1-Hydroxy-1'-hydroperoxydicyclohexyl peroxide
78-59-1	Isophorone
78-78-4	Isopentane
78-79-5	Isoprene
78-81-9	Isobutylamine (Butylamine isomers)
78-83-1	Isobutyl alcohol
78-85-3	Methacrolein
78-87-5	1,2-Dichloropropane
78-92-2	*sec*-Butyl alcohol
78-93-3	2-Butanone
78-94-4	Methyl vinyl ketone
78-96-6	1-Amino-2-propanol
79-00-5	1,1,2-Trichloroethane
79-01-6	Trichloroethylene
79-04-9	Chloroacetyl chloride
79-06-1	Acrylamide
79-07-2	2-Chloroacetamide
79-09-4	Propionic acid
79-10-7	Acrylic acid
79-11-8	Chloroacetic acid
79-20-9	Methyl acetate
79-21-0	Peracetic acid
79-22-1	Methyl chlorocarbonate (Methyl chloroformate)
79-24-3	Nitroethane
79-27-6	1,1,2,2-Tetrabromoethane
79-29-8	2,3-Dimethylbutane (Hexane isomers)
79-34-5	1,1,2,2-Tetrachloroethane
79-36-7	Dichloroacetyl chloride
79-41-4	Methacrylic acid

CAS number	Substance
79-44-7	Dimethylcarbamoyl chloride
79-46-9	2-Nitropropane
80-05-7	Bisphenol A (2,2-Bis(4-hydroxyphenyl)propane)
80-15-9	α,α-Dimethylbenzyl hydroperoxide
80-62-6	Methacrylic acid methyl ester
81-14-1	1-(4-*tert*-Butyl-2,6-dimethyl-3,5-dinitrophenyl)ethanone
81-15-2	1-*tert*-Butyl-3,5-dimethyl-2,4,6-trinitrobenzene
81-81-2	Warfarin
81-84-5	Naphthalic anhydride
82-45-1	1-Aminoanthraquinone
83-79-4	Rotenone
84-65-1	Anthraquinone
84-74-2	Dibutyl phthalate
85-01-8	Phenanthrene
85-42-7	Hexahydrophthalic anhydride
85-44-9	Phthalic anhydride
85-68-7	Butylbenzyl phthalate
86-30-6	*N*-Nitrosodiphenylamine
86-50-0	Azinphos-methyl
86-57-7	1-Nitronaphthalene
86-88-4	1-Naphthylthiourea
87-59-2	2,3-Xylidine
87-61-6	1,2,3-Trichlorobenzene
87-62-7	2,6-Xylidine
87-68-3	Hexachloro-1,3-butadiene
87-86-5	Pentachlorophenol
88-10-8	Diethylcarbamoyl chloride
88-12-0	*N*-Vinyl-2-pyrrolidone
88-72-2	2-Nitrotoluene
88-73-3	*o*-Chloronitrobenzene
88-88-0	Picryl chloride
88-89-1	Picric acid
88-99-3	*o*-Phthalic acid
90-01-7	2-(Hydroxymethyl)phenol (formaldehyde condensation product with phenol)
90-04-0	*o*-Anisidine
90-13-1	1-Chloronaphthalene (Chlorinated naphthalenes)
90-30-2	*N*-Phenyl-1-naphthylamine
90-43-7	*o*-Phenylphenol
90-94-8	Michler's ketone
91-08-7	Toluene-2,6-diisocyanate
91-15-6	*o*-Phthalodinitrile
91-17-8	Decalin
91-20-3	Naphthalene
91-23-6	2-Nitroanisole
91-29-2	4-Nitro-4'-aminodiphenylamine-2-sulfonic acid
91-59-8	2-Naphthylamine
91-94-1	3,3'-Dichlorobenzidine
91-95-2	3,3'-Diaminobenzidine
92-52-4	Biphenyl
92-67-1	4-Aminobiphenyl
92-70-6	3-Hydroxy-2-naphthalenecarboxylic acid
92-84-2	Phenothiazine
92-87-5	Benzidine
92-93-3	4-Nitrobiphenyl
93-15-2	Methyleugenol
93-76-5	2,4,5-Trichlorophenoxyacetic acid

CAS number	Substance
94-36-0	Dibenzoyl peroxide
94-75-7	2,4-Dichlorophenoxyacetic acid
94-96-2	2-Ethyl-1,3-hexanediol
95-14-7	1*H*-Benzotriazole
95-33-0	*N*-Cyclohexyl-2-benzothiazolesulfenamide
95-48-7	*o*-Cresol
95-50-1	1,2-Dichlorobenzene
95-51-2	*o*-Chloroaniline
95-53-4	*o*-Toluidine
95-54-5	*o*-Phenylenediamine
95-63-6	1,2,4-Trimethylbenzene
95-64-7	3,4-Xylidine
95-68-1	2,4-Xylidine
95-69-2	4-Chloro-*o*-toluidine
95-70-5	Toluene-2,5-diamine
95-76-1	3,4-Dichloroaniline
95-78-3	2,5-Xylidine
95-79-4	5-Chloro-*o*-toluidine
95-80-7	Toluene-2,4-diamine
95-95-4	2,4,5-Trichlorophenol
96-12-8	1,2-Dibromo-3-chloropropane
96-13-9	2,3-Dibromo-1-propanol
96-14-0	3-Methylpentane (Hexane isomers)
96-18-4	1,2,3-Trichloropropane
96-23-1	1,3-Dichloro-2-propanol
96-24-2	3-Chloro-1,2-propanediol (α-Chlorohydrin)
96-29-7	Butanone oxime
96-33-3	Acrylic acid methyl ester
96-34-4	Chloroacetic acid methyl ester
96-37-7	Methylcyclopentane (Hexane (all isomers except *n*-Hexane))
96-45-7	Ethylene thiourea
96-48-0	γ-Butyrolactone
97-00-7	1-Chloro-2,4-dinitrobenzene
97-18-7	Bithionol
97-39-2	Di-*o*-tolylguanidine
97-53-0	Eugenol
97-54-1	Isoeugenol
97-56-3	*o*-Aminoazotoluene
97-63-2	Methacrylic acid ethyl ester
97-77-8	Disulfiram
97-88-1	*n*-Butyl methacrylate
97-90-5	Ethylene glycol dimethacrylate
98-00-0	Furfuryl alcohol
98-01-1	Furfural
98-07-7	Benzyl trichloride
98-29-3	*p*-*tert*-Butylcatechol
98-51-1	*p*-*tert*-Butyl toluene
98-54-4	*p*-*tert*-Butyl phenol
98-73-7	4-*tert*-Butylbenzoic acid
98-82-8	Cumene
98-83-9	α-Methyl styrene
98-87-3	Benzyl dichloride
98-88-4	Benzoyl chloride
98-95-3	Nitrobenzene
99-08-1	3-Nitrotoluene
99-54-7	3,4-Dichloronitrobenzene

CAS number	Substance
99-55-8	5-Nitro-*o*-toluidine
99-99-0	4-Nitrotoluene
100-00-5	*p*-Chloronitrobenzene
100-01-6	4-Nitroaniline
100-21-0	*p*-Phthalic acid
100-37-8	2-Diethylaminoethanol
100-40-3	4-Vinylcyclohexene
100-41-4	Ethylbenzene
100-42-5	Styrene
100-44-7	Benzyl chloride
100-51-6	Benzyl alcohol
100-52-7	Benzaldehyde
100-61-8	*N*-Methylaniline
100-63-0	Phenylhydrazine
100-74-3	*N*-Ethylmorpholine
100-75-4	*N*-Nitrosopiperidine
100-97-0	Hexamethylenetetramine
101-14-4	4,4'-Methylene-bis(2-chloroaniline)
101-61-1	4,4'-Methylene-bis(*N*,*N*-dimethylaniline)
101-67-7	4,4'-Dioctyldiphenylamine
101-68-8	4,4'-Methylene diphenyl isocyanate (MDI)
101-77-9	4,4'-Diaminodiphenylmethane
101-80-4	4,4'-Oxydianiline
101-83-7	Dicyclohexylamine
101-84-8	Diphenyl ether
101-90-6	Diglycidyl resorcinol ether
102-71-6	Triethanolamine
102-82-9	Tri-*n*-butylamine
103-09-3	2-Ethylhexyl acetate
103-11-7	Acrylic acid 2-ethylhexyl ester
103-71-9	Phenyl isocyanate
104-12-1	4-Chlorophenyl isocyanate
104-54-1	Cinnamyl alcohol
104-55-2	Cinnamaldehyde
104-57-4	Benzyl formate
104-76-7	2-Ethyl-1-hexanol
104-91-6	4-Nitrosophenol
104-94-9	*p*-Anisidine
105-38-4	Vinyl propionate
105-39-5	Chloroacetic acid ethyl ester
105-46-4	*sec*-Butyl acetate
105-59-9	Methyldiethanolamine
105-60-2	ε-Caprolactam
105-67-9	2,4-Xylenol (2,4-Dimethylphenol)
105-74-8	Dilauroyl peroxide
106-24-1	Geraniol
106-35-4	3-Heptanone
106-44-5	*p*-Cresol
106-46-7	1,4-Dichlorobenzene
106-47-8	*p*-Chloroaniline
106-49-0	*p*-Toluidine
106-50-3	*p*-Phenylenediamine
106-51-4	Quinone
106-58-1	1,4-Dimethylpiperazine
106-65-0	Dimethyl succinate
106-87-6	4-Vinyl-1-cyclohexene dioxide

CAS number	Substance
106-88-7	1,2-Butylene oxide
106-89-8	Epichlorohydrin
106-92-3	Allyl glycidyl ether
106-93-4	1,2-Dibromoethane
106-94-5	Propyl bromide
106-97-8	*n*-Butane
106-99-0	1,3-Butadiene
107-02-8	Acrolein
107-05-1	Allyl chloride
107-06-2	1,2-Dichloroethane
107-07-3	2-Chloroethanol
107-13-1	Acrylonitrile
107-15-3	Ethylenediamine
107-18-6	Allyl alcohol
107-19-7	Propargyl alcohol
107-20-0	Chloroacetaldehyde
107-21-1	Ethylene glycol
107-22-2	Glyoxal
107-30-2	Monochlorodimethyl ether
107-31-3	Formic acid methyl ester
107-41-5	Hexylene glycol
107-49-3	TEPP
107-64-2	Dimethyldioctadecylammonium chloride
107-66-4	Di-*n*-butyl phosphate
107-71-1	*tert*-Butyl peracetate
107-75-5	Hydroxycitronellal
107-83-5	2-Methylpentane (Hexane isomers)
107-87-9	2-Pentanone
107-98-2	Propylene glycol 1-methyl ether
108-01-0	*N,N*-Dimethylaminoethanol
108-03-2	1-Nitropropane
108-05-4	Vinyl acetate
108-10-1	Hexone
108-11-2	4-Methyl-2-pentanol
108-20-3	Isopropyl ether
108-21-4	Isopropyl acetate
108-22-5	Isopropenyl acetate
108-24-7	Acetic anhydride
108-31-6	Maleic anhydride
108-39-4	*m*-Cresol
108-42-9	*m*-Chloroaniline
108-45-2	*m*-Phenylenediamine
108-46-3	Resorcinol (1,3-Benzenediol)
108-65-6	Propylene glycol 1-methyl ether-2-acetate
108-67-8	1,3,5-Trimethylbenzene (Mesitylene)
108-68-9	3,5-Xylenol (3,5-Dimethylphenol)
108-69-0	3,5-Xylidine
108-70-3	1,3,5-Trichlorobenzene
108-77-0	Cyanuric chloride
108-83-8	Diisobutyl ketone
108-84-9	*sec*-Hexyl acetate
108-87-2	Methylcyclohexane
108-88-3	Toluene (Toluol)
108-90-7	Chlorobenzene
108-91-8	Cyclohexylamine
108-93-0	Cyclohexanol

CAS number	Substance
108-94-1	Cyclohexanone
108-95-2	Phenol
109-02-4	*N*-Methylmorpholine
109-16-0	Triethylene glycol dimethacrylate
109-17-1	Tetraethylene glycol dimethacrylate
109-59-1	2-Isopropoxyethanol
109-60-4	Propyl acetate
109-66-0	*n*-Pentane
109-73-9	*n*-Butylamine
109-79-5	Butanethiol
109-86-4	Ethylene glycol monomethyl ether
109-87-5	Dimethoxymethane
109-89-7	Diethylamine
109-94-4	Formic acid ethyl ester
109-99-9	Tetrahydrofuran
110-00-9	Furan
110-01-0	Tetrahydrothiophene (THT)
110-02-1	Thiophene
110-05-4	Di-*tert*-butyl peroxide
110-12-3	Methyl-2-hexanone
110-19-0	Isobutyl acetate
110-22-5	Diacetyl peroxide
110-25-8	Oleoyl sarcosine
110-42-9	Methyl decanoate
110-43-0	2-Heptanone
110-49-6	Ethylene glycol monomethyl ether acetate
110-54-3	*n*-Hexane
110-65-6	Butynediol
110-80-5	Ethylene glycol monoethyl ether
110-82-7	Cyclohexane
110-83-8	Cyclohexene
110-85-0	Piperazine
110-86-1	Pyridine
110-91-8	Morpholine
111-15-9	Ethylene glycol monoethyl ether acetate
111-27-3	1-Hexanol
111-30-8	Glutaraldehyde
111-40-0	Diethylenetriamine
111-42-2	Diethanolamine
111-44-4	2,2'-Dichlorodiethyl ether
111-46-6	Diethylene glycol
111-65-9	*n*-Octane
111-76-2	Ethylene glycol monobutyl ether
111-77-3	Diethylene glycol monomethyl ether
111-87-5	1-Octanol
111-90-0	Diethylene glycol monoethyl ether
111-96-6	Diethylene glycol dimethyl ether
112-07-2	Ethylene glycol monobutyl ether acetate
112-24-3	Triethylenetetramine
112-27-6	Triethylene glycol
112-34-5	Diethylene glycol monobutyl ether
112-40-3	Dodecane
112-53-8	1-Dodecanol
112-72-1	1-Tetradecanol
112-80-1	Oleic acid
112-85-6	Behenic acid

CAS number	Substance
112-92-5	1-Octadecanol
114-26-1	Propoxur
115-07-1	Propylene
115-10-6	Dimethyl ether
115-11-7	Isobutene
115-28-6	1,4,5,6,7,7-Bicyclo[2.2.1]hept-5-ene-2,3-dicarboxylic acid
115-70-8	2-Amino-2-ethyl-1,3-propanediol
115-86-6	Triphenylphosphate
115-96-8	Tris(2-chloroethyl)phosphate
116-14-3	Tetrafluoroethene
117-81-7	Di(2-ethylhexyl) phthalate (DEHP)
117-84-0	Dioctyl phthalate
118-48-9	*N*-Carboxyanthranilic anhydride
118-74-1	Hexachlorobenzene
118-91-2	*o*-Chlorobenzoic acid
118-96-7	2,4,6-Trinitrotoluene
119-34-6	2-Nitro-4-aminophenol
119-90-4	3,3'-Dimethoxybenzidine
119-93-7	3,3'-Dimethylbenzidine
120-12-7	Anthracene
120-61-6	Terephthalic acid dimethyl ester
120-71-8	5-Methyl-*o*-anisidine
120-82-1	1,2,4-Trichlorobenzene
121-44-8	Triethylamine
121-45-9	Trimethylphosphite
121-69-7	*N*,*N*-Dimethylaniline
121-73-3	*m*-Chloronitrobenzene
121-75-5	Malathion
121-91-5	*m*-Phthalic acid
122-39-4	Diphenylamine
122-40-7	α-Amylcinnamaldehyde
122-60-1	Phenyl glycidyl ether (PGE)
122-66-7	Hydrazobenzene
122-99-6	2-Phenoxyethanol
123-05-7	2-Ethylhexanal
123-30-8	4-Aminophenol
123-31-9	Hydroquinone
123-38-6	Propionaldehyde
123-42-2	Diacetone alcohol
123-51-3	Isoamyl alcohol
123-54-6	Acetylacetone
123-72-8	Butyraldehyde (*n*-Butanal)
123-73-9	Crotonaldehyde
123-75-1	Pyrrolidine
123-86-4	*n*-Butyl acetate
123-91-1	1,4-Dioxane
123-92-2	3-Methylbutyl acetate (Amyl acetate)
124-17-4	Diethylene glycol monobutyl ether acetate
124-38-9	Carbon dioxide
124-40-3	Dimethylamine
124-68-5	2-Amino-2-methyl-1-propanol
126-11-4	2-Hydroxymethyl-2-nitro-1,3-propanediol
126-71-6	Triisobutylphosphate
126-73-8	Tributyl phosphate
126-99-8	2-Chloroprene
127-00-4	*sec*-Propylene chlorohydrin (1-Chloro-2-propanol)

CAS number	Substance
127-18-4	Tetrachloroethylene
127-19-5	*N,N*-Dimethyl acetamide
127-20-8	2,2-Dichloropropionic acid sodium salt
128-37-0	2,6-Di-*tert*-butyl-*p*-cresol (3,5-Di-*tert*-butyl-4-hydroxytoluene) (BHT)
128-39-2	2,6-Di-*tert*-butylphenol
129-00-0	Pyrene
129-16-8	Merbromin
129-79-3	2,4,7-Trinitrofluorenone
131-17-9	Diallyl phthalate
132-27-4	Sodium *o*-phenylphenol
132-32-1	3-Amino-9-ethylcarbazole
135-88-6	*N*-Phenyl-2-naphthylamine
137-05-3	Methyl 2-cyanoacrylate
137-17-7	2,4,5-Trimethylaniline
137-26-8	Thiram
137-32-6	2-Methyl-1-butanol (pentanol isomers)
138-86-3	Limonene
139-65-1	4,4'-Thiodianiline
140-88-5	Acrylic acid ethyl ester
140-95-4	1,3-Bis(hydroxymethyl)urea
141-32-2	Acrylic acid *n*-butyl ester
141-43-5	2-Aminoethanol
141-78-6	Ethyl acetate
141-79-7	Mesityl oxide
141-97-9	Acetoacetic acid ethyl ester
142-82-5	*n*-Heptane
143-07-7	Lauric acid
143-22-6	Triethylene glycol *n*-butyl ether
143-28-2	Oleyl alcohol
143-33-9	Sodium cyanide
143-50-0	Chlordecone
144-62-7	Oxalic acid
148-18-5	Diethyldithiocarbamate sodium
148-79-8	Thiabendazole
149-30-4	2-Mercaptobenzothiazole
149-57-5	2-Ethylhexanoic acid
150-60-7	Dibenzyl disulfide
151-50-8	Potassium cyanide
151-56-4	Ethylenimine
151-67-7	Halothane
156-59-2	*cis*-1,2-Dichloroethylene
156-60-5	*trans*-1,2-Dichloroethylene
156-62-7	Calcium cyanamide
189-55-9	Dibenzo[*a,i*]pyrene (pyrolysis product)
189-64-0	Dibenzo[*a,h*]pyrene (pyrolysis product)
191-26-4	Anthanthrene
191-30-0	Dibenzo[*a,l*]pyrene (pyrolysis product)
192-65-4	Dibenzo[*a,e*]pyrene (pyrolysis product)
193-39-5	Indeno[1,2,3-*cd*]pyrene (pyrolysis product)
205-82-3	Benzo[*j*]fluoranthene (pyrolysis product)
205-99-2	Benzo[*b*]fluoranthene (pyrolysis product)
207-08-9	Benzo[*k*]fluoranthene (pyrolysis product)
218-01-9	Chrysene (pyrolysis product)
239-35-0	Benzo[*b*]naphtho-[2,1-*d*]thiophene
288-32-4	Imidazole
300-76-5	Naled

CAS number	Substance
302-01-2	Hydrazine
303-47-9	Ochratoxin A
306-83-2	2,2-Dichloro-1,1,1-trifluoroethane
309-00-2	Aldrin
319-84-6	α-HCH (1,2,3,4,5,6-Hexachlorocyclohexane)
319-85-7	β-HCH (1,2,3,4,5,6-Hexachlorocyclohexane)
330-55-2	Linuron (*N*'-(3,4-Dichlorophenyl)-*N*-methoxy-*N*-methylurea)
333-41-5	Diazinon
334-88-3	Diazomethane
335-67-1	Perfluorooctanoic acid
335-93-3	Silver perfluorooctanoate
335-95-5	Sodium perfluorooctanoate
373-02-4	Nickel acetate
409-21-2	Silicon carbide
420-04-2	Cyanamide
460-19-5	Cyanogen
461-58-5	Dicyanodiamide
463-51-4	Ketene
463-82-1	*tert*-Pentane
470-17-7	Isoalantolactone (Sesquiterpene lactones)
477-43-0	Dehydrocostus lactone (Sesquiterpene lactones)
479-45-8	*N*-Methyl-*N*,2,4,6-tetranitroaniline
492-80-8	Auramine
496-72-0	Toluylene-3,4-diamine
504-29-0	2-Aminopyridine
505-60-2	Bis(β-chloroethyl)sulfide (mustard gas)
506-77-4	Cyanogen chloride
508-59-8	Parthenin (Sesquiterpene lactones)
509-14-8	Tetranitromethane
510-15-6	Chlorobenzilate
512-56-1	Trimethyl phosphate
513-79-1	Cobalt(II) carbonate
514-10-3	Abietic acid
526-73-8	1,2,3-Trimethylbenzene
532-27-4	2-Chloroacetophenone
534-52-1	4,6-Dinitro-*o*-cresol
535-80-8	*m*-Chlorobenzoic acid
538-75-0	Dicyclohexylcarbodiimide
540-59-0	1,2-Dichloroethylene *sym*
540-73-8	1,2-Dimethylhydrazine
540-84-1	2,2,4-Trimethylpentane
540-88-5	*tert*-Butyl acetate
541-41-3	Chloroformic acid ethyl ester
541-73-1	1,3-Dichlorobenzene
541-85-5	5-Methyl-3-heptanone
542-56-3	Isobutyl nitrite
542-75-6	1,3-Dichloropropene
542-88-1	Bischloromethyl ether
542-92-7	Cyclopentadiene
543-27-1	Chloroformic acid isobutyl ester
544-63-8	Myristic acid
546-43-0	Alantolactone (Sesquiterpene lactones)
552-30-7	Trimellitic anhydride
553-21-9	Costunolide (Sesquiterpene lactones)
556-52-5	Glycidol (Glycide)
557-05-1	Zinc stearate

CAS number	Substance
560-21-4	2,3,3-Trimethylpentane (Octane)
563-47-3	3-Chloro-2-methylpropene
564-02-3	2,2,3-Trimethylpentane (Octane)
565-75-3	2,3,4-Trimethylpentane (Octane)
576-26-1	2,6-Xylenol (2,6-Dimethylphenol)
581-89-5	2-Nitronaphthalene
583-48-2	3,4-Dimethylhexane (Octane)
583-60-8	1-Methylcyclohexan-2-one
584-02-1	3-Pentanol
584-79-2	Allethrin
584-84-9	Toluene-2,4-diisocyanate
584-94-1	2,3-Dimethylhexane (Octane)
587-85-9	Phenyl mercury
589-43-5	2,4-Dimethylhexane (Octane)
589-53-7	4-Methylheptane (Octane)
589-81-1	3-Methylheptane (Octane)
591-78-6	2-Hexanone
592-13-2	2,5-Dimethylhexane (Octane)
592-27-8	2-Methylheptane (Octane)
592-34-7	Chloroformic acid *n*-butyl ester
592-41-6	1-Hexene
593-70-4	Chlorofluoromethane
594-42-3	Perchloromethyl mercaptan
594-72-9	1,1-Dichloro-1-nitroethane
594-82-1	2,2,3,3-Tetramethylbutane (Octane)
598-56-1	*N,N*-Dimethyl ethylamine
598-75-4	3-Methyl-2-butanol (pentanol isomers)
600-25-9	1-Chloro-1-nitropropane
601-77-4	*N*-Nitrosodiisopropylamine
602-87-9	5-Nitroacenaphthene
603-35-0	Triphenyl phosphine
604-75-1	Oxazepam
608-93-5	Pentachlorobenzene
609-20-1	2,6-Dichloro-*p*-phenylenediamine
609-26-7	2-Methyl-3-ethylpentane (Octane)
612-64-6	*N*-Nitrosoethylphenylamine
614-00-6	*N*-Nitrosomethylphenylamine
615-05-4	2,4-Diaminoanisole
619-99-8	3-Ethylhexane (Octane)
620-11-1	3-Pentyl acetate
620-92-8	4,4'-Methylenebisphenol (formaldehyde condensation product with phenol)
621-64-7	*N*-Nitrosodi-*n*-propylamine
623-05-2	4-(Hydroxymethyl)phenol (formaldehyde condensation product with phenol)
624-41-9	2-Methylbutyl acetate (Amyl acetate)
624-83-9	Methyl isocyanate
624-86-2	*O*-Ethylhydroxylamine
625-16-1	1,1-Dimethylpropyl acetate (Amyl acetate)
625-36-5	3-Chloropropanoyl chloride
625-45-6	Methoxyacetic acid
626-38-0	1-Methylbutyl acetate (Amyl acetate)
627-13-4	*n*-Propyl nitrate
627-44-1	Ethyl mercury
627-93-0	Dimethyl adipate
628-63-7	1-Pentyl acetate (Amyl acetate)
628-96-6	Ethylene glycol dinitrate
630-08-0	Carbon monoxide

CAS number	Substance
632-22-4	Tetramethyl urea (TMU)
632-99-5	Magenta (basic fuchsin hydrochloride)
634-66-2	1,2,3,4-Tetrachlorobenzene
634-90-2	1,2,3,5-Tetrachlorobenzene
646-06-0	1,3-Dioxolane (Dioxacyclopentane)
674-82-8	Diketene
680-31-9	Hexamethylphosphoric acid triamide
693-21-0	Diethylene glycol dinitrate
693-23-2	Dodecanedioic acid
700-13-0	Trimethylhydroquinone
730-40-5	Disperse Orange 3
760-23-6	3,4-Dichloro-1-butene
763-69-9	Ethyl 3-ethoxypropionate
764-41-0	1,4-Dichloro-2-butene
770-35-4	1-Phenoxy-2-propanol
811-97-2	1,1,1,2-Tetrafluoroethane
818-61-1	Acrylic acid hydroxyethyl ester
822-06-0	1,6-Hexamethylene diisocyanate
823-40-5	Toluene-2,6-diamine
838-88-0	4,4'-Methylene-bis(2-methylaniline)
868-77-9	2-Hydroxyethyl methacrylate
868-85-9	Dimethyl hydrogen phosphite
870-08-6	Dioctyltin oxide (n-Octyltin compounds)
872-50-4	*N*-Methyl-2-pyrrolidone
920-37-6	2-Chloroacrylonitrile
923-26-2	Methacrylic acid 2-hydroxypropyl ester
924-16-3	*N*-Nitrosodi-*n*-butylamine
929-06-6	2-(2-Aminoethoxy)ethanol
930-55-2	*N*-Nitrosopyrrolidine
935-92-2	Trimethylquinone
996-35-0	*N,N*-Dimethylisopropylamine
999-61-1	Acrylic acid hydroxypropyl ester
1070-70-8	1,4-Butanediol diacrylate
1085-98-9	Dichlofluanid
1116-54-7	*N*-Nitrosodiethanolamine
1119-40-0	Dimethyl glutarate
1120-71-4	1,3-Propane sultone
1121-03-5	2,4-Butane sultone
1163-19-5	Decabromobiphenyl ether
1239-45-8	Ethidium bromide
1241-94-7	Diphenyl 2-ethylhexyl phosphate
1300-73-8	Xylidine
1302-74-5	Aluminium oxide (Emery)
1302-78-9	Bentonite
1303-28-2	Arsenic pentoxide
1303-86-2	Boron oxide
1305-62-0	Calcium hydroxide
1305-78-8	Calcium oxide
1306-19-0	Cadmium oxide
1306-23-6	Cadmium sulfide
1307-96-6	Cobalt(II) oxide
1308-06-1	Cobalt(II,III) oxide
1309-37-1	Fe_2O_3 (iron oxides, pigmentary synthetic)
1309-38-2	Fe_3O_4 (iron oxides, pigmentary synthetic)
1309-48-4	Magnesium oxide
1309-64-4	Antimony trioxide

CAS number	Substance
1310-14-1	alpha-FeO(OH) (iron oxides, pigmentary synthetic)
1310-73-2	Sodium hydroxide
1313-27-5	Molybdenum trioxide
1313-99-1	Nickel monoxide
1314-06-3	Nickel sesquioxide
1314-13-2	Zinc oxide
1314-56-3	Phosphorus pentoxide
1314-62-1	Vanadium pentoxide
1314-80-3	Phosphorus pentasulfide
1317-35-7	Manganous-manganic oxide
1317-42-6	Cobalt(II) sulfide
1317-43-7	Nemalite
1317-60-8	alpha-Fe_2O_3 (iron oxides, pigmentary synthetic)
1318-02-1	Zeolites
1319-77-3	Cresol
1321-64-8	Pentachloronaphthalene
1321-65-9	Trichloronaphthalene
1321-74-0	Divinylbenzene
1327-33-9	Antimony trioxide
1327-53-3	Arsenic trioxide
1330-20-7	Xylene
1332-21-4	Asbestos
1332-58-7	Kaolin(ite)
1333-86-4	Carbon black
1335-87-1	Hexachloronaphthalene
1335-88-2	Tetrachloronaphthalene
1338-23-4	Methyl ethyl ketone peroxide
1344-28-1	Aluminium oxide
1344-37-2	C.I. pigment yellow 34
1345-04-6	Antimony trisulfide
1345-25-1	Iron(II) oxide
1402-68-2	Aflatoxins
1461-22-9	Tributyltin chloride
1464-53-5	Diepoxybutane
1477-55-0	*m*-Xylylenediamine
1484-13-5	Vinylcarbazole
1565-94-2	Bisphenol A diglycidyl methacrylate
1569-02-4	Propylene glycol monoethyl ether
1570-64-5	4-Chloro-2-methylphenol
1589-47-5	Propylene glycol 2-methyl ether
1633-83-6	1,4-Butane sultone
1634-04-4	*tert*-Butyl methyl ether
1663-39-4	*tert*-Butyl acrylate
1667-11-4	4-Chloromethyl-biphenyl
1675-54-3	Bisphenol A diglycidyl ether
1680-21-3	Triethylene glycol diacrylate
1738-25-6	Dimethylaminopropionitrile
1746-01-6	2,3,7,8-Tetrachlorodibenzo-*p*-dioxin
1748-81-8	Carabrone (Sesquiterpene lactones)
1758-61-8	Dicyclohexyl peroxide
1817-47-6	*p*-Nitrocumene
1836-75-5	Nitrofen (2,4-Dichlorophenyl-*p*-nitrophenyl ether)
1854-23-5	4,4'-(2-Ethyl-2-nitro-1,3-propanediyl)bismorpholine
1854-26-8	Dimethylol dihydroxyethyleneurea
1891-29-8	Lactucin (Sesquiterpene lactones)
1897-45-6	Chlorothalonil

CAS number	Substance
1910-42-5	Paraquat
1912-24-9	Atrazine
1983-10-4	Tributyltin fluoride
2082-81-7	1,4-Butanediol dimethacrylate
2104-64-5	EPN, *O*-Ethyl-*O*-(4-nitrophenyl)phenylthiophosphonate
2136-89-2	*o*-Chlorobenzotrichloride
2155-70-6	Tributyltin methacrylate
2156-56-1	Dichloroacetic acid sodium salt
2179-59-1	Allyl propyl disulfide
2203-14-7	4-*tert*-Butyl-2,6-bis(hydroxymethyl)phenol (formaldehyde condensation product with ptBP)
2224-44-4	4-(2-Nitrobutyl)morpholine
2234-13-1	Octachloronaphthalene
2238-07-5	Diglycidyl ether (DGE)
2243-62-1	1,5-Diaminonaphthalene
2303-16-4	Diallate
2346-44-3	4-[(4-Hydroxy-3-(hydroxymethyl)phenyl)methyl]-2-(hydroxymethyl)phenol (formaldehyde condensation product with phenol)
2358-84-1	Diethylene glycol dimethacrylate
2381-21-7	1-Methylpyrene
2385-85-5	Mirex
2395-00-8	Potassium perfluorooctanoate
2409-55-4	2-*tert*-Butyl-*p*-cresol
2425-77-6	2-Hexyl-1-decanol
2425-79-8	1,4-Butanediol diglycidyl ether
2426-08-6	*n*-Butyl glycidyl ether (BGE)
2431-50-7	2,3,4-Trichloro-1-butene
2455-24-5	Tetrahydrofurfuryl methacrylate
2465-27-2	Auramine hydrochloride
2467-02-9	2,2'-Methylenebisphenol (formaldehyde condensation product with phenol)
2467-03-0	2,4'-Methylenebisphenol (formaldehyde condensation product with phenol)
2527-58-4	2,2'-Dithiobis(*N*-methylbenzamide)
2530-83-8	γ-Glycidoxypropyltrimethoxysilane
2551-62-4	Sulfur hexafluoride
2634-33-5	1,2-Benzisothiazol-3(2*H*)-one
2682-20-4	2-Methyl-2,3-dihydroisothiazol-3-one
2687-25-4	Toluylene-2,3-diamine
2807-30-9	Ethylene glycol mono-*n*-propyl ether
2832-19-1	Chloroacetamide-*N*-methylol (CAM)
2832-40-8	Disperse Yellow 3
2855-13-2	3-Aminomethyl-3,5,5-trimethyl-cyclohexylamine (Isophorone diamine)
2872-52-8	Disperse Red 1
2937-59-9	2,6-Bis(Hydroxymethyl)phenol (formaldehyde condensation product with phenol)
2937-60-2	2,4-Bis(Hydroxymethyl)phenol (formaldehyde condensation product with phenol)
2937-61-3	2,4,6-Tris(Hydroxymethyl)phenol (formaldehyde condensation product with phenol)
3033-62-3	Bis(2-dimethylaminoethyl)ether
3033-77-0	Glycidyl trimethylammonium chloride
3091-25-6	Monooctyltin trichloride (n-Octyltin compounds)
3129-91-7	Dicyclohexylamine nitrite
3173-72-6	1,5-Naphthylene diisocyanate
3179-89-3	Disperse Red 17
3296-90-0	2,2-bis(bromomethyl)-1,3-propanediol
3302-10-1	Isononanoic acid
3327-22-8	(3-Chloro-2-hydroxypropyl)trimethylammonium chloride
3333-52-6	Tetramethyl succinonitrile

CAS number	Substance
3333-67-3	Nickel carbonate
3524-68-3	Pentaerythritol triacrylate
3542-36-7	Dioctyltin dichloride (n-Octyltin compounds)
3687-31-8	Lead arsenate
3687-46-5	Decyl oleate
3689-24-5	TEDP
3811-73-2	Sodium pyrithione
3825-26-1	Ammonium perfluorooctanoate
4016-14-2	Isopropyl glycidyl ether (IGE)
4074-88-8	Diethylene glycol diacrylate
4098-71-9	Isophorone diisocyanate
4259-15-8	Bis[*O,O*-bis(2-ethylhexyl) phosphorodithioato-*S,S'*]-zinc-(T-4)
4342-36-3	Tributyltin benzoate
4435-53-4	3-Methoxy-*n*-butyl acetate
4524-95-2	2-Methyl-2-azabicyclo[2.2.1]heptane
4602-84-0	Farnesol
4635-59-0	4-Chlorobutanoyl chloride
4719-04-4	*N,N',N''*-Tris(β-hydroxyethyl)-hexahydro-1,3,5-triazine
5064-31-3	Nitrilotriacetic acid trisodium salt
5216-25-1	*p*-Chlorobenzotrichloride
5307-14-2	2-Nitro-*p*-phenylenediamine
5333-42-6	2-Octyl-1-dodecanol
5470-11-1	Hydroxylamine hydrochloride
5503-41-3	Rhodium(II) acetate
5625-90-1	4,4'-Methylenedimorpholine
5714-22-7	Sulfur pentafluoride
5912-86-7	*cis*-Isoeugenol
5915-41-3	Terbuthylazine
5932-68-3	*trans*-Isoeugenol
5989-27-5	*d*(+)-Limonene
5989-54-8	*l*(−)-Limonene
6032-29-7	2-Pentanol
6358-64-1	2,5-Dimethoxy-4-chloroaniline
6419-19-8	Aminotris(methylenephosphonic acid)
6423-43-4	Propylene glycol dinitrate
6440-58-0	1,3-Dimethylol-5,5-dimethyl hydantoin
6638-87-5	4-*tert*-Butyl-2-(hydroxymethyl)phenol (formaldehyde condensation product with ptBP)
6754-13-8	Helenalin (Sesquiterpene lactones)
6789-99-7	Tetrahydrobenzotriazole
7005-47-2	2-Dimethylamino-2-methyl-1-propanol
7085-85-0	Ethyl 2-cyanoacrylate
7397-62-8	Hydroxyacetic acid butyl ester
7411-49-6	3,3'-Diaminobenzidine tetrahydrochloride
7414-83-7	1-Hydroxyethane-1,1-diphosphonate, disodium salt
7429-90-5	Aluminium
7439-92-1	Lead
7439-96-5	Manganese
7439-97-6	Mercury
7439-98-7	Molybdenum
7440-02-0	Nickel
7440-05-3	Palladium
7440-06-4	Platinum
7440-16-6	Rhodium
7440-22-4	Silver
7440-24-6	Strontium
7440-25-7	Tantalum

CAS number	Substance
7440-28-0	Thallium
7440-31-5	Tin
7440-33-7	Tungsten
7440-36-0	Antimony
7440-38-2	Arsenic
7440-39-3	Barium
7440-41-7	Beryllium
7440-43-9	Cadmium
7440-47-3	Chromium
7440-48-4	Cobalt
7440-50-8	Copper
7440-57-5	Gold
7440-58-6	Hafnium
7440-62-2	Vanadium
7440-65-5	Yttrium
7440-67-7	Zirconium
7446-09-5	Sulfur dioxide
7553-56-2	Iodine
7572-29-4	Dichloroacetylene
7580-67-8	Lithium hydride
7631-86-9	Silica, amorphous
7631-90-5	Sodium bisulfite
7631-95-0	Sodium molybdate(VI) (Molybdenum compounds)
7637-07-2	Boron trifluoride
7646-85-7	Zinc chloride
7647-01-0	Hydrogen chloride
7647-10-1	Palladium chloride
7647-14-5	Sodium chloride
7664-38-2	Phosphoric acid
7664-39-3	Hydrogen fluoride
7664-41-7	Ammonia
7664-93-9	Sulfuric acid
7665-72-7	*tert*-Butyl glycidyl ether
7681-52-9	Sodium hypochlorite
7681-57-4	Sodium metabisulfite
7696-12-0	Tetramethrin
7697-37-2	Nitric acid
7699-41-4	Fused silica
7718-54-9	Nickel chloride
7719-09-7	Thionyl chloride
7719-12-2	Phosphorus trichloride
7722-84-1	Hydrogen peroxide
7723-14-0	Phosphorus, yellow
7726-95-6	Bromine
7727-21-1	Potassium persulfate (Alkali persulfates)
7727-43-7	Barium sulfate
7727-54-0	Ammonium persulfate
7733-02-0	Zinc sulfate
7747-35-5	5-Ethyl-3,7-dioxa-1-azabicyclo[3.3.0]octane (EDAO)
7758-19-2	Sodium chlorite
7758-97-6	Lead chromate
7773-06-0	Ammonium sulfamate
7775-27-1	Sodium persulfate (Alkali persulfates)
7778-18-9	Calcium sulfate (anhydrite)
7778-39-4	Arsenic acid
7778-44-1	Calcium arsenate

CAS number	Substance
7779-27-3	1,3,5-Triethylhexahydro-1,3,5-triazine
7779-90-0	Zinc phosphate
7782-41-4	Fluorine
7782-42-5	Graphite
7782-49-2	Selenium
7782-50-5	Chlorine
7782-65-2	Germanium tetrahydride
7782-79-8	Hydrazoic acid
7783-06-4	Hydrogen sulfide
7783-07-5	Hydrogen selenide
7783-42-8	Thionyl fluoride
7784-42-1	Arsine
7784-46-5	Sodium arsenite (Arsenic and inorganic arsenic compounds)
7786-34-7	Mevinphos
7786-81-4	Nickel sulfate
7789-82-4	Calcium molybdate(VI) (Molybdenum compounds)
7790-91-2	Chlorine trifluoride
7790-94-5	Chlorosulfonic acid
7803-49-8	Hydroxylamine
7803-51-2	Phosphine
7803-52-3	Stibine
7803-57-8	Hydrazine hydrate
8001-35-2	Chlorinated camphene
8001-54-5	Benzalkonium chloride
8002-26-4	Tall oil, distilled
8003-22-3	D&C Yellow No. 11 (C.I. Solvent Yellow 33)
8003-34-7	Pyrethrum
8006-64-2	Turpentine
8007-18-9	Nickel titanic yellow pigment
8022-00-2	Demeton-methyl
8050-09-7	Rosin (Colophony)
8052-42-4	Bitumen
8065-48-3	Demeton
9001-00-7	Bromelain
9001-73-4	Papain
9001-89-2	6-Phytase
9002-86-2	PVC
9003-27-4	Poly(isobutylene)
9006-04-6	Natural rubber latex
9006-65-9	Polydimethyl siloxanes, linear
9014-01-1	Subtilisin
9016-00-6	Polydimethyl siloxanes, linear
9016-87-9	"Polymeric MDI"
10024-97-2	Nitrous oxide
10025-67-9	Sulfur monochloride
10025-87-3	Phosphorus oxychloride
10026-13-8	Phosphorus pentachloride
10026-24-1	Cobalt(II) sulfate
10028-15-6	Ozone
10034-76-1	Calcium sulfate (hemihydrate)
10035-10-6	Hydrogen bromide
10039-54-0	Hydroxylamine sulfate
10043-35-3	Boric acid
10046-00-1	Hydroxylamine hydrogen sulfate
10049-04-4	Chlorine dioxide
10049-07-7	Rhodium (III) chloride

CAS number	Substance
10101-41-4	Calcium sulfate (dihydrate)
10102-44-0	Nitrogen dioxide
10108-64-2	Cadmium chloride
10124-36-4	Cadmium sulfate
10139-58-9	Rhodium (III) nitrate
10241-05-1	Molybdenum pentachloride (Molybdenum compounds)
10453-86-8	Resmethrin
10489-46-0	Rhodium sulfate
10595-95-6	*N*-Nitrosomethylethylamine
10605-21-7	Carbendazim
11070-44-3	Methyltetrahydrophthalic anhydride
11097-69-1	Chlorinated biphenyls
11138-47-9	Sodium perborate
12011-76-6	Dawsonite
12022-37-6	gamma-FeO(OH) (iron oxides, pigmentary synthetic)
12027-67-7	Ammonium molybdate(VI) (Molybdenum compounds)
12030-97-6	Potassium titanate
12035-36-8	Nickel dioxide
12035-72-2	Nickel subsulfide
12054-48-7	Nickel hydroxide
12056-46-1	Potassium titanate
12056-49-4	Potassium titanate
12056-51-8	Potassium titanate
12056-53-0	Potassium titanate
12070-12-1	Tungsten carbide (Hard metal)
12134-66-6	gamma-Fe_2O_3 (iron oxides, pigmentary synthetic)
12174-11-7	Attapulgite
12181-28-1	alpha-FeO(OH) (iron oxides, pigmentary synthetic)
12184-22-4	Molybdocene dichloride (Molybdenum compounds)
12244-57-4	Sodium aurothiomalate
12286-12-3	Magnesium oxide sulfate
12298-43-0	Halloysite
12427-38-2	Manganous ethylenebis(dithiocarbamate) (Maneb)
12510-42-8	Erionite
12604-58-9	Ferrovanadium
12656-85-8	C.I. pigment red 104 (Molybdate orange)
13007-92-6	Chromium carbonyl
13048-33-4	1,6-Hexanediol diacrylate
13106-76-8	Ammonium molybdate (Molybdenum compounds)
13356-20-2	Monooctyltin oxide (n-Octyltin compounds)
13360-57-1	Dimethylsulfamoyl chloride
13397-24-5	Calcium sulfate (gypsum)
13463-40-6	Iron pentacarbonyl
13463-67-7	Titanium dioxide
13464-58-9	Arsenous acid (Arsenic and inorganic arsenic compounds)
13494-80-9	Tellurium
13530-65-9	Zinc chromate
13569-65-8	Rhodium chloride trihydrate
13752-51-7	4-((Morpholinothiocarbonyl)thio)morpholine (OTOS)
13825-90-6	Silane (Silicon tetrahydride)
13838-16-9	Enflurane
13952-84-6	*sec*-Butylamine
13983-17-0	Wollastonite
14075-53-7	Potassium tetrafluoroborate
14464-46-1	Cristobalite
14484-64-1	Ferbam

CAS number	Substance
14548-60-8	Benzyl alcohol mono(poly)hemiformal
14807-96-6	Talc
14808-60-7	Quartz
14861-17-7	4-(2,4-Dichlorophenoxy)benzenamine
14972-70-4	Sodium hexachlororhodate (III) hydrate (Rhodium)
14977-61-8	Chromyl chloride
14998-27-7	Chlorite
15096-52-3	Cryolite (sodium aluminium fluoride)
15159-40-7	*N*-Chloroformylmorpholine
15336-18-2	Ammonium hexachlororhodate(III) (Rhodium)
15467-20-6	Nitrilotriacetic acid disodium salt
15468-32-3	Tridymite
15501-74-3	Sepiolite
15571-58-1	Dioctyltin bis(2-ethylhexyl thioglycolate) (n-Octyltin compounds)
15625-89-5	Trimethylolpropane triacrylate
15827-60-8	Diethylenetriaminepenta(methylenephosphonic acid)
15922-78-8	Sodium pyrithione
16065-83-1	Chromium(III) compounds
16091-18-2	Dioctyltin maleate (n-Octyltin compounds)
16096-31-4	Diglycidyl hexanediol
16731-55-8	Potassium metabisulfite
16812-54-7	Nickel sulfide
17702-41-9	Decaborane
17804-35-2	Benomyl
17831-71-9	Tetraethylene glycol diacrylate
18307-23-8	Sepiolite
18454-12-1	Lead chromate oxide
18662-53-8	Nitrilotriacetic acid trisodium salt monohydrate
18994-66-6	Nitrilotriacetic acid monosodium salt
19287-45-7	Diborane
19430-93-4	3,3,4,4,5,5,6,6,6-Nonafluoro-1-hexene
19624-22-7	Pentaborane
20018-09-1	4-(Diiodomethylsulfonyl)-toluene
20554-84-1	Parthenolide (Sesquiterpene lactones)
20706-25-6	Ethylene glycol monopropyl ether acetate (2-Propoxyethyl acetate)
20765-98-4	Rhodium (III) chloride trihydrate
20816-12-0	Osmium tetroxide
21243-68-5	4-[(4-Hydroxyphenyl)methyl]-2-(hydroxymethyl)phenol (formaldehyde condensation product with phenol)
21645-51-2	Aluminium hydroxide
21652-27-7	1-Hydroxyethyl-2-heptadecenyl-imidazoline
22042-96-2	Diethylenetriaminepenta(methylene-phosphonic acid) sodium salts
22398-80-7	Indium phosphide
22967-92-6	Methyl mercury
23209-59-8	Calcium sodium metaphosphate
23696-28-8	Olaquindox (*N*-(2-Hydroxyethyl)-3-methyl-2-quinoxalinecarboxamide 1,4-dioxide)
23971-84-8	Anthecotulide (Sesquiterpene lactones)
24124-25-2	Tributyltin linoleate
24623-77-6	Aluminium hydroxide oxide
25013-15-4	Methyl styrene
25013-16-5	*tert*-Butyl-4-hydroxyanisole (BHA)
25154-52-3	Nonyl phenol
25154-54-5	Dinitrobenzene
25167-67-3	*n*-Butene
25167-70-8	2,4,4-Trimethylpentene

CAS number	Substance
25265-71-8	Dipropylene glycol
25321-14-6	Dinitrotoluene
25322-68-3	Polyethylene glycol (PEG)
25322-69-4	Polypropylene glycol (PPG)
25376-45-8	*o*-Toluenediamine
25551-13-7	Trimethylbenzene
25584-83-2	Acrylic acid hydroxypropyl ester (all isomers)
25586-43-0	Monochloronaphthalenes (Chlorinated naphthalenes)
25637-99-4	Hexabromocyclododecane
25639-42-3	Methylcyclohexanol
26002-80-2	Phenothrin
26125-61-1	*p*-Aramid
26172-55-4	5-Chloro-2-methyl-2,3-dihydroisothiazol-3-one
26401-86-5	Monooctyltin tris(isooctyl thioglycolate) (n-Octyltin compounds)
26401-97-8	Dioctyltin bis(isooctyl thioglycolate) (n-Octyltin compounds)
26444-49-5	Diphenyl cresyl phosphate
26530-20-1	2-Octyl-4-isothiazolin-3-one
26628-22-8	Sodium azide
26675-46-7	Isoflurane
26761-40-0	Diisodecyl phthalate
26896-18-4	Isononanoic acid
26966-75-6	*o*-Toluylenediamine (mixture of isomers)
27107-89-7	Monooctyltin tris(2-ethylhexyl thioglycolate) (n-Octyltin compounds)
27208-37-3	Cyclopenta[*cd*]pyrene
27213-78-1	*p-tert*-Butylcatechol
27458-92-0	Isotridecanol
27478-34-8	Dinitronaphthalene
27579-97-1	(−)-Frullanolide (Sesquiterpene lactones)
28272-18-6	Pyrethrosin (Sesquiterpene lactones)
28523-86-6	Sevoflurane
28553-12-0	Diisononyl phthalate
28699-88-9	Dichloronaphthalene (Chlorinated naphthalenes)
29222-48-8	Trimethylpentane (all isomers)
29385-43-1	Methyl-1*H*-benzotriazole
29387-86-8	Propylene glycol *n*-butyl ether
29911-28-2	Dipropylene glycol *n*-butyl ether
30618-84-9	Glyceryl monothioglycolate
30899-19-5	Pentanol
31027-31-3	4-Isopropylphenyl isocyanate
31906-04-4	4-(4-Hydroxy-4-methyl pentyl)-3-cyclohexene-1-carboxaldehyde
32534-81-9	Pentabromodiphenyl ether
32536-52-0	Octabromodiphenyl ether
33204-39-6	Arteglasin A (Sesquiterpene lactones)
33568-99-9	Dioctyltin bis(isooctyl maleate) (n-Octyltin compounds)
34123-59-6	Isoproturon (*N*-(4-Isopropylphenyl)-*N'*,*N'*-dimethylurea)
34590-94-8	Dipropylene glycol monomethyl ether
35001-25-3	Laurenobiolide (Sesquiterpene lactones)
35691-65-7	1,2-Dibromo-2,4-dicyanobutane
35851-08-2	4-*tert*-Butyl-2-(5-*tert*-butyl-2-hydroxy-3-(hydroxymethyl)benzyloxy-methyl)-6-(hydroxymethyl)phenol (formaldehyde condensation product with ptBP)
36653-82-4	1-Hexadecanol
37278-89-0	Xylanases
37288-11-2	3-Phytase
39117-96-9	5-*tert*-Butyl-2-hydroxy-3-(hydroxymethyl)benzaldehyde (formaldehyde condensation product with ptBP)

CAS number	Substance
40776-40-7	(+)-Frullanolide (Sesquiterpene lactones)
41683-62-9	1,2-Dichloromethoxyethane
42978-66-5	Tripropylene glycol diacrylate
51630-58-1	Fenvalerate
52315-07-8	Cypermethrin
52645-53-1	Permethrin
52918-63-5	Deltamethrin
53250-83-2	2-Chloro-4-methylsulfonylbenzoic acid
53469-21-9	Chlorinated biphenyls
54827-17-7	Tetramethylbenzidine
54839-24-6	1-Ethoxy-2-propanol acetate
55406-53-6	3-Iodo-2-propynyl butylcarbamate
55720-99-5	Chlorinated biphenyl oxide
57018-52-7	Propylene glycol mono-*tert*-butyl ether
57041-67-5	Desflurane
59231-34-4	Isodecyl oleate
59766-31-3	Potassium titanate
60676-86-0	Quartz glass
61583-60-6	Zinc molybdate (Molybdenum compounds)
61790-53-2	Diatomaceous earth (uncalcined)
61792-09-4	Diethylenetriaminepenta(methylenephosphonic acid) 5Na salt
63148-62-9	Polydimethyl siloxanes, linear
63449-39-8	Chlorinated paraffins
64742-48-9	White spirit
64742-49-0	White spirit
64742-88-7	White spirit
65980-75-8	Potassium pentachlororhodate(III) (Rhodium)
65997-15-1	Portland cement
66204-44-2	*N,N'*-Methylene-bis(5-methyloxazolidine)
68155-78-2	Diethylenetriaminepenta(methylenephosphonic acid) 7Na salt
68359-37-5	Cyfluthrin
68855-54-9	Calcined diatomaceous earth
69669-44-9	Alkyl benzenesulfonates C10–C14, linear
70657-70-4	Propylene glycol 2-methyl ether-1-acetate
74091-64-8	2,5(2,6)-Bis(isocyanatomethyl)bicyclo[2.2.1]heptane
80443-41-0	Tebuconazole
80584-91-4	Triazintriyltriiminotrihexanoic acid
85117-50-6	Alkyl benzenesulfonates C10–C14, linear
85409-17-2	Tributyltin naphthenate
88377-66-6	Bis(1-((5-chloro-2-hydroxyphenyl)azo)-2-naphthalenolato(2-hydrogen))-chromate-1-tetradecanamine
93841-74-8	Diethylenetriaminepenta(methylenephosphonic acid) 6Na salt
93841-75-9	Diethylenetriaminepenta(methylenephosphonic acid) 9Na salt
93841-76-0	Diethylenetriaminepenta(methylenephosphonic acid) 10Na salt
94987-75-4	Diethylenetriaminepenta(methylenephosphonic acid) 2Na salt
94987-76-5	Diethylenetriaminepenta(methylenephosphonic acid) 1Na salt
94987-77-6	Diethylenetriaminepenta(methylenephosphonic acid) 4Na salt
95015-06-8	Diethylenetriaminepenta(methylenephosphonic acid) 3Na salt
95183-54-3	Diethylenetriaminepenta(methylenephosphonic acid) 8Na salt
95481-62-2	Dicarboxylic acid (C4–C6) dimethylester, mixture
98711-09-2	4-[(2-Hydroxyphenyl)methyl]-2,6-bis(hydroxymethyl)phenol (formaldehyde condensation product with phenol)
103223-10-5	2-[(4-Hydroxy-3-(hydroxymethyl)phenyl)methyl]-6-(hydroxymethyl)phenol (formaldehyde condensation product with phenol)

CAS number	Substance
103223-11-6	4-[(4-Hydroxy-3,5-bis(hydroxymethyl)phenyl)methyl]-2-(hydroxymethyl)phenol (formaldehyde condensation product with phenol)
111109-77-4	Dipropylene glycol dimethyl ether
116230-20-7	2-(2-(2-Azabicyclo[2.2.1]hept-2-yl)ethoxy)-ethanol
134954-21-5	α-Peroxyachifolide (Sesquiterpene lactones)
137506-60-6	Cobalt(II) carbonate
293733-21-8	6-Amino-2-ethoxynaphthalene
316355-46-1	4-*tert*-Butyl-2-(5-*tert*-butyl-2-hydroxybenzyloxymethyl)-6-(hydroxymethyl)phenol (formaldehyde condensation product with ptBP)
499219-06-6	4-*tert*-Butyl-2,6-bis-(5-*tert*-butyl-2-hydroxy-3-hydroxymethyl-benzyloxymethyl)phenol (formaldehyde condensation product with ptBP)
499219-07-7	4-*tert*-Butyl-2-(5-*tert*-butyl-2-hydroxybenzyloxymethyl)-6-(5-*tert*-butyl-2-hydroxy-3-hydroxymethylbenzyloxymethyl)phenol (formaldehyde condensation product with ptBP)

Members of the Commission and Permanent Guest Contributors

Members

Frau Professor Dr. A. Hartwig (Vorsitzende), Technische Universität Berlin, Fakultät III – Lebensmittelchemie / Sekr.TIB 4/3-1, Gustav-Meyer-Allee 25, 13355 Berlin

Frau Dr. rer. nat. I.-D. Adler, Marktplatz 15B, 85375 Neufahrn

Professor Dr. rer. nat. J. Angerer, Institut und Poliklinik für Arbeits-, Sozial- und Umweltmedizin der Universität Erlangen-Nürnberg, Schillerstraße 25–29, 91054 Erlangen

Dr. rer. nat. M. Bader, Medizinische Hochschule Hannover, Abteilung Arbeitsmedizin, Carl-Neuberg-Straße 1, 30625 Hannover

Dr. rer. nat. M. Blaszkewicz, Institut für Arbeitsphysiologie an der Universität Dortmund, Abteilung Analytische Chemie, Ardeystraße 67, 44139 Dortmund

Professor Dr. med. Dr. rer. nat. H. M. Bolt, Institut für Arbeitsphysiologie an der Universität Dortmund, Ardeystraße 67, 44139 Dortmund

Professor Dr. T. Brüning, BGFA-Forschungsinstitut für Arbeitsmedizin der Deutschen Gesetzlichen Unfallversicherung, Institut der Ruhr-Universität Bochum, Bürkle-de-la-Camp-Platz 1, 44789 Bochum

Professor Dr. Dr. med. habil. G. Csanády, Helmholtz Zentrum München – Deutsches Forschungszentrum für Gesundheit und Umwelt, Ingolstädter Landstraße 1, 85764 Neuherberg

Professor Dr. med. H. Drexler, Institut und Poliklinik für Arbeits-, Sozial- und Umweltmedizin der Universität Erlangen-Nürnberg, Schillerstraße 25–29, 91054 Erlangen

Frau Professor Dr. med. M. Fartasch, BGFA-Forschungsinstitut für Arbeitsmedizin der Deutschen Gesetzlichen Unfallversicherung, Institut der Ruhr-Universität Bochum, Bürkle-de-la-Camp-Platz 1, 44789 Bochum

Professor Dr. rer. nat. Dr. med. habil. J. Filser, Helmholtz Zentrum München – Deutsches Forschungszentrum für Gesundheit und Umwelt, Ingolstädter Landstraße 1, 85764 Neuherberg

Professor Dr. med Dr. rer. nat. H.-P. Gelbke, CinTox (Consulting in Toxicology), Dr. Kausch-Straße 6a, 67251 Freinsheim

Priv. Doz. Dr. rer. nat. T. Göen, Institut und Poliklinik für Arbeits-, Sozial- und Umweltmedizin der Universität Erlangen-Nürnberg, Schillerstraße 25–29, 91054 Erlangen

Dr. med. R. Grebenstein, Robert Bosch GmbH, Hugofelsweg 4, 87509 Immenstadt

Professor Dr. med. H. Greim, Technische Universität München, Institut für Toxikologie, Hohenbachernstraße 15–17, 85354 Freising-Weihenstephan.

List of MAK and BAT Values 2008. DFG, Deutsche Forschungsgemeinschaft

ISBN: 978-3-527-32305-0

Professor Dr. med. E. Hallier, Georg-August-Universität Göttingen, Abteilung für Arbeits- und Sozialmedizin, Waldweg 37, 37073 Göttingen

Professor Dr. rer. biol. hum. U. Heinrich, Fraunhofer-Institut für Toxikologie und experimentelle Medizin, Nikolai-Fuchs-Straße 1, 30625 Hannover

Frau Professor Dr. med. G. Leng, Bayer Industry Services, BIS-SUA-GHA-GSS, L9, 51368 Leverkusen

Professor Dr. med. Dipl.-Ing. S. Letzel, Institut für Arbeits-, Sozial- und Umweltmedizin der Johannes-Gutenberg-Universät, Zahlbacher Straße 67, 55131 Mainz

Professor Dr. med. R.D. Merget, BGFA-Forschungsinstitut für Arbeitsmedizin der Deutschen Gesetzlichen Unfallversicherung, Institut der Ruhr-Universität Bochum, Bürkle-de-la-Camp-Platz 1, 44789 Bochum

Priv. Doz. Dr. rer. medic. P. Morfeld, Institut für Epidemiologie und Risikobewertung in der Arbeitswelt der Evonik Industries, Rüttenscheider Straße 1–3, 45128 Essen

Priv. Doz. Dr. rer. nat. M. Müller, Georg-August-Universität Göttingen, Zentrum für Umwelt- und Arbeitsmedizin, Waldweg 37, 37073 Göttingen

Professor Dr. med. D. Nowak, Institut und Poliklinik für Arbeits- und Umweltmedizin der Ludwig-Maximilians-Universität München, Ziemssenstraße 1, 80336 München

Professor Dr. rer. nat. Dr. agr. habil. H. Parlar, TU München, Wissenschaftszentrum Weihenstephan für Ernährung, Landnutzung und Umwelt, Lehrstuhl für Chemisch-Technische Analyse und Chemische Lebensmitteltechnologie, Weihenstephaner Steig 23, 85354 Freising

Professor Dr. med. A. W. Rettenmeier, Universitätsklinikum der Gesamthochschule Essen, Institut für Hygiene und Arbeitsmedizin, Hufelandstraße 55, 45122 Essen

Dipl.-Ing. K.-H. Schaller, Institut und Poliklinik für Arbeits-, Sozial- und Umweltmedizin der Universität Erlangen-Nürnberg, Schillerstraße 25–29, 91054 Erlangen

Professor Dr. med. A. Schnuch, IVDK-Zentrale/Institut an der Georg-August-Universität Göttingen, Universitäts-Hautklinik, von-Siebold-Straße 3, 37075 Göttingen

Professor Dr. med. R. Stahlmann, Charité-Universitätsmedizin Berlin, Campus Benjamin Franklin, Institut für Klinische Pharmakologie und Toxikologie, Garystraße 5, 14195 Berlin

Professor Dr. med. K. Straif, Carcinogen Identification and Evaluation, International Agency for Research on Cancer, World Health Organization, 150 Cours Albert Thomas, 69372 Lyon Cedex 08, Frankreich

Frau Dr. med. G. Stropp, Bayer Health Care AG, Pharma-Forschungszentrum, Geb. 514, Institut für Toxikologie, 42096 Wuppertal

Professor Dr. med. Dr. rer. nat. H.W. Thielmann, Deutsches Krebsforschungszentrum, Im Neuenheimer Feld 280, 69120 Heidelberg

Dr. C. van Thriel, Institut für Arbeitsphysiologie an der Universität Dortmund, Ardeystraße 67, 44139 Dortmund

Professor Dr. med. Dipl. Chem. G. Triebig, Institut und Poliklinik für Arbeits- und Sozialmedizin des Universitätsklinikums Heidelberg, Hospitalstraße 1, 69115 Heidelberg

Professor Dr. rer. nat. Dr. med. habil. K. Ulm, Institut für Medizinische Statistik und Epidemiologie der TU München, Klinikum Rechts der Isar, Ismaninger Straße 22, 81675 München

Professor Dr. med. W. Uter, Friedrich-Alexander-Universität Erlangen-Nürnberg, Institut für Medizininformatik, Biometrie und Epidemiologie, Waldstraße 6, 91054 Erlangen

Guest Contributors

Professor Dr. rer. nat. H. Blome, BGIA – Institut für Arbeitsschutz der Deutschen Gesetzlichen Unfallversicherung, Alte Heerstraße 111, 53757 Sankt Augustin

Dr. rer. nat. R. Hebisch, Bundesanstalt für Arbeitsschutz und Arbeitsmedizin, Friedrich-Henkel-Weg 1–25, 44149 Dortmund

Professor Dr. med. vet. H.-B. Richter-Reichhelm, Bundesinstitut für Risikobewertung, Thielallee 88–92, 14195 Berlin

Dr. med. H. Wellhäußer, Berufsgenossenschaft der chemischen Industrie, Fachreferat Arbeitsmedizin–Bereich: Prävention, Kurfürsten-Anlage 62, 69115 Heidelberg

Program Director (Deutsche Forschungsgemeinschaft)

Frau Dr. rer. nat. I. Ohlert, Deutsche Forschungsgemeinschaft, Kennedyallee 40, 53175 Bonn. Postanschrift: 53170 Bonn

Secretariat of the Commission

Frau Dr. rer. nat. H. Greim, Technische Universität Berlin, Fakultät III – Lebensmittelchemie / Sekr. TIB 4/3-1, Gustav-Meyer-Allee 25, 13355 Berlin

Constitution and Procedures of the Commission for the Investigation of Health Hazards of Chemical Compounds in the Work Area

I.

The activity of the Commission for the Investigation of Health Hazards of Chemical Compounds in the Work Area is based on the following regulations of the statutes of the Deutsche Forschungsgemeinschaft.

§ 1
Purpose of the Association

The Deutsche Forschungsgemeinschaft (German Research Foundation) serves all branches of science and the humanities by funding research projects and facilitating cooperation among researchers. It devotes particular attention to the education and advancement of young researchers. It promotes equality between men and women in the scientific and academic communities. It advises parliaments and public authorities on scientific matters and fosters relations with the private sector and between scientists and academics at home and abroad.

§ 6
Senate

1. The Senate shall consist of 39 members from the scientific and academic communities. The President of the Hochschulrektorenkonferenz (Association of Universities and Other Higher Education Institutions in Germany), the Chairman of the Union der Akademien der Wissenschaften in der Bundesrepublik Deutschland (Union of the German Academies of Sciences and Humanities) and the President of the Max-Planck-Gesellschaft (Max-Planck Society) are *ex officio* members of the Senate. The remaining 36 members shall be voted into a three-year term by the General Assembly; each year one-third of the senators leave the Senate. The composition of elected members should take into account an appropriate distribution of the humanities, natural sciences and the applied sciences, including the technical and agricultural sciences. The composition should also take into consideration members who conduct research in and outside the university. However, in order to assure that a suitable representative is not denied election on the basis of trying to attain a certain balance, no set distribution shall be stipulated.

. . .

6. The Senate shall attend to common matters of concern in research, promote cooperation in research, advise government offices in scientific and academic questions, and represent the interests of research in Germany in relation to research abroad. The Senate may recommend and initiate research activities and should work towards the coordination of those projects which have begun separately.
8. Within the scope of its mandate, the Senate may establish committees whose members need not be members of the Senate.

II.

On 1st July, 1986 the Senate of the Deutsche Forschungsgemeinschaft resolved the following principles for the Constitution and Procedure of the Commission for the Investigation of Health Hazards of Chemical Compounds in the Work Area:

1. The Senate has assigned to the Deutsche Forschungsgemeinschaft's Commission for the Investigation of Health Hazards of Chemical Compounds in the Work Area the responsibility of investigating the scientific foundations for the protection of workers' health from the effects of toxic chemicals at the workplace. The most important practical results of the Commission's work are scientific recommendations for the establishment of MAK and BAT values, for the classification of carcinogenic substances and for the evaluation of

embryotoxic and/or foetotoxic effects and of germ cell mutagens as well as the investigation and evaluation of analytical methods for controlling exposure and for examining observance of threshold values for health protection at the workplace. In addition, the Commission investigates further current problems of hazards to health caused by occupational exposures and proposes possible appropriate solutions.

A two-step procedure appears to be the best solution for the realization of health protection measures at the workplace which are in line with the current state of the science: The results of the Commission's work already mentioned above are annually reviewed and published by the Deutsche Forschungsgemeinschaft. At the same time they are handed to the Bundesminister für Arbeit und Sozialordnung who examines the recommendations, also taking nonscientific viewpoints into account, and who then makes them legally binding in an appropriate form – altered or unaltered as a basis for health protection.

2. The Commission works in scientific freedom and independence. It is not subject to instructions regarding selection or priority setting for the examination of substances and other matters to be investigated. It is the Commission's duty, however, to take up suggestions, in so far as they are of scientific significance, from industrial users and as far as possible to treat with precedence suggestions from the Bundesminister für Arbeit und Sozialordnung who is responsible for health protection at the workplace.
3. With respect to other organizations for which occupational safety plays a substantial role ("Länderausschuß für Arbeitsschutz und Sicherheitstechnik (LASI)" (Federal Committee for Occupational Safety and Technical Security), "Bundesverband der Deutschen Industrie" (Federation of German Industries), "Hauptverband der gewerblichen Berufsgenossenschaften"(Central Association of Industrial Injuries Insurance Institutes), "Deutscher Gewerkschaftsbund" (German Trade Union Federation)) the Commission observes the rules of procedure* which are published in the supplementary yellow pages of the Commission's annual Report. These rules of procedure ensure the complete transparency of the Commission's work programme by means of the advance announcement of planned changes and additions.** A most comprehensive information basis for the Commission's recommendations is ensured by the request to supply the Commission with information and commentaries and the associated possibility of involving appropriate scientific experts in the decision-making process.

   The reasons for MAK and BAT values, for the classification of carcinogenic substances or substances suspected of having carcinogenic potential and for the evaluation of embryotoxic and/or foetotoxic effects and germ cell mutagens are published in the form of detailed scientific documentation ("Begründungen").
4. The sole object of the Commission's work is to protect, as far as possible and necessary, and in line with the most up to date scientific information, the health of workers and of their offspring. The Commission regards health as the highest value which it does not weigh up against other factors. Therefore, only scientific arguments regarding health at the workplace are considered in discussions and decision-making. Other aspects such as competitive sociopolitical, economic, technological and other nonscientific reasons are excluded.

   Members of the Commission do not possess the knowledge required for a qualified evaluation of economic, technical and sociopolitical aspects.
5. For the reasons stated in 4., requests for participation of experts, other than those concerned with health aspects of protection at work, in the Commission's discussions cannot be complied with.
6. At the same time the Commission does not undervalue the necessity for political decisions in the process of realizing protection at work. It does, however, reject mixing political with scientific judgements in its own work.
7. By publishing its recommendations, the Commission contributes to fulfilling the constitutional obligation of the Deutsche Forschungsgemeinschaft to provide advice on scientific matters to parliaments and public authorities. Should the Bundesminister für Arbeit und Sozialordnung (see 1. above) deviate in any particular case from the recommendations, the Commission considers it essential that he makes the reasons known.
8. The presidency and governing body of the Deutsche Forschungsgemeinschaft can check observance of the rules of procedure, but ensure unchanged and immediate publication of the Commission's results, in so far as there are no imperative opposing reasons.

---

* see p. XXIV of this report
** see p. V of this report

III.

Newly appointed Members and Permanent Guest Contributors of the Commission for the Investigation of Health Hazards of Chemical Compounds in the Work Area receive written notice from the President of the Deutsche Forschungsgemeinschaft in which the following fundamentals of the Commission's work are laid down:

In order to fulfil the statutory functions of the Deutsche Forschungsgemeinschaft as advisers to the legislative and executive organs, the Senate has set up Commissions for various fields of knowledge, for example, for protection at work, protection of health and protection of the environment. The Commission in which you have been appointed is one of these.

The Commissions have the responsibility of ascertaining the current state of scientific data available in the respective field and of formulating it in such a way that the government authorities to be advised are in a position to reach competent decisions on their own responsibility. To this end it is desirable that in the individual Commissions the scientific position is elaborated so that it can be upheld by all members. Such a consensus is then represented in public as the standpoint of the Deutsche Forschungsgemeinschaft.

In view of this responsibility of the Commission, scientists are appointed members *ad personam* in their capacity as authoritative experts and not as representatives of the institutions or companies in which they work.

As well as these members there are also permanent guest contributors working in the Commissions. Scientists and other experts from public authorities are appointed permanent guest contributors with advisory function and may take on research assignments as well as official responsibilities. As they belong to institutes potentially affected by the Commissions's advice they have no voting rights. In this way a possible conflict of interests should be avoided from the outset.

The Senate appoints the Commissions for periods of office lasting 3 years each. Members and permanent guest contributors are also appointed for three years and can be reappointed once. A further extension of a personal mandate is only possible in justified exceptional cases.

The strict division aimed at between recognition of a scientific standpoint and its "application" in the broadest sense, be it from the political, legal, economic or other social point of view, presupposes that extrascientific problems of the government bodies the Commission is required to advise do not find admittance into the vote of the Commission. Political consequences of scientific facts, problems of realization, decisions about the reasonableness of particular risks, economic aspects, etc, do not belong within the responsibility of the Deutsche Forschungsgemeinschaft nor its Commissions.

For the procedure of the Commissions, discussions as well as data and facts referred to in the discussions are dealt with in strict confidentiality up until their publication by the Deutsche Forschungsgemeinschaft as a Report from the Commission concerned. Nobody, through appointment in a Commission, may gain a competitive advantage by exploiting advance information.

Substances in the lists of MAK values [1]) and BAT values [2]) reviewed in 2007/2008

(* in Sections IIa, IIb, III, IV, V, XII, XIII, XIV and XV; ° dismissed from consideration)

MAK Values

Changes

* Barium sulfate [7727-43-7]
pregnancy risk group C

* Calcium sulfate Anhydrite [7778-18-9] Hemihydrate [10034-76-1]
Dihydrate [10101-41-4] Gypsum [13397-24-5]
pregnancy risk group C

* *p*-Chloroaniline [106-47-8]
additional designation Sh

* Cobalt [7440-48-4] and its compounds
additional designation H

* Diethylcarbamoyl chloride [88-10-8]
review of classification: no change

* Dimethyl sulfoxide [67-68-5]
MAK value 50 ml/m³ equivalent to 160 mg/m³ — previous value: section IIb
peak limitation I(2)
pregnancy risk group D

* Ethylene glycol monomethyl ether [109-86-4]
MAK value 1 ml/m³ equivalent to 3,2 mg/m³ — previous value: 5 ml/m³ equivalent to 16 mg/m³

* Ethylene glycol monomethyl ether acetate [110-49-6]
MAK value 1 ml/m³ equivalent to 4,9 mg/m³ — previous value: 5 ml/m³ equivalent to 25 mg/m³

* Heptachlor [76-44-8]
MAK value 0,05 mg/m³ **I** — previous value: 0,5 mg/m³ **I**
peak limitation II(8) — II(2)
pregnancy risk group D
carcinogen category 4 — 3B

* Hexane (all isomers except *n*-Hexane)
MAK value 500 ml/m³ equivalent to 1800 mg/m³ — previous value: 200 ml/m³ equivalent to 720 mg/m³

* Magnesium oxide [1309-48-4]
pregnancy risk group C

* Methoxyacetic acid [625-45-6]
MAK value 1 ml/m³ equivalent to 3,7 mg/m³ — previous value: 5 ml/m³ equivalent to 19 mg/m³
peak limitation II(8) — I(2)
additional designation H

* *m*-Phenylenediamine [108-45-2]
additional designation Sh

* *N*-Phenyl-1-naphthylamine [90-30-2]
classification in section IIb

* PVC [9002-86-2]
pregnancy risk group C

---

1 *Toxikologisch-arbeitsmedizinische Begründung von MAK-Werten*, WILEY-VCH, D-69451 Weinheim.
2 *Arbeitsmedizinisch-toxikologische Begründungen für BAT-Werte*, WILEY-VCH, D-69451 Weinheim.

- * Pyridine [110-86-1]
  carcinogen category 3B
  additional designation H
  MAK value has been withdrawn — previous value: 5 ml/m³ equivalent to 16 mg/m³; peak limitation II (2) not applicable
- * Silicon carbide [409-21-2]
  pregnancy risk group C
- * Tantalum [7440-25-7]
  pregnancy risk group C
- * Tetraethyllead [78-00-2]
  pregnancy risk group B — previous classification: D
- * Tetramethyllead [75-74-1]
  pregnancy risk group B — previous classification: D
- * Titanium dioxide [13463-67-7]
  carcinogen category 3A
  MAK value has been withdrawn — previous value: 1,5 mg/m³ **R**; pregnancy risk group C not applicable
- * Zinc oxide fume [1314-13-2]
  review of classification: no change

New Entries

- * Aminotris(methylenephosphonic acid) [6419-19-8]
- * Benzalkonium chloride [8001-54-5]
- * Chromium(III) compounds
- * Di-*n*-butyl phosphate [107-66-4]
- * Disperse Orange 3 [730-40-5]
- * Disperse Red 1 [2872-52-8]
- * Disperse Red 17 [3179-89-3]
- * Disperse Yellow 3 [2832-40-8]
- * Ethylenediaminetetraacetic acid (EDTA) [60-00-4]
- * Isononanoic acid [26896-18-4]
- * Isoprene (2-Methyl-1,3-butadiene) [78-79-5]
- * *n*-Octyltin compounds (as Sn [7440-31-5])
- * Phenothiazine [92-84-2]
- * Tall oil, distilled [8002-26-4]
- * Thiabendazole [148-79-8]

Biological Tolerance Values

BAT Values Changes

- * Aluminium [7429-90-5]
  BAT 60 µg/g creatinine — previous value: 200 µg/l
- * Carbon disulfide [75-15-0]
  BAT 2 mg/g creatinine — previous value: 4 mg/g creatinine
- * Chlorobenzene [108-90-7]
  BAT 25/150 mg/g creatinine — previous value: 35/175 mg/g creatinine
- * Ethylene glycol monobutyl ether [111-76-2]
  BAT 100/200 mg/l — previous value: 100 mg/l
- * Ethylene glycol monobutyl ether acetate [112-07-2]
  BAT 100/200 mg/l — previous value: 100 mg/l

* Trimethylbenzene (all isomers)
  BAT 400 mg/g creatinine previous value: 600 mg/g creatinine

Exposure Equivalents for Carcinogenic Substances, EKA changes

BLW Changes

BAR Changes

BAT Values New Entries

* 1-Ethoxy-2-propanol [1569-02-4]
* 1-Ethoxy-2-propyl acetate [54839-24-6]
* Ethylene glycol monomethyl ether [109-86-4]
* Ethylene glycol monomethyl ether acetate [110-49-6]

Exposure Equivalents for Carcinogenic Substances, EKA New Entries

BLW New Entries

BAR New Entries

* Chromium [7440-47-3] and its inorganic compounds
* 2,4,6-Trinitrotoluene [118-96-7]

Substances being Examined for the Establishment of MAK Values and BAT Values

The "Commission for the Investigation of Health Hazards of Chemical Compounds in the Work Area" of the Deutsche Forschungsgemeinschaft is discussing changes of, or additions to, the MAK values and BAT values of the following substances for the 2009 List (Report 45) and subsequent lists:

MAK Values (Changes and New entries)

a. Changes

(MAK values, sensitizing substances, carcinogens, embryotoxic and/or foetotoxic substances, germ cell mutagens)

Substance	Discussed Change	Reason
Acetic anhydride [108-24-7]	Examination of MAK value	Suggestion from the Commission
Acrylates (monomers and oligomers)	Examination for sensitizing effect	Suggestion from the Commission
Acrylic acid hydroxyethyl ester [818-61-1]	Establishment of MAK value	Suggestion from the Ausschuß für Gefahrstoffe
Aldrin [309-00-2]	Examination of MAK value	Suggestion from the Commission
Alkali persulfates	Establishment of MAK value	Suggestion from the Commission
Allyl propyl disulfide [2179-59-1]	Examination of MAK value	Suggestion from the Commission
Aluminium [7429-90-5] and its oxides [1344-28-1], [1302-74-5] and hydroxides [21645-51-2], [24623-77-6]	Examination of MAK value Examination of reproductive toxicity	Suggestion from the Commission
Ammonia [7664-41-7]	Examination of MAK value	Suggestion from the Commission
Ammonium persulfate [7727-54-0]	Establishment of MAK value	Suggestion from the Commission
Animal hair, epithelia and other materials derived from animals	Establishment of MAK value	Suggestion from the Commission
o-Anisidine [90-04-0]	Examination for sensitization potential	Suggestion from the Commission
Atrazine [1912-24-9]	Examination for carcinogenic effect Examination for germ cell mutagenicity	Suggestion from the Commission
Auramine [492-80-8] and its hydrochloride [2465-27-2]	Examination of carcinogenic potential Examination for germ cell mutagenicity	Suggestion from the Commission
Azinphos-methyl [86-50-0]	Examination for carcinogenic effect	Suggestion from the Commission

Substance	Discussed Change	Reason
Barium compounds (soluble)	Examination of MAK value	Suggestion from the Commission
Benomyl [17804-35-2]	Establishment of MAK value Examination for carcinogenic effect	Suggestion from the Commission
Benzidine [92-87-5]	Examination of carcinogenic potential	Suggestion from the Commission
1*H*-Benzotriazole [95-14-7]	Examination for carcinogenic effect	Suggestion from the Commission
Benzyl chloride [100-44-7]	Examination for germ cell mutagenicity	Suggestion from the Commission
2,2-Bis(4-hydroxyphenyl)-propane (Bisphenol A) [80-05-7]	Examination for germ cell mutagenicity	Suggestion from the Commission
Bitumen [8052-42-4]	Examination of carcinogenic potential	Suggestion from the Commission
Boron [7440-42-8] and its inorganic compounds	Establishment of MAK values	Suggestion from the Commission
Bromelain [9001-00-7]	Establishment of MAK value	Suggestion from the Commission
1,4-Butanediol diglycidyl ether [2425-79-8]	Establishment of MAK value	Suggestion from the Commission
Butanone oxime [96-29-7]	Examination of carcinogenic potential	Suggestion from the Commission
tert-Butyl acrylate [1663-39-4]	Establishment of MAK value	Suggestion from BG Chemie
tert-Butyl hydroperoxide [75-91-2]	Examination of MAK value Examination of carcinogenic potential	Suggestion from the Commission
tert-Butyl-4-hydroxy-anisole (BHA) [25013-16-5]	Examination for carcinogenic effect	Suggestion from the Commission
Calcium sulfate (gypsum) [7778-18-9]	Examination of MAK value	Suggestion from the Commission
Camphor [76-22-2]	Examination of MAK value	Suggestion from the Commission
ε-Caprolactam [105-60-2]	Examination of MAK value	Suggestion from the Commission
Carbaryl [63-25-2]	Examination of MAK value	Suggestion from the Commission
Carbendazim [10605-21-7]	Establishment of MAK value Examination for carcinogenic effect	Suggestion from the Commission Suggestion from the Ausschuß für Gefahrstoffe
Carbon dioxide [124-38-9]	Examination of MAK value	Suggestion from the Commission
Carbon monoxide [630-08-0]	Examination of reproductive toxicity	Suggestion from the Commission
N-Carboxyanthranilic anhydride [118-48-9]	Establishment of MAK value	Suggestion from BG Chemie
Cellulases	Establishment of MAK values	Suggestion from the Commission

Substance	Discussed Change	Reason
Cereal flour dusts	Examination for sensitization potential	Suggestion from the Commission
Chlordane [57-74-9]	Examination of MAK value Examination of carcinogenic potential	Suggestion from the Commission
Chlordecone [143-50-0]	Examination of carcinogenic potential	Suggestion from the Commission
Chlorinated biphenyls [53469-21-9]	Examination of MAK value	Suggestion from the Commission
Chlorinated biphenyls (54% chlorine) [11097-69-1]	Examination of MAK value	Suggestion from the Commission
Chloroacetic acid methyl ester [96-34-4]	Examination of sensitization potential	Suggestion from the Commission
Chloroacetyl chloride [79-04-9]	Establishment of MAK value	Suggestion from users
o-Chloroaniline [95-51-2]	Establishment of MAK value	Suggestion from the Commission
m-Chloroaniline [108-42-9]	Establishment of MAK value	Suggestion from the Commission
Chlorodifluoromethane [75-45-6]	Examination of MAK value	Suggestion from the Commission
1-Chloro-2,4-dinitro-benzene [97-00-7]	Establishment of MAK value	Suggestion from the Commission
2-Chloroethanol [107-07-3]	Examination of MAK value	Suggestion from the Commission
3-Chloro-2-methylpropene [563-47-3]	Examination of carcinogenic potential Examination for sensitization potential	Suggestion from the Commission
p-Chloronitrobenzene (1-Chloro-4-nitrobenzene) [100-00-5]	Examination of carcinogenic potential	Suggestion from users
Chloropicrin [76-06-2]	Examination of MAK value	Suggestion from the Commission
3-Chloro-1,2-propanediol (α-Chlorohydrin) [96-24-2]	Examination for germ cell mutagenicity	Suggestion from the Commission
Chlorpromazine (2-Chloro-10-(3-dimethyl-aminopropyl)pheno-thiazine) [50-53-3]	Establishment of MAK value	Suggestion from the Commission
Chromium carbonyl [13007-92-6]	Examination of carcinogenic potential	Suggestion from the Commission
Chromium(VI) compounds	Examination of the carcinogenic potential for man	Suggestion from the Commission
Chromyl chloride [14977-61-8]	Examination for germ cell mutagenicity	Suggestion from the Commission
Cresol (all isomers) [1319-77-3]	Examination for carcinogenic effect	Suggestion from the Commission

Substance	Discussed Change	Reason
Cumene [98-82-8]	Examination for carcinogenic effect	Suggestion from the Commission
Cyclohexanol [108-93-0]	Examination of MAK value	Suggestion from the Commission
Cyclohexanone [108-94-1]	Examination for carcinogenic effect	Suggestion from the Commission
DDT (Dichlorodiphenyl-trichloroethane) [50-29-3]	Examination of MAK value	Suggestion from the Commission
Decaborane [17702-41-9]	Examination of MAK value	Suggestion from the Commission
Demeton-methyl [8022-00-2]	Examination of MAK value	Suggestion from the Commission
Diallyl phthalate [131-17-9]	Examination for carcinogenic effect	Suggestion from the Commission
Dibenzoyl peroxide [94-36-0]	Examination of MAK value Examination for carcinogenic effect	Suggestion from the Commission
3,3'-Dichlorobenzidine [91-94-1]	Examination of carcinogenic potential Examination for sensitization potential	Suggestion from the Commission
2,2'-Dichlorodiethyl ether [111-44-4]	Examination of MAK value	Suggestion from the Commission
1,1-Dichloroethane [75-34-3]	Examination of MAK value Examination for carcinogenic effect	Suggestion from the Commission
1,2-Dichloroethylene *sym* [540-59-0]	Examination of MAK value	Suggestion from the Commission
Dichlorofluoromethane (FC-21) [75-43-4]	Examination of MAK value	Suggestion from the Commission
Dichloromethane [75-09-2]	Examination for germ cell mutagenicity	Suggestion from the Commission
1,3-Dichloropropene [542-75-6]	Examination for germ cell mutagenicity	Suggestion from the Commission
1,2-Dichloro-1,1,2,2-tetra-fluoroethane (FC-114) [76-14-2]	Examination of MAK value	Suggestion from the Commission
Dichlorvos (DDVP) [62-73-7]	Examination for carcinogenic effect Examination for sensitization potential	Suggestion from the Commission
Dicyclohexylcarbodiimide [538-75-0]	Examination for carcinogenic effect	Suggestion from BG Chemie
Dicyclopentadiene [77-73-6]	Examination of MAK value	Suggestion from the Commission
Dieldrin [60-57-1]	Examination of MAK value	Suggestion from the Commission
Diesel engine emissions	Examination of carcinogenic potential	Suggestion from the Commission

Substance	Discussed Change	Reason
Diethylenetriamine [111-40-0]	Establishment of MAK value	Suggestion from BG Chemie
1,1-Difluoroethylene (Vinylidene fluoride) [75-38-7]	Examination of carcinogenic potential	Suggestion from the Commission
Diglycidyl hexanediol [16096-31-4]	Establishment of MAK value	Suggestion from the Commission
Dimethylamine [124-40-3]	Examination of MAK value	Suggestion from the Ausschuß für Gefahrstoffe
α,α-Dimethylbenzyl hydroperoxide [80-15-9]	Establishment of MAK value Examination for carcinogenic effect	Suggestion from the Commission
1,1-Dimethylhydrazine [57-14-7]	Examination of sensitizing effects on the airways	Suggestion from the Commission
1,2-Dimethylhydrazine [540-73-8]	Examination of sensitizing effects on the airways	Suggestion from the Commission
Dimethyl sulfate [77-78-1]	Examination of carcinogenic potential	Suggestion from the Commission
Dimethylsulfoxide [67-68-5]	Examination of percutaneous absorption	Suggestion from the Commission
4,6-Dinitro-*o*-cresol [534-52-1]	Examination for sensitization potential	Suggestion from the Commission
Dinitrotoluene (isomers) [25321-14-6]	Examination of carcinogenic potential	Suggestion from the Commission
Dipropylene glycol monomethyl ether (mixture of isomers) [34590-94-8]	Examination of MAK value	Suggestion from the Commission
Dispersion blue 106/124	Establishment of MAK value	Suggestion from the Commission
EPN, *O*-Ethyl-*O*-(4-nitrophenyl)phenylthiophosphonate [2104-64-5]	Examination of MAK value	Suggestion from the Commission
Ethylene glycol [107-21-1]	Examination of MAK value Examination of percutaneous absorption	Suggestion from the Commission
Ethylene glycol dimethacrylate [97-90-5]	Establishment of MAK value	Suggestion from the Commission
Ethylene glycol dinitrate [628-96-6]	Examination of MAK value	Suggestion from the Commission
Ethylene glycol mono-*n*-propyl ether [2807-30-9]	Examination of MAK value	Suggestion from the Commission
Ethylene glycol monopropyl ether acetate [20706-25-6]	Examination of MAK value	Suggestion from the Commission
Ethyl ether [60-29-7]	Examination of MAK value	Suggestion from the Commission
2-Ethyl-1-hexanol [104-76-7]	Examination for carcinogenic effect	Suggestion from the Commission

Substance	Discussed Change	Reason
Farnesol [4602-84-0]	Establishment of MAK value	Suggestion from the Commission
Fenthion [55-38-9]	Examination of MAK value	Suggestion from the Commission
Fibrous dust, inorganic	Establishment of MAK values Examination of carcinogenic potential Examination of the durability in the organism	Suggestion from the Commission
Formaldehyde [50-00-0]	Examination of carcinogenic potential	Suggestion from the Commission
Formaldehyde condensation products with phenol	Establishment of MAK values	Suggestion from the Commission
General threshold limit value for dust (respirable fraction)	Examination of MAK value Examination for carcinogenic effect Examination for prenatal toxicity	Suggestion from the Commission
General threshold limit value for dust (inhalable fraction)	Examination of MAK value Examination for prenatal toxicity	Suggestion from the Commission
Glyceryl monothioglycolate [30618-84-9]	Establishment of MAK value	Suggestion from the Commission
Glycidol [556-52-5]	Examination for germ cell mutagenicity	Suggestion from the Commission
Glycidyl trimethylammonium chloride [3033-77-0]	Examination of carcinogenic potential	Suggestion from the Commission
Halothane [151-67-7]	Examination of MAK value	Suggestion from the Commission
Heptane (all isomers except *n*-Heptane)	Establishment of MAK value	Suggestion from the Ausschuß für Gefahrstoffe
Hexachlorobenzene [118-74-1]	Examination of embryotoxic and/or fetotoxic effect	Suggestion from the Commission
Hexachloro-1,3-butadiene [87-68-3]	Examination of MAK value Examination for carcinogenic effect	Suggestion from the Commission
1,2,3,4,5,6-Hexachlorocyclohexane (techn. mixture)	Examination of MAK value	Suggestion from the Commission
Hexachloroethane [67-72-1]	Examination for carcinogenic effect	Suggestion from the Commission
Hexahydrophthalic anhydride [85-42-7]	Establishment of MAK value	Suggestion from the Commission
Hexamethylphosphoric acid triamide [680-31-9]	Examination for germ cell mutagenicity Examination of carcinogenic potential	Suggestion from the Commission
2-Hexanone [591-78-6]	Examination of MAK value	Suggestion from the Commission

Substance	Discussed Change	Reason
Hydraulic fluids and lubricants (components)	Establishment of MAK values Examination for sensitization potential	Suggestion from the Commission
Hydrazine hydrate [7803-57-8] and hydrazine salts	Examination for carcinogenic effect	Suggestion from the Commission
Hydrazoic acid [7782-79-8]	Examination of MAK value	Suggestion from the Commission
Hydroxylamine [7803-49-8]	Establishment of MAK value Examination for carcinogenic effect	Suggestion from the Commission
Iron oxide fume [1345-25-1], [1309-37-1]	Establishment of MAK value	Suggestion from the Commission
Iron oxides [1345-25-1], [1309-37-1]	Examination of MAK value Examination for prenatal toxicity	Suggestion from the Commission
Iron pentacarbonyl [13463-40-6]	Examination of MAK value	Suggestion from the Commission
Isophorone diisocyanate [4098-71-9]	Examination of MAK value	Suggestion from the Commission
2-Isopropoxyethanol [109-59-1]	Examination of MAK value	Suggestion from the Commission
Magnesium oxide fume [1309-48-4]	Establishment of MAK value	Suggestion from the Commission
Malathion [121-75-5]	Examination of MAK value	Suggestion from the Commission
Maleic anhydride [108-31-6]	Examination of MAK value	Suggestion from the Commission
Manganese [7439-96-5] and its inorganic compounds	Examination of MAK value	Suggestion from the Commission
Manganous ethylenebis-(dithiocarbamate) (Maneb) [12427-38-2]	Examination for carcinogenic effect	Suggestion from users
Mercury (metallic mercury [7439-97-6] and inorganic mercury compounds)	Examination of MAK value Examination for prenatal toxicity	Suggestion from the Commission
Metal-working fluids, components	Examination of toxicity and carcinogenicity	see p. 189 of this report
Methacrylic acid 2-hydroxypropyl ester [923-26-2]	Establishment of MAK value	Suggestion from the Ausschuß für Gefahrstoffe
Methoxychlor (DMDT) [72-43-5]	Examination of MAK value	Suggestion from the Commission
Methylamine [74-89-5]	Examination of MAK value	Suggestion from the Commission
4,4'-Methylene-bis(2-methylaniline) [838-88-0]	Examination for sensitization potential	Suggestion from the Commission
Methyl isocyanate [624-83-9]	Examination of MAK value Examination of sensitization potential	Suggestion from the Commission

Substance	Discussed Change	Reason
Methyl styrene [25013-15-4] [98-83-9]	Examination of MAK value Examination for carcinogenic effect	Suggestion from the Commission
Methyltetrahydrophthalic anhydride [11070-44-3]	Establishment of MAK value	Suggestion from the Commission
N-Methyl-*N*,2,4,6-tetra-nitroaniline [479-45-8]	Examination for percutaneous absorption	Suggestion from the Commission
Mevinphos [7786-34-7]	Examination of MAK value	Suggestion from the Commission
Molybdenum compounds	Examination for carcinogenic effect	Suggestion from BG Chemie
Monomethylhydrazine [60-34-4]	Establishment of MAK value Examination for carcinogenic effect	Suggestion from users
2-Naphthylamine [91-59-8]	Examination of carcinogenic potential	Suggestion from the Commission
1-Naphthylthiourea [86-88-4]	Examination of MAK value	Suggestion from the Commission
4-Nitro-4'-aminodiphenyl-amine-2-sulfonic acid [91-29-2]	Establishment of MAK value	Suggestion from the Commission
4-Nitrosophenol [104-91-6]	Examination for carcinogenic effect	Suggestion from BG Chemie
Nitrous oxide [10024-97-2]	Examination of MAK value	Suggestion from the Commission
Organic peroxides	Examination for carcinogenic effect	Suggestion from users
4,4'-Oxydianiline [101-80-4]	Examination of sensitization potential	Suggestion from the Commission
Paraquat [1910-42-5]	Examination of MAK value	Suggestion from the Commission
Parathion [56-38-2]	Examination of MAK value	Suggestion from the Commission
Pentaborane [19624-22-7]	Examination of MAK value	Suggestion from the Commission
Pentachloroethane [76-01-7]	Examination for carcinogenic effect	Suggestion from the Commission
Pentachlorophenol [87-86-5]	Examination for germ cell mutagenicity	Suggestion from the Commission
Perchloromethyl mercaptan [594-42-3]	Examination for carcinogenic effect	List of Suspected Carcinogens
Phenyl isocyanate [103-71-9]	Establishment of MAK value	Suggestion from the Commission
N-Phenyl-2-naphthylamine [135-88-6]	Examination for sensitization potential	Suggestion from the Commission
Phosphine [7803-51-2]	Examination of MAK value Examination for carcinogenic effect	Suggestion from the Commission
Plants containing sesqui-terpene lactones	Establishment of MAK values	Suggestion from the Commission

Substance	Discussed Change	Reason
Portland cement [65997-15-1]	Examination of MAK value Examination for prenatal toxicity	Suggestion from the Commission
Propoxur [114-26-1]	Examination of MAK value	Suggestion from the Commission
Propylene glycol dinitrate [6423-43-4]	Examination of MAK value	Suggestion from the Commission
Propylene glycol 1-methyl ether-2-acetate [108-65-6]	Examination of MAK value	Suggestion from the Ausschuß für Gefahrstoffe
	Examination for percutaneous absorption	Suggestion from the Commission
Propylene oxide [75-56-9]	Examination for germ cell mutagenicity	Suggestion from the Commission
n-Propyl nitrate [627-13-4]	Examination of MAK value	Suggestion from the Commission
Ricinus proteins	Establishment of MAK value	Suggestion from the Commission
Rosin (Colophony) [8050-09-7]	Establishment of MAK value	Suggestion from the Commission
Sidestream smoke (passive smoking at the workplace)	Examination for germ cell mutagenicity	Suggestion from the Commission
Silicon carbide [409-21-2] (without fibres)	Examination of MAK value	Suggestion from the Commission
Soya bean constituents	Establishment of MAK value	Suggestion from the Commission
Styrene [100-42-5]	Examination of MAK value	Suggestion from the Commission
Sulfur dioxide [7446-09-5]	Examination of MAK value	Suggestion from the Commission
Sulfur hexafluoride [2551-62-4]	Examination of MAK value	Suggestion from the Commission
TEPP [107-49-3]	Examination of MAK value	Suggestion from the Commission
1,1,2,2-Tetrachloroethane [79-34-5]	Examination of carcinogenic potential	Suggestion from the Commission
Thiourea [62-56-6]	Examination of sensitization potential	Suggestion from the Commission
Tin compounds, organic	Examination of MAK value	Suggestion from the Commission
Toluene (Toluol) [108-88-3]	Examination of MAK value	Suggestion from the Commission
Tributyl phosphate [126-73-8]	Examination of percutaneous absorption	Suggestion from the Commission
1,2,3-Trichlorobenzene [87-61-6]	Examination of MAK value	Suggestion from the Commission
1,3,5-Trichlorobenzene [108-70-3]	Examination of MAK value	Suggestion from the Commission
1,1,2-Trichloroethane [79-00-5]	Examination of MAK value	Suggestion from the Commission
1,1,2-Trichloro-1,2,2-trifluoroethane (FC-113) [76-13-1]	Examination of MAK value	Suggestion from the Commission

Substance	Discussed Change	Reason
Triethanolamine [102-71-6]	Establishment of MAK value Examination for carcinogenic effect	Suggestion from the Commission
Trimellitic anhydride (fume) [552-30-7]	Examination of MAK value	Suggestion from the Commission
Trimethyl phosphate [512-56-1]	Examination of germ cell mutagenicity	Suggestion from the Commission
4-Vinylcyclohexene [100-40-3]	Examination of carcinogenic potential	Suggestion from the Commission
Vinylidene chloride [75-35-4]	Examination of carcinogenic potential	Suggestion from the Commission
Warfarin [81-81-2]	Examination of MAK value	Suggestion from the Commission
Woods	Examination for sensitization potential	Suggestion from the Commission
Xylene [1330-20-7]	Examination of embryotoxic and/or fetotoxic effect	Suggestion from the Commission
m-Xylylenediamine [1477-55-0]	Establishment of MAK value	Suggestion from the Commission
Zinc chloride fume [7646-85-7]	Examination of MAK value	Suggestion from the Commission
Zinc oxide fume [1314-13-2]	Examination of MAK value Examination for prenatal toxicity	Suggestion from the Commission

b. New Entries

Substance	Discussed Classification	Reason
Aerosol, general threshold limit value (respirable fraction)	Establishment of MAK value	Suggestion from the Commission
Aerosols of inorganic acids	Examination for carcinogenic effect	Suggestion from the Commission
1-Aminoanthraquinone [82-45-1]	Establishment of MAK value	Suggestion from BG Chemie
p-Aminoazobenzene [60-09-3]	Examination for carcinogenic effect	Suggestion from the Commission
Anthracene [120-12-7]	Establishment of MAK value	Suggestion from the Commission
Anthraquinone [84-65-1]	Establishment of MAK value Examination for carcinogenic effect	Suggestion from the Commission Suggestion from BG Chemie
Arsenic compounds, organic	Examination of carcinogenic potential	Suggestion from the Commission
2-(2-(2-Azabicyclo[2.2.1]-hept-2-yl)ethoxy)-ethanol [116230-20-7]	Establishment of MAK value	Suggestion from the Bundesanstalt für Arbeitsschutz und Arbeitsmedizin

Substance	Discussed Classification	Reason
Bentonite [1302-78-9]	Establishment of MAK value	Suggestion from the Commission
Benzyl formate [104-57-4]	Establishment of MAK value	Suggestion from users
1,4,5,6,7,7-Bicyclo[2.2.1]-hept-5-ene-2,3-dicarboxylic acid [115-28-6]	Examination for carcinogenic effect	Suggestion from the Commission
2,2-bis(bromomethyl)-1,3-propanediol [3296-90-0]	Examination for carcinogenic effect	Suggestion from the Commission
Bis(1-((5-chloro-2-hydroxy-phenyl)azo)-2-naphthalen-olato(2-))-chromate-1-tetra-decanamine [88377-66-6]	Establishment of MAK value	Suggestion from the Bundesanstalt für Arbeitsschutz und Arbeitsmedizin
2,5(2,6)-Bis(isocyanato-methyl)bicyclo[2.2.1]heptane [74091-64-8]	Establishment of MAK value	Suggestion from the Bundesanstalt für Arbeitsschutz und Arbeitsmedizin
n-Butene [25167-67-3]	Examination for carcinogenic effect	Suggestion from the Commission
Butylbenzyl phthalate [85-68-7]	Establishment of MAK value Examination of reproductive toxicity	Suggestion from the Commission
1-(4-*tert*-Butyl-2,6-dimethyl-3,5-dinitro-phenyl)ethanone [81-14-1]	Establishment of MAK value	Suggestion from the Commission
1-*tert*-Butyl-3,5-dimethyl-2,4,6-trinitrobenzene [81-15-2]	Establishment of MAK value	Suggestion from the Commission
Butyraldehyde (*n*-Butanal) [123-72-8]	Establishment of MAK value	Suggestion from the Ausschuß für Gefahrstoffe
γ-Butyrolactone [96-48-0]	Establishment of MAK value	Suggestion from users
Calcium hydroxide [1305-62-0]	Establishment of MAK value	Suggestion from the Commission
2-Chloroacetamide [79-07-2]	Establishment of MAK value	Suggestion from BG Chemie
Chloroacetic acid ethyl ester [105-39-5]	Establishment of MAK value	Suggestion from users
2-Chloroacetophenone [532-27-4]	Establishment of MAK value Examination for carcinogenic effect	Suggestion from users Suggestion from the Commission
Chlorobenzilate [510-15-6]	Examination for carcinogenic effect	Suggestion from the Commission
o-Chlorobenzotrichloride [2136-89-2]	Examination for carcinogenic effect	Suggestion from BG Chemie
4-Chlorobutanoyl chloride [4635-59-0]	Establishment of MAK value	Suggestion from BG Chemie

Substance	Discussed Classification	Reason
(3-Chloro-2-hydroxy-propyl)trimethyl-ammonium chloride [3327-22-8]	Establishment of MAK value Examination for carcinogenic effect	Suggestion from the Commission Suggestion from BG Chemie
4-Chloro-2-methylphenol [1570-64-5]	Establishment of MAK value	Suggestion from the Commission
2-Chloro-4-methylsulfonyl-benzoic acid [53250-83-2]	Establishment of MAK value	Suggestion from the Bundesanstalt für Arbeitsschutz und Arbeitsmedizin
3-Chloropropanoyl chloride [625-36-5]	Examination for carcinogenic effect	Suggestion from the Commission
Chlorosulfonic acid [7790-94-5]	Establishment of MAK value	Suggestion from BG Chemie
Colourants containing phenylenediamine	Examination for carcinogenic effect	Suggestion from the Commission
Creosote/Tar oil	Examination for carcinogenic effect	Suggestion from the Bundesministerium für Umwelt, Naturschutz & Reaktorsicherheit
Cryolite (sodium aluminium fluoride) [15096-52-3]	Establishment of MAK value	Suggestion from the Commission
Cyanuric chloride [108-77-0]	Establishment of MAK value	Suggestion from the Commission
N-Cyclohexyl-2-benzo-thiazolesulfenamide [95-33-0]	Establishment of MAK value	Suggestion from the Commission
Cypermethrin [52315-07-8]	Establishment of MAK value	Suggestion from the Commission
D&C Yellow No. 11 (C.I. Solvent Yellow 33) [8003-22-3]	Examination for carcinogenic effect	Suggestion from the Commission
Decabromobiphenyl ether [1163-19-5]	Establishment of MAK value	Suggestion from the Commission
Decalin [91-17-8]	Examination for carcinogenic effect	Suggestion from the Commission
Deltamethrin [52918-63-5]	Establishment of MAK value	Suggestion from the Commission
Desflurane [57041-67-5]	Establishment of MAK value	Suggestion from the Commission
Diallate [2303-16-4]	Examination for carcinogenic effect	Suggestion from the Commission
2,3-Dibromo-1-propanol [96-13-9]	Examination for carcinogenic effect	Suggestion from the Commission
Dibutyl phthalate [84-74-2]	Establishment of MAK value	Suggestion from the Commission
Dichlofluanid [1085-98-9]	Examination of reproductive toxicity	Suggestion from users
Dichloroacetic acid [79-43-6] and its sodium salt [2156-56-1]	Examination for carcinogenic effect	Suggestion from BG Chemie

Substance	Discussed Classification	Reason
Dichloroacetyl chloride [79-36-7]	Examination for carcinogenic effect	Suggestion from BG Chemie
3,4-Dichloro-1-butene [760-23-6]	Examination for carcinogenic effect	Suggestion from BG Chemie
2,6-Dichloro-*p*-phenylene-diamine [609-20-1]	Examination for carcinogenic effect	Suggestion from BG Chemie
Diethylene glycol mono-methyl ether [111-77-3]	Establishment of MAK value	Suggestion from the Commission
Diisodecyl phthalate [26761-40-0]	Establishment of MAK value	Suggestion from the Commission
Diisononyl phthalate [28553-12-0]	Establishment of MAK value	Suggestion from the Commission
N,N-Dimethylamino-ethanol [108-01-0]	Establishment of MAK value	Suggestion from the Commission
2-Dimethylamino-2-methyl-1-propanol [7005-47-2]	Establishment of MAK value	Suggestion from the Commission
Dimethyldioctadecyl-ammonium chloride [107-64-2]	Establishment of MAK value	Suggestion from the Commission
Dioctyl phthalate [117-84-0]	Establishment of MAK value	Suggestion from the Commission
Diphenylamine [122-39-4]	Establishment of MAK value	Suggestion from the Commission
Diphenyl 2-ethylhexyl phosphate [1241-94-7]	Establishment of MAK value	Suggestion from BG Chemie
Dipropylene glycol *n*-butyl ether [29911-28-2]	Establishment of MAK value	Suggestion from users
Dipropylene glycol dimethyl ether [111109-77-4]	Establishment of MAK value	Suggestion from the Commission
Di-*o*-tolylguanidine [97-39-2]	Establishment of MAK value Examination for sensitization potential	Suggestion from BG Chemie
Dodecane [112-40-3]	Examination for tumour-promoting effect	Suggestion from users
Enzyme dusts (e. g. proteases)	Examination of sensitization potential	Suggestion from the Commission
Ethylenediaminetetraacetic acid tetrasodium salt (Na EDTA) [64-02-8]	Establishment of MAK value	Suggestion from the Commission
2-Ethylhexanal [123-05-7]	Establishment of MAK value	Suggestion from BG Chemie
2-Ethylhexyl acetate [103-09-3]	Establishment of MAK value	Suggestion from users
O-Ethylhydroxylamine [624-86-2]	Establishment of MAK value	Suggestion from the Bundesanstalt für Arbeitsschutz und Arbeitsmedizin
Fenvalerate [51630-58-1]	Establishment of MAK value	Suggestion from the Commission

Substance	Discussed Classification	Reason
Fine dust, inorganic, poorly soluble, non-fibrous, including ultrafine particles	Establishment of MAK values Examination for carcinogenic effect	Suggestion from the Commission
γ-Glycidoxypropyltri-methoxysilane [2530-83-8]	Establishment of MAK value	Suggestion from the Commission
Glycidyl compounds	Examination for sensitization potential	Suggestion from the Commission
Hexabromocyclododecane [25637-99-4]	Establishment of MAK value	Suggestion from the Commission
1-Hexene [592-41-6]	Examination for carcinogenic effect	Suggestion from the Commission
1-Hydroxyethane-1,1-di-phosphonate, disodium salt [7414-83-7]	Establishment of MAK value	Suggestion from the Commission
Hydroxylamine sulfate [10039-54-0]	Establishment of MAK value	Suggestion from the Commission
Iron oxides, pigmentary synthetic e. g. [1310-14-1; 12022-37-6; 1309-37-1; 12134-66-6; 1309-38-2]	Establishment of MAK value Examination for prenatal toxicity	Suggestion from the Commission
Iron sulfate [7720-78-7], [10028-22-5]	Establishment of MAK value	Suggestion from the Commission
Isobutene [115-11-7]	Examination for carcinogenic effect	Suggestion from BG Chemie
Isobutyl nitrite [542-56-3]	Examination for carcinogenic effect	Suggestion from the Commission
Isopropyl bromide [75-26-3]	Examination for reproductive toxicity	Suggestion from the Commission
Isoproturon (*N*-(4-Iso-propylphenyl)-*N'*,*N'*-di-methylurea) [34123-59-6]	Examination for carcinogenic effect	Suggestion from the Ausschuß für Gefahrstoffe
Kaolin(ite) [1332-58-7]	Establishment of MAK value	Suggestion from the Commission
(L)-Lactate esters	Establishment of MAK value	Suggestion from users
Leather dust	Examination for carcinogenic effect	Suggestion from the Commission
Linuron (*N'*-(3,4-Dichloro-phenyl)-*N*-methoxy-*N*-methylurea) [330-55-2]	Examination for carcinogenic effect	Suggestion from the Ausschuß für Gefahrstoffe
Magenta (basic fuchsin hydrochloride) [632-99-5]	Examination for carcinogenic effect	Suggestion from the Commission
Methacrolein [78-85-3]	Examination for carcinogenic effect	Suggestion from BG Chemie
Methanesulfonic acid ethyl ester [62-50-0]	Establishment of MAK value	Suggestion from the Commission

Substance	Discussed Classification	Reason
Methanesulfonic acid methyl ester [66-27-3]	Establishment of MAK value	Suggestion from the Commission
2-Methyl-2-azabicyclo-[2.2.1]heptane [4524-95-2]	Establishment of MAK value	Suggestion from the Bundesanstalt für Arbeitsschutz und Arbeitsmedizin
Methyl decanoate [110-42-9]	Establishment of MAK value	Suggestion from users
Methyleugenol [93-15-2]	Examination for carcinogenic effect	Suggestion from BG Chemie
Mirex [2385-85-5]	Examination for carcinogenic effect	Suggestion from the Commission
4-((Morpholinothio-carbonyl)-thio)morpholine (OTOS) [13752-51-7]	Examination for carcinogenic effect	Suggestion from the Bundesanstalt für Arbeitsschutz und Unfall-forschung
Nitrogen oxides [10102-43-9],[10102-44-0]	Question of a common MAK value	Examination by the Commission
Nonyl phenol [25154-52-3]	Establishment of MAK value	Suggestion from the Commission
Octabromodiphenyl ether [32536-52-0]	Establishment of MAK value	Suggestion from the Commission
Organic dusts	Establishment of MAK values Examination for carcinogenic effect	Suggestion from the Commission
Organic fibres (dust)	Examination for carcinogenic effect	Suggestion from the Commission
Oxalic acid [144-62-7]	Establishment of MAK value	Suggestion from the Commission
Oxazepam [604-75-1]	Examination for carcinogenic effect	Suggestion from the Commission
Pentabromodiphenyl ether [32534-81-9]	Establishment of MAK value	Suggestion from the Commission
Pentachlorobenzene [608-93-5]	Establishment of MAK value	Suggestion from the Commission
Perfluorooctanesulfonic acids	Establishment of MAK value	Suggestion from the Commission
Permethrin [52645-53-1]	Establishment of MAK value	Suggestion from the Commission
Petrol engine emissions	Examination for carcinogenic effect	Suggestion from the Commission
Phenolphthalein [77-09-8]	Examination for carcinogenic effect	Suggestion from the Commission
o-Phthalodinitrile [91-15-6]	Establishment of MAK value	Suggestion from BG Chemie
Potassium tetrafluoro-borate [14075-53-7]	Establishment of MAK value	Suggestion from BG Chemie
1-Propanol [71-23-8]	Establishment of MAK value	Suggestion from the Commission
Propionaldehyde [123-38-6]	Establishment of MAK value	Suggestion from the Commission
Propyl bromide [106-94-5]	Examination for reproductive toxicity	Suggestion from the Commission

Substance	Discussed Classification	Reason
Propylene [115-07-1]	Examination for carcinogenic effect	Suggestion from the Commission
sec-Propylene chlorohydrin (1-chloro-2-propanol) [127-00-4]	Establishment of MAK value	Suggestion from users
Propylene glycol *n*-butyl ether [29387-86-8]	Establishment of MAK value	Suggestion from users
Propylene glycol mono-*tert*-butyl ether [57018-52-7]	Examination for carcinogenic effect	Suggestion from the Commission
Salicylic acid [69-72-7]	Establishment of MAK value	Suggestion from the Commission
Sevoflurane [28523-86-6]	Establishment of MAK value	Suggestion from the Commission
Silane (Silicon tetrahydride) [13825-90-6]	Establishment of MAK value	Inquiry from users
Sodium aurothiomalate [12244-57-4]	Establishment of MAK value Examination for carcinogenic effect	Suggestion from the Commission
Sodium chloride (aerosol) [7647-14-5]	Establishment of MAK value Examination for tumour-promoting effect	Suggestion from the Commission
Sodium chlorite [7758-19-2]	Establishment of MAK value	Suggestion from the Commission
Sodium hypochlorite [7681-52-9]	Establishment of MAK value	Suggestion from the Commission
Sodium perborate [11138-47-9]	Establishment of MAK value	Suggestion from the Commission
Tebuconazole [80443-41-0]	Establishment of MAK value	Suggestion from users
Terbuthylazine [5915-41-3]	Establishment of MAK value	Suggestion from the Commission
Terephthalic acid dimethyl ester [120-61-6]	Establishment of MAK value	Suggestion from BG Chemie
Tetrachlorobenzenes [95-94-3, 634-66-2, 634-90-2]	Establishment of MAK value	Suggestion from the Commission
Tetramethylbenzidine [54827-17-7]	Examination for carcinogenic effect	Suggestion from users
Thioglycolic acid [68-11-1]	Establishment of MAK value	Suggestion from BG Chemie
Thionyl chloride [7719-09-7]	Establishment of MAK value	Suggestion from the Commission
Thionyl fluoride [7783-42-8]	Establishment of MAK value	Suggestion from users
Thiophene [110-02-1]	Establishment of MAK value	Suggestion from the Commission
Titanium dioxide, silanized	Establishment of MAK value	Suggestion from users
Toluene-2,6-diamine [823-40-5]	Examination for sensitization potential	Suggestion from the Commission

Substance	Discussed Classification	Reason
o-Toluylenediamine (mixture of isomers) [26966-75-6]	Examination for carcinogenic effect	Suggestion from the Ausschuß für Gefahrstoffe
Trimethylhydroquinone [700-13-0]	Examination for sensitization potential	Suggestion from BG Chemie
2,4,4-Trimethylpentene [25167-70-8]	Establishment of MAK value	Suggestion from the Commission
Trimethylquinone [935-92-2]	Establishment of MAK value Examination for sensitization potential	Suggestion from BG Chemie
Tris(2-chloroethyl)-phosphate [115-96-8]	Establishment of MAK value Examination for carcinogenic effect	Suggestion from the Commission
Vinyl propionate [105-38-4]	Examination for carcinogenic effect	Suggestion from BG Chemie
Welding fumes	Establishment of MAK value	Suggestion from users
White spirit [64742-88-7], [64742-49-0], [64742-48-9]	Establishment of MAK value	Suggestion from the Commission
2,4-Xylenol (2,4-dimethyl-phenol) [105-67-9]	Establishment of MAK value Examination for sensitization potential	Suggestion from BG Chemie
2,6-Xylenol (2,6-dimethyl-phenol) [576-26-1]	Establishment of MAK value Examination for sensitization potential	Suggestion from BG Chemie
3,5-Xylenol (3,5-dimethyl-phenol) [108-68-9]	Establishment of MAK value Examination for sensitization potential	Suggestion from BG Chemie
Zeolites (non-fibrous) [1318-02-1]	Establishment of MAK value	Suggestion from the Commission
Zinc [7440-66-6] and its compounds	Establishment of MAK values	Suggestion from the Commission

Biological Tolerance Values (Changes and new entries)

a. Changes

Substance	Reason
Acrylonitrile [107-13-1]	Suggestion from the Commission
4-Aminobiphenyl [92-67-1]	Suggestion from the Commission
Arsenic [7440-38-2] and its inorganic compounds	Suggestion from the Commission
Benzene [71-43-2]	Suggestion from the Commission
Benzidine [92-87-5] and its salts	Suggestion from the Commission
Beryllium [7440-41-7] and its inorganic compounds	Suggestion from the Commission
Cadmium [7440-43-9] and its inorganic compounds	Suggestion from the Commission
Cumene [98-82-8]	Suggestion from the Commission
Cyclohexane [110-82-7]	Suggestion from the Commission
4,4'-Diaminodiphenylmethane [101-77-9]	Suggestion from the Commission
1,2-Dichlorobenzene [95-50-1]	Suggestion from the Commission
N,N-Dimethyl acetamide [127-19-5]	Suggestion from the Commission
Dimethylformamide [68-12-2]	Examination by the Commission
Ethylene glycol monobutyl ether [111-76-2]	Examination by the commission
Ethylene glycol monobutyl ether acetate [112-07-2]	Examination by the commission
Ethylene glycol monoethyl ether [110-80-5]	Examination by the Commission
Formic acid methyl ester [107-31-3]	Suggestion from the Commission
Isopropyl alcohol [67-63-0]	Suggestion from the Commission
Lead [7439-92-1] and its compounds	Suggestion from the Commission
Manganese [7439-06-5] and its inorganic compounds	Suggestion from the Commission
Mercury, inorganic compounds	Suggestion from the Commission
2-Naphthylamine [91-59-8]	Suggestion from the Commission
Nickel [7440-02-0] and its compounds	Suggestion from the Commission
Styrene [100-42-5]	Suggestion from the Commission
Toluene (Toluol) [108-88-3]	Suggestion from the Commission
Toluene-2,4-diamine [95-80-7]	Suggestion from the Commission
Trichloroethylene [79-01-6]	Suggestion from the Commission
Vinyl chloride [75-01-4]	Suggestion from the Commission

b. New Entries

Substance	Reason
Barium [7440-39-3]	Suggestion from the Commission
Chromium(III) compounds	Suggestion from the Commission
1,5-Diaminonaphthalene [2243-62-1]	Suggestion from the Commission
3,3'-Dichlorobenzidine [91-94-1]	Suggestion from the Commission
Di(2-ethylhexyl) phthalate (DEHP) [117-81-7]	Suggestion from the Commission
3,3'-Dimethoxybenzidine [119-90-4]	Suggestion from the Commission
2,5-Dimethoxy-4-chloroaniline [6358-64-1]	Suggestion from the Commission
Glycidol [556-52-5]	Suggestion from the Commission
Glyoxal [107-22-2]	Suggestion from the Commission
4-Nitroaniline [100-01-6]	Suggestion from the Commission
PAH, parameter: 1-hydroxypyrene [5315-79-7]	Suggestion from the Commission
Perfluoroctansulfate	Suggestion from the Commission
Selenium [7782-49-2] and its inorganic compounds	Suggestion from the Commission
Toluene-2,4-diisocyanate [584-84-9]	Suggestion from the Commission
Toluene-2,6-diisocyanate [91-08-7]	Suggestion from the Commission
o-Toluidine [95-53-4]	Suggestion from the Commission
Xylidine (isomers):	Suggestion from the Commission
2,3-Xylidine [87-59-2], 2,5-Xylidine [95-78-3], 3,4-Xylidine [95-64-7], 3,5-Xylidine [108-69-0] 2,4-Xylidine [95-68-1] and 2,6-Xylidine [87-62-7]	Suggestion from the Commission

The Commission requests that company physicians, the manufacturers and users of industrial chemicals, research institutes dealing with these compounds, as well as boards of control and other governmental institutions, submit the names of any additional substances which occur at the workplace and have not as yet been considered.

Scientific and technical data and information applying to the compounds listed above should be submitted by

1st February 2009

to the

Geschäftsstelle der Deutschen Forschungsgemeinschaft
53170 Bonn

Prof. Dr. Andrea Hartwig
Chair of the Commission for the Investigation
of Health Hazards of Chemical Compounds
in the Work Area

Procedure of the Commission for the Investigation of Health Hazards of Chemical Compounds in the Work Area for making Changes in or Additions to the List of MAK and BAT Values

1. Notice of discussed new entries and changes is given, as a rule, one year in advance with the issue of the List of MAK and BAT Values, generally on July 1st. Where MAK values are to be changed, the new intended value is reported as well as the reason for the change (new sources of reference, additional information, justified petitions). The notice of discussed new entries and changes serves as a request from the Commission for submission by February 1 of the following year of written reports with pertinent information and commentary. The Commission will respond by May 1 to the reports received. If factual issues cannot be clarified either in written form or by telephone, the Commission calls in one (or when different workplaces having nonidentical exposure conditions are affected, several) technically qualified representative(s) from the involved areas for ultimate counsel. The Commission plus the organizations listed in the following sentence must agree by vote on the selection of the consultant(s). The notice of discussed new entries and changes is officially reported by the Commission to the "Länderausschuß für Arbeitsschutz und Sicherheitstechnik (LASI)" (Federal Committee for Occupational Safety and Technical Security), the "Bundesverband der Deutschen Industrie" (Federation of German Industries), the "Hauptverband der gewerblichen Berufsgenossenschaften" (Central Association of Industrial Injuries Insurance Institutes) and the "Deutsche Gewerkschaftsbund" (the German Trade Union Federation).
2. In cases where the scientific documentation is not adequate for the new entry of a substance or for a change in value, the decision for renewed consideration is reset for one year later.
3. The Commission makes use of advance bulletins in urgent cases where a decision as to a new entry or change must be reached quickly in order to avert health damage. In this way the Commission can deal with the affected branches of industry or the central organizations without the usual notification procedure and without counsel. For the advance bulletins of such decisions the Commission always provides detailed scientific justification which is published in the technical journals and which is sent together with the advance bulletin to the places and organizations named in the final sentence of paragraph 1 above.

Standing Order for the MAK and BAT Values

The List of Maximum Concentrations and Biological Tolerance Values at the Workplace is updated annually. By using the Order Card below, a standing order can be entered that guarantees annual delivery of the List. This

- eliminates the need to send repeated renewal orders and
- ensures immediate availability of the most recent data.

Please tear here

Order Form

Yes, I would like to order (please add the number of copies):

___ **List of MAK and BAT Values**
(standing order) This order shall become effective with the 2009 edition and remain valid until it is cancelled in writing.

The MAK-Collection for Occupational Health and Safety

___ HELMUT GREIM (Ed.)
Part I: MAK Value Documentations
Volume 23 978-3-527-31595-6 2007 308 pp Hbk
€ 159.00 /£ 120.00 /US$ 230.00

___ HELMUT GREIM (Ed.)
Part I: MAK Value Documentations
Volume 24 978-3-527-31594-2 2007 196 pp Hbk
€ 109.00 /£ 85.00 /US$ 160.00

___ HANS DREXLER (Ed.)
Part II: BAT Value Documentations
Volume 4 978-3-527-27049-1 2005 243 pp Hbk
€ 109.00 /£ 85.00 /US$ 160.00

___ HARUN PARLAR (Ed.)
Part III: Air Monitoring Methods
Volume 10 978-3-527-31601-4 2007 187 pp Hbk
€ 109.00 /£ 85.00 /US$ 160.00

___ JÜRGEN ANGERER (Ed.)
Part IV: MAK Value Documentations
Volume 11 978-3-527-31596-3 2007 321 pp Hbk
€ 179.00 /£ 135.00 /US$ 260.00

All prices are approx prices and subject to change.

MAK 2008

Order Form

Yes, I would like to order (please add the number of copies):

___ **List of MAK and BAT Values**
(standing order) This order shall become effective with the 2009 edition and remain valid until it is cancelled in writing.

The MAK-Collection for Occupational Health and Safety

___ HELMUT GREIM (Ed.)
Part I: MAK Value Documentations
Volume 23 978-3-527-31595-6 2007 308 pp Hbk
€ 159.00 /£ 120.00 /US$ 230.00

___ HELMUT GREIM (Ed.)
Part I: MAK Value Documentations
Volume 24 978-3-527-31594-2 2007 196 pp Hbk
€ 109.00 /£ 85.00 /US$ 160.00

___ HANS DREXLER (Ed.)
Part II: BAT Value Documentations
Volume 4 978-3-527-27049-1 2005 243 pp Hbk
€ 109.00 /£ 85.00 /US$ 160.00

___ HARUN PARLAR (Ed.)
Part III: Air Monitoring Methods
Volume 10 978-3-527-31601-4 2007 187 pp Hbk
€ 109.00 /£ 85.00 /US$ 160.00

___ JÜRGEN ANGERER (Ed.)
Part IV: MAK Value Documentations
Volume 11 978-3-527-31596-3 2007 321 pp Hbk
€ 179.00 /£ 135.00 /US$ 260.00

All prices are approx prices and subject to change.

MAK 2008

Name

Street

City, Postal Code, Country

Date

Signature

Reply

Stamp

WILEY-VCH
Customer Service Books
P. O. Box 10 11 61

69451 Weinheim
Germany

Name

Street

City, Postal Code, Country

Date

Signature

Reply

Stamp

John Wiley & Sons, Inc.
Customer Care Center
Consumer Accounts
10475 Crosspoint Blvd.
Indianapolis, IN 46256
USA